NONLINEAR FILTERING AND SMOOTHING

NONLINEAR FILTERING AND SMOOTHING:

AN INTRODUCTION TO MARTINGALES, STOCHASTIC INTEGRALS AND ESTIMATION

VENKATARAMA KRISHNAN

Indian Institute of Science
Bangalore, India
and
University of Lowell
Lowell, Massachusetts

A Wiley-Interscience Publication

JOHN WILEY & SONS

New York Chichester Brisbane Toronto Singapore

Library of Congress Cataloging in Publication Data:

Krishnan, Venkatarama
Nonlinear filtering and smoothing.

"A Wiley-Interscience publication."
Bibliography: p.
Includes index.
1. Martingales (Mathematics) 2. Integrals, Stochastic.
3. Estimation theory. I. Title.

QA274.5.K74 1984 519.2'87 83-16712
ISBN 0-471-89840-6

Printed in the United States of America

10 9 8 7 6 5 4 3 2 1

TO MY FAMILY

Kamala
Gayathri
Hemalekha
Amma

PREFACE

This book is the outcome of a course on martingales and estimation theory being given since the fall of 1977 by the author at the Indian Institute of Science, Bangalore, to engineering graduate students with a basic knowledge of probability theory. The continued rapid advances in the martingale approach to filtering and smoothing problems made it necessary to give the engineering students a clear physical understanding of the fundamental concepts in this area. As a consequence, applicational aspects have been stressed throughout the book. Starting with the basic concepts of probability and stochastic processes in Chapters 1 and 2, martingales and square integrable martingales have been introduced in Chapters 3 and 4. Chapter 5 covers white noise and white noise integrals with an introduction to Fourier transforms and spectral measures. Chapters 6 and 7 deal with stochastic integrals and stochastic differential equations and the associated Ito calculus and extensions to the Ito calculus. Differences between white noise differential equations and the corresponding stochastic differential equations have been clearly brought out. After having defined the Stratonovich integral, the correction terms needed for computational purposes to convert the Ito stochastic differential equation to the Stratonovich form have been derived. Chapter 8 contains the derivation of optimal nonlinear filtering representation in a form slightly different from that of the classic work of Fujisaki, Kallianpur, and Kunita (15). At this stage it was felt necessary that some time ought to be spent on the classical Kalman filter (optimal linear Gaussian nonstationary filter), the heuristic derivation of which is contained in Chapter 9. In the same chapter the Kalman filter has been derived as a special case of the general nonlinear filtering representation. In Chapter 10 fault detection problems using the nonlinear filtering representation are considered, and Chapter 11 contains some of the results of the work on smoothing problems carried out by the author and his students during the early seventies.

This book is written by an engineer for engineers. As far as possible, the physical understanding of the problem has been stressed, and as a result rigorous mathematical proofs have in some cases given way to heuristic proofs. Rigorous proofs have also been given and in some of those cases they lead to a better physical understanding of the problem. In some other cases proofs have been referred to other textbooks. This book has been class tested for the past several years, and the generous feedback from colleagues and graduate students from two continents has helped the author to present it in this particular form.

During the preparation of this book the two-volume work by Lipster and Shiryaev (34) and the book by Kallianpur (29) have appeared on the market. This book follows the same martingale approach to filtering and smoothing problems as these other two books, but the presentation is kept at a lower level. A third book by Bremaud (5) on point processes has also appeared on the market. This book also carries some aspects of point processes, but again at a lower level of presentation. It has been the intent of the author to give a concise physical understanding of the principles of martingales, stochastic integrals, and estimation theory from an applicational point of view at a level where an engineering student with a basic probability theory background can comprehend. For more intensive studies, including mathematical rigor, the student can refer to the books mentioned above. Selected problems have also been included at the end of every chapter to enhance the utility of the book.

The references given at the end are by no means exhaustive, but only reflect the relevance they bear to the material in the book.

In writing this book the author has been greatly influenced by the now classic works of Wong, Kailath, Kallianpur, Segall, and Lipster and Shiryaev. He has freely drawn on their works and would like to express his scientific debt of gratitude to these authors.

This book could not have been written but for the direct and indirect support obtained from many sources in India and in the U.S.A. The author is thankful to the students who took the course and suggested many improvements. In particular, he would like to mention J. Viswanathan, C. E. Venimadhavan, K. R. Ramakrishnan, and H. S. Jamadagni for technical discussions on the material of the book. S. L. Yadav of the Tata Institute of Fundamental Research, Bangalore, gave him suggestions for improving the clarity of presentation of earlier chapters. He is thankful to Professor Joseph L. Hibey of the University of Notre Dame and Dr. Wolf Jachimowicz of WBC Extrusion Products, Lowell, for the long hours spent in formulating the fault detection problem and the painstaking discussions on the clarity of its presentation. He is indebted to Professor Harold J. Kushner and Professor Thomas Kailath for their critical review and excellent suggestions for improving the quality of presentation. He appreciates the support given to him by Herb Sandberg and Allen Dushman by extending him facilities at the Dynamics Research Corporation, Wilmington, Massachusetts, for finishing parts of the book. He also appreciates the facilities extended to him at the University of

Lowell and the facilities provided for him by the Indian Institute of Science, Bangalore. He is thankful to the Ministry of Education and Culture, Government of India, who gave him financial assistance through the Curriculum Development Cell established at the Indian Institute of Science for the preparation of the initial manuscript. The preparation of the final manuscript was self-supported.

The author places on record with a deep sense of appreciation the unstinting cooperation given by B. Seshachalam who involved himself enthusiastically in this project from the beginning and superbly typed the initial and the final manuscripts and the many revisions in between. He is also thankful to G. Krishnamurthy for the art work.

During the preparation of the final manuscript I faced extremely difficult times. During this difficult and trying period, my wife, Kamala, my daughters, Gayathri and Hemalekha, and my mother were a constant source of inspiration to me with their unwavering support, without which this book would never have seen the light of day. It is fitting that I dedicate this book to them. I am also grateful to Professor S. V. Rangaswamy of the Indian Institute of Science, who helped me over some of the difficulties.

Finally, I acknowledge with great pleasure the constant encouragement given to me by David Kaplan and the Wiley staff; their skills in transforming a rough manuscript into a finished book amazes me.

दृष्ट्वेदं मानुषं रूपं तव सौम्यं जनार्दन।
इदानीमस्मि संवृत्तः सचेताः प्रकृतिं गतः ॥

Bhagavad-Gita
Canto XI

VENKATARAMA KRISHNAN

Lowell, Massachusetts
November 1983

CONTENTS

NONLINEAR FILTERING AND SMOOTHING

1 BASIC CONCEPTS OF PROBABILITY THEORY

1.1 INTRODUCTION

Probability theory is the mathematical study of phenomena occurring due to chance mechanism. If we toss a coin, we cannot say a priori whether we will get heads or tails. Outcomes of a random experiment can be analyzed or modeled only in an abstract manner. A random experiment or a mathematical experiment is one in which the possible outcomes may be finite or infinite. In the experiment of tossing a coin there are two outcomes, heads and tails. In the tossing of a die there are six outcomes. On the other hand, the weight of a full-term new-born baby may vary continuously from 4 to 10 pounds. Each of these outcomes is known as an *elementary outcome*. The collection of all elementary outcomes of a random experiment is called *sample space* and is denoted by Ω. In set terminology the sample space is termed the *universal* set. Thus, the sample space Ω is a set consisting of mutually exclusive, collectively exhaustive listing of all possible outcomes of a random experiment. That is, $\Omega = \{\omega_1, \omega_2, \ldots, \omega_n\}$ denotes the set of all finite outcomes, $\Omega = \{\omega_1, \omega_2, \ldots\}$ denotes the set of all countably infinite outcomes, and $\Omega = \{0 \le t \le T\}$ denotes the set of uncountably infinite outcomes.

1.2 ALGEBRA OF SETS

Let Ω represent the sample space which is a collection of ω-points as defined earlier. The various set operations are (1) *complementation*, (2) *union*, and (3) *intersection*. Let A and B be two subsets of the sample space Ω, denoted by

$A \subset \Omega$, $B \subset \Omega$. The complement of A, denoted by A^c, represents the set of all ω-points not contained in A:

$$A^c = \{\omega: \quad \omega \notin A\} \tag{1.2.1}$$

Evidently the complement of Ω is the empty set $\varnothing$. Two sets A and B are equal if and only if A is contained in B and B is contained in A:

$$A = B \Leftrightarrow A \subset B \quad \text{and} \quad B \subset A \tag{1.2.2}$$

The union of sets A and B, denoted by $A \cup B$ or $A + B$, represents the occurrence of ω-points in either A or B. Similarly, the intersection of sets A and B, denoted by $A \cap B$ or AB, represents the occurrence of ω-points in A and B. Clearly, if there is no commonality of ω-points in A and B, then $A \cap B$ is the empty set $\varnothing$.

$$\begin{aligned} A \cup B &= \{\omega: \quad \omega \in A \quad \text{or} \quad \omega \in B\} \\ A \cap B &= \{\omega: \quad \omega \in A \quad \text{and} \quad \omega \in B\} \end{aligned} \tag{1.2.3}$$

Example 1.2.1

Let Ω be the ω-points on the real line R.

$$\Omega = \{\omega: \quad -\infty < \omega < \infty\}$$

Define

$$\begin{aligned} A &= \{\omega: \quad \omega \in (-\infty, a)\} = \{\omega < a\} \\ B &= \{\omega: \quad \omega \in (b, c)\} = \{b < \omega < c\} \end{aligned}$$

Then the set operations yield

$$\begin{aligned} A^c &= \{a \le \omega < \infty\} \\ B^c &= \{-\infty < \omega \le b\} \cup \{c \le \omega < \infty\} \end{aligned}$$

$$A \cup B = \begin{bmatrix} \{\omega < a\} & c < a \\ \{\omega < c\} & b < a < c \\ \{\omega < a\} \cup \{b < \omega < c\} & a < b \end{bmatrix}$$

$$A \cap B = \begin{bmatrix} \{b < \omega < c\} & c < a \\ \{b < \omega < a\} & b < a < c \\ \varnothing & a < b \end{bmatrix}$$

The unions and intersections of an arbitrary collection of sets are defined by

$$\begin{aligned} \bigcup_{n \in N} A_n &= \{\omega: \quad \omega \in A_n \text{ for some } n \in N\} \\ \bigcap_{n \in N} A_n &= \{\omega: \quad \omega \in A_n \text{ for all } n \in N\} \end{aligned} \tag{1.2.4}$$

where N is an arbitrary index set which may be finite or countably infinite.

The unions and intersections follow the reflexive, commutative, associative, and distributive laws.

The complements $(\bigcup_{n\in N} A_n)^c$ and $(\bigcap_{n\in N} A_n)^c$ are given by de Morgan's laws as follows:

$$\begin{aligned}\left(\bigcup_{n\in N} A_n\right)^c &= \{\omega\colon \quad \omega \text{ does not belong to any } A_n,\, n \in N\}\\ &= \{\omega\colon \quad \omega \notin A_n \text{ for all } n \in N\}\\ &= \bigcap_{n\in N} A_n^c \qquad (1.2.5)\end{aligned}$$

$$\begin{aligned}\left(\bigcap_{n\in N} A_n\right)^c &= \{\omega\colon \quad \omega \text{ does not belong to each and every } A_n,\, n \in N\}\\ &= \{\omega\colon \quad \omega \text{ does not belong to some } A_n,\, n \in N\}\\ &= \bigcup_{n\in N} A_n^c \qquad (1.2.6)\end{aligned}$$

Sequences

A sequence of sets A_n, $n \in N$, is *increasing* if $A_{n+1} \supset A_n$ and *decreasing* if $A_{n+1} \subset A_n$ for every $n \in N$.

A sequence which is either increasing or decreasing is called a *monotone* sequence. We can write the limits (N countably infinite) of monotone sequences as

$$\begin{aligned}\lim_{n\to\infty} A_n &= \lim{}_n A_n = \bigcup_{n=1}^{\infty} A_n = A \quad \text{increasing}\\ \lim_{n\to\infty} A_n &= \lim{}_n A_n = \bigcap_{n=1}^{\infty} A_n = A \quad \text{decreasing}\end{aligned} \qquad (1.2.7)$$

The limit of monotone sequences $\{A_n\}$ is written as $A_n \uparrow A$ when it is increasing and $A_n \downarrow A$ when it is decreasing.

Example 1.2.2

Let Ω be the real line R. If $A_n = \{\omega\colon \quad 0 < \omega < a - 1/n\}$, then $A_n \uparrow A = \{\omega\colon \quad 0 < \omega < a\}$. On the other hand, if $B_n = \{\omega\colon \quad 0 < \omega < a + 1/n\}$, then $B_n \downarrow B = \{\omega\colon \quad 0 < \omega \leq a\}$.

We can define a *superior limit* and an *inferior limit* for any sequence $\{A_n\}$ not necessarily monotone. We first define sequences $\{B_n\}$ and $\{C_n\}$ derived from $\{A_n\}$ as follows:

$$\begin{aligned} B_n &= \sup_{k \geq n} A_k = \bigcup_{k=n}^{\infty} A_k \\ &= \{\omega: \quad \omega \text{ belongs to at least one of } A_n, A_{n+1}, \ldots\} \end{aligned} \tag{1.2.8}$$

$$\begin{aligned} C_n &= \inf_{k \geq n} A_k = \bigcap_{k=n}^{\infty} A_k \\ &= \{\omega: \quad \omega \text{ belongs to all } A_k \text{ except } A_1, A_2, \ldots, A_{n-1}\} \end{aligned} \tag{1.2.9}$$

Clearly the sequences $\{B_n\}$ and $\{C_n\}$ are monotone and decreasing and increasing, respectively. We can now define a limit from eq. 1.2.7 for these monotone sequences:

$$\begin{aligned} B &= \lim_{n \to \infty} B_n = \lim_n B_n = \bigcap_{n=1}^{\infty} B_n = \bigcap_{n=1}^{\infty} \bigcup_{k=n}^{\infty} A_k \\ &= \lim_{n \to \infty} \sup A_n = \lim \sup_n A_n \\ &= \{\omega: \quad \omega \text{ belongs to infinitely many } A_n\} \end{aligned}$$

$$\begin{aligned} C &= \lim_{n \to \infty} C_n = \lim_n C_n = \bigcup_{n=1}^{\infty} C_n = \bigcup_{n=1}^{\infty} \bigcap_{k=n}^{\infty} A_k \\ &= \lim_{n \to \infty} \inf A_n = \lim \inf_n A_n \\ &= \{\omega: \quad \omega \text{ belongs to all but a finite number of } A_n\} \end{aligned}$$

Hence

$$\lim \sup_n A_n \supset \lim \inf_n A_n$$

If $\lim \sup_n A_n = \lim \inf_n A_n$, then $\{A_n\}$ is a convergent sequence and $\lim_n A_n = A$, say, exists, that is,

$$\lim \sup_n A_n = \lim \inf_n A_n = \lim_n A_n = A \tag{1.2.10}$$

Example 1.2.3

Let A_k be the set of points (x, y) of the Cartesian plane R^2 in the region $\{0 \leq x < k, 0 \leq y < 1/k\}$, that is,

$$A_k = \left\{x, y \in R^2: \quad 0 \leq x < k, 0 \leq y < \frac{1}{k}\right\}$$

Here $\{A_k\}$ does not belong to the monotone class.

But

$$B_n = \bigcup_{k=n}^{\infty} A_k = \left\{x, y \in R^2: \quad 0 \le x < \infty, 0 \le y < \frac{1}{n}\right\}$$

is a decreasing sequence, and hence

$$B = \lim_n B_n = \bigcap_{n=1}^{\infty} B_n = \{x, y \in R^2: \quad 0 \le x < \infty, y = 0\} = \limsup_n A_n$$

Similarly,

$$C_n = \bigcap_{k=n}^{\infty} A_k = \{x, y \in R^2: \quad 0 \le x < n, y = 0\}$$

is an increasing sequence, and hence

$$C = \lim_n C_n = \bigcup_{n=1}^{\infty} C_n = \{x, y \in R^2: \quad 0 \le x < \infty, y = 0\} = \liminf_n A_n$$

Since $\limsup_n A_n = \liminf_n B_n = \{x, y \in R^2: \quad 0 \le x < \infty, \ y = 0\}$, we have $\lim_n A_n = B = C = \{x, y \in R^2: \quad 0 \le x < \infty, y = 0\}$.

Example 1.2.4

Let Ω be the positive real line R^+. Consider the sequence

$$A_n = \left\{\omega \in \Omega: \quad 0 < \omega < a + \frac{(-1)^n}{n}\right\}$$

Here

$$B_n = \begin{cases} \left\{\omega \in \Omega: \quad 0 < \omega < a + \dfrac{1}{n}, n \text{ even}\right\} \\ \left\{\omega \in \Omega: \quad 0 < \infty < a + \dfrac{1}{n+1}, n \text{ odd}\right\} \end{cases}$$

$$\limsup_n A_n = \{\omega \in \Omega: \quad 0 < \omega \le a\}$$

Similarly

$$C_n = \begin{cases} \left\{\omega \in \Omega: \quad 0 < \omega < a - \dfrac{1}{n}, n \text{ odd}\right\} \\ \left\{\omega \in \Omega: \quad 0 < \omega < a - \dfrac{1}{n+1}, n \text{ even}\right\} \end{cases}$$

$$\liminf_n A_n = \{\omega \in \Omega: \quad 0 < \omega < a\}$$

Since $\limsup_n A_n \neq \liminf_n A_n$, the sequence $\{A_n\}$ does not converge and has no limit.

Even though the limit of a sequence may not exist, superior and inferior limits will always exist, as is evident from the definitions.

1.3 FIELDS, σ-FIELDS, AND EVENTS

We define $\mathcal{A}$ as the nonempty class of subsets drawn from the sample space Ω. We say that the class $\mathcal{A}$ is a *field* or an *algebra* of sets in Ω if it satisfies the following definition.

Definition 1.3.1 Field or Algebra

A class of a collection of subsets $A_j \subset \Omega$ denoted by $\mathcal{A}$ is a field when the following conditions are satisfied:

1. If $A_i \in \mathcal{A}$, then $A_i^c \in \mathcal{A}$.
2. If $\{A_i = i = 1, 2, \ldots, n\} \in \mathcal{A}$, then $\bigcup_{i=1}^{n} A_i \in \mathcal{A}$. (1.3.1)

Given the above two conditions, de Morgan's law ensures that finite intersections also belong to the field. Thus a class of subsets is a field if and only if it is closed under all finite set operations like unions, intersections, and complementations. Since every Boolean algebra of sets is isomorphic to an algebra of subsets of Ω, we can also call the field a *Boolean field* or *Boolean algebra*. Every field contains as elements the sample space Ω and the empty set $\varnothing$.

Example 1.3.1

Let $\Omega = R$ and consider a class $\mathcal{A}$ of all intervals of the form $(a, b]$, that is, $\{x \in R\colon \ a < x \leq b\}$:

$$
\begin{aligned}
(a,b] \cap (c,d] &= \varnothing && a < b < c < d \\
&= (c,b] && a < c < b < d \\
&= (a,d] && c < a < d < b \\
&= (c,d] && a < c < d < b \\
&= (a,b] && c < a < b < d
\end{aligned}
$$

Clearly the class $\mathcal{A}$ is closed under intersections. However,

$$(a, b]^c = (-\infty, a] \cup (b, \infty) \notin \mathcal{A}$$

$$(a, b] \cup (c, d] \notin \mathcal{A} \qquad \text{if } a < b < c < d$$

The class $\mathcal{A}$ is not a field.

Example 1.3.2

The smallest field containing $A \subset \Omega$ is

$$\mathcal{A} = \{\Omega, \varnothing, A, A^c\}$$

If a class of subsets is closed under finite set operations, it does not necessarily mean that it is also closed under countably infinite set operations. Very often we come across the sequence of sets $\{A_n\}$ as $n \to \infty$ and the convergence of such sequences ($\limsup_n A_n$, $\liminf_n A_n$). In Example 1.3.1 the class $\mathcal{A}$ is closed under finite intersections. If we now take countably infinite intersections, $\bigcap_{n=1}^{\infty}(a - 1/n, b] = [a, b] \notin \mathcal{A}$. If a class of sets $\mathcal{F}$ drawn from the sample space Ω is closed under all countably infinite set operations, then that class $\mathcal{F}$ is called a *σ-field* or *σ-algebra*.

Definition 1.3.2 σ-Field or σ-Algebra

A class of a countably infinite collection of subsets $A_j \subset \Omega$ denoted by $\mathcal{F}$ is a σ-field when the following conditions are satisfied:

1. If $A_i \in \mathcal{F}$, then $A_i^c \in \mathcal{F}$.
2. If $\{A_i, i = 1, 2, \dots\} \in \mathcal{F}$, then $\bigcup_{i=1}^{\infty} A_i \in \mathcal{F}$. (1.3.2)

In general a σ-field is a field, but a field may not be a σ-field.

Example 1.3.3

Let $\Omega = R$ and $\mathcal{A}$ be the class of all intervals of the form $(-\infty, a]$, $(b, c]$, and (d, ∞):

$$(b, c]^c = (-\infty, b] \cup (c, \infty) \in \mathcal{A}$$

$$(d, \infty)^c = (-\infty, d] \in \mathcal{A}$$

$$(-\infty, a]^c = (a, \infty) \in \mathcal{A}$$

From Example 1.3.1 the class $\mathcal{A}$ is closed under finite intersections. Similarly it can also be shown that $\mathcal{A}$ is closed under finite unions. Hence the class $\mathcal{A}$ is a field. However, for infinite intersections of the form

$$\bigcap_{n=1}^{\infty}\left(b-\frac{1}{n}, c\right) = [b, c) \notin \mathcal{Q}$$

the class $\mathcal{Q}$ is not a σ-field.

Proposition 1.3.1 Intersection of σ-Fields

The *intersection* of any nonempty but arbitrary collection of σ-fields in Ω is a σ-field in Ω.

In general the arbitrary *union* of a collection of σ-fields may not be a σ-field.

Many of the examples given above illustrate that an arbitrary class $\mathcal{Q}$ of subsets of Ω may or may not be a σ-field. However, we can always construct the smallest σ-field over $\mathcal{Q}$ which will contain $\mathcal{Q}$ and will be denoted by $\sigma(\mathcal{Q}) = \mathcal{F}$. This will always exist since $\sigma(\mathcal{Q})$ can be defined as the intersection of all σ-fields containing $\mathcal{Q}$. If $\sigma_1(\mathcal{Q}), \sigma_2(\mathcal{Q}), \ldots$ are all σ-fields containing $\mathcal{Q}$, then

$$\sigma(\mathcal{Q}) = \bigcap_{i=1}^{\infty} \sigma_i(\mathcal{Q})$$

Further the minimal σ-field thus generated is unique. We shall call $\sigma(\mathcal{Q})$ the σ-field generated by $\mathcal{Q}$.

Example 1.3.4

Let the sample space Ω contain ω-points of the toss of a die. Ω is the set $\{1,2,3,4,5,6\}$. We shall now define a class of sets

$$\mathcal{Q} = \{\varnothing, \Omega, \{1,3,5\}, \{2,4,6\}, \{2,4\}\}$$

Clearly $\mathcal{Q}$ is not a field since $\{1,3,5\} \cup \{2,4\} = \{1,2,3,4,5\}$ is not in $\mathcal{Q}$. However, we can generate the field containing $\mathcal{Q}$ by

$$\sigma(\mathcal{Q}) = \mathcal{F} = \{\mathcal{Q}, \{1,3,5,6\}, \{6\}, \{1,2,3,4,5\}\}$$

which is indeed a σ-field, and we can show that it is the minimal σ-field generated by $\mathcal{Q}$.

So far we have not considered the nature of the sample space Ω, except that it is nonempty. A set A and a class of subsets of A called *open sets* of A, such that this class contains ∅ and A, and closed under finite intersections and arbitrary unions, is called a *topological space*. If Ω is a topological space, an example being the real line R, the minimum σ-field over the collection of open sets of the topological space is called the Borel σ-field or Borel field, as given by the following definition.

Definition 1.3.3 Borel σ-Field

The minimum σ-field generated by the collection of open sets of a topological space Ω is called the *Borel σ-field* or *Borel field*. Members of this σ-field are called *Borel sets*.

Clearly the Borel σ-field is a σ-field, and hence each closed set is also a Borel set.

The important topological space with which we will be concerned is the real line R. The collection of Borel sets on the real line is denoted by $\mathcal{R}$. Each open interval is a member of $\mathcal{R}$. From the relationships

$$
\begin{aligned}
(a, b] &= \bigcap_{n=1}^{\infty} \left(a, b + \frac{1}{n}\right) \\
[a, b) &= \bigcap_{n=1}^{\infty} \left(a - \frac{1}{n}, b\right) \\
[a, b] &= \bigcap_{n=1}^{\infty} \left(a - \frac{1}{n}, b + \frac{1}{n}\right)
\end{aligned}
\tag{1.3.3}
$$

we find that the intervals $(a, b]$, $[a, b)$ and $[a, b]$ are Borel sets. Hence the Borel field $\mathcal{R}$ contains all subsets of the form given above and their complements, countable unions, and intersections, Each set $\{b\} = [b, b] = (-\infty, b) \cap (b, \infty)$ consisting of a single point b is in $\mathcal{R}$, and so are countable unions of single points.

A suitable model of the random experiment is therefore a sample space Ω and a σ-field $\mathcal{F}$ of subsets of Ω. The space $(\Omega, \mathcal{F})$ thus created is called a *measurable space*. Subsets of Ω which are elements in the σ-field are called *events*. Elements of Ω are *points*.

If $\{A_i, i = 1, 2, \ldots, n\}$ is a class of disjoint sets of Ω such that $\bigcup_{i=1}^{n} A_i = \Omega$, then the $\{A_i\}$ collectively exhaust Ω. The class $\{A_i\}$ is called a *partition* of Ω.

Definition 1.3.4 Atom

Let $\mathcal{F}$ be a σ-field of subsets of a sample space Ω. We call a set $A \neq \varnothing$ an *atom* of $\mathcal{F}$ if $A \in \mathcal{F}$ and if

$$B \subset A, \text{ then either } B = \varnothing \quad \text{or} \quad B = A \tag{1.3.4}$$

Atoms are irreducible elements of a σ-field. If there are two σ-fields, $\mathcal{F}_1 \subset \mathcal{F}_2$, then the atoms of $\mathcal{F}_1$ are sets in $\mathcal{F}_2$. Since every atom in $\mathcal{F}_1$ is a union of atoms of $\mathcal{F}_2$, the atoms of $\mathcal{F}_1$ give a coarser partition of Ω than the atoms of $\mathcal{F}_2$.

Example 1.3.5

In Example 1.3.4 where $\Omega = \{1, 2, 3, 4, 5, 6\}$ we define two σ-fields

$$\mathcal{F}_1 = \{\varnothing, \Omega, \{1, 3, 5\}, \{2, 4, 6\}\}$$

$$\mathcal{F}_2 = \{\varnothing, \Omega, \{1, 3, 5\}, \{2, 4, 6\}, \{2, 4\}, \{1, 3, 5, 6\}, \{6\}, \{1, 2, 3, 4, 5\}\}$$

Clearly $\mathcal{F}_1 \subset \mathcal{F}_2$ and the atoms of $\mathcal{F}_1$ are $\{1, 3, 5\}$ and $\{2, 4, 6\}$. The atoms of $\mathcal{F}_2$ are $\{1, 3, 5\}$, $\{2, 4\}$, and $\{6\}$. Hence $\mathcal{F}_2$ gives a finer partition of Ω than $\mathcal{F}_1$.

1.4 PROBABILITY SPACE

A *probability measure* is a set function P defined on a σ-field $\mathcal{F}$ of subsets of a sample space Ω such that it satisfies the following axioms of Kolmogorov for any $A \in \mathcal{F}$:

1. $P(A) \geq 0$ (nonnegativity)
2. $P(\Omega) = 1$ (normalization)
3. $P(\bigcup_{n=1}^{\infty} A_n) = \sum_{n=1}^{\infty} P(A_n)$ (σ-additivity) (1.4.1)
   with $A_n \in \mathcal{F}$, and A_i and A_j being pairwise disjoint.

Any set function μ defined on a measurable space $(\Omega, \mathcal{F})$ satisfying axioms 1 and 3 is called a *measure*. A probability measure is a *normed* or *scaled* measure because of axiom 2. There are other measures, such as counting measure, Lebesgue-measure, and spectral measure, which are not necessarily normalized. However, any bounded measure with suitable normalization can be converted into a probability measure. If $\mu(A)$ is finite for each $A \in \mathcal{F}$, then μ is a *finite* measure. However, if $\mu(A) = \infty$ but if there exists a sequence $\{A_n\}$ of members of $\mathcal{F}$ such that $A \subset \bigcup_{n=1}^{\infty} A_n$ and $\mu(A_n)$ is finite for each n, then μ is a *σ-finite* measure. An example of a measure that is σ-finite is length defined on the space $(R, \mathcal{R})$. The triplet $(\Omega, \mathcal{F}, \mu)$ is a *measure space*. The measure space $(\Omega, \mathcal{F}, P)$ is called a *probability space*, which serves to describe any random experiment where

1. Ω is a nonempty set called the sample space, whose elements are the elementary outcomes of a random experiment.
2. $\mathcal{F}$ is a σ-field of subsets of Ω.
3. P is a probability measure defined on the measurable space $(\Omega, \mathcal{F})$.

A *signed* measure (Halmos, 18, p. 118) is a σ-additive set function μ defined on a measurable space $(\Omega, \mathcal{F})$ taking positive and negative values such that $\mu(\varnothing) = 0$ and assuming at most one of two values, $+\infty$ or $-\infty$.

As an example if we define a measure $\nu(A) = \mu_1(A) - \mu_2(A)$, then ν is a signed measure. The Jordan–Hahn decomposition theorem (Halmos, 18, p. 123) guarantees that a signed measure ν can be given as the difference between two measures, $\nu = \nu^+ - \nu^-$, one of which is finite.

We would now like to enquire whether a probability measure P defined on a field $\mathfrak{F}$ can be extended to the σ-field generated by $\mathfrak{F}$. The answer is in the affirmative, as given by the following proposition (Halmos, 18, p. 54).

Proposition 1.4.1 Extension of Probability Measure

Let $\mathfrak{F}$ be a field and let $\sigma(\mathfrak{F})$ be the σ-field generated by $\mathfrak{F}$. Let P be the probability measure defined on the measurable space $(\Omega, \mathfrak{F})$. Then there exists a unique probability measure $\bar{P}$ defined on the measurable space $(\Omega, \sigma(\mathfrak{F}))$ such that for any A in $\mathfrak{F}$, $\bar{P}(A) = P(A)$.

Example 1.4.1

Let $\Omega = R$ be the real line. Let $\mathfrak{F}$ be the σ-field generated by the class of all intervals. For any finite interval $(a, b]$ we shall define a measure μ given by $\mu((a, b]) = b - a, b > a$. Then μ can be extended to a unique σ-finite measure on $(R, \mathfrak{R})$. Note that the measure of any countable number of points on the real line is zero.

Completion (Doob, 14, pp. 48, 606)

Next we discuss the concept of completion of a probability space. Let us assume that there is a subset Λ_0 which is measurable in $(\Omega, \mathfrak{F}, P)$ and has a measure 0, that is, $P(\Lambda_0) = 0$. Hence Λ_0 is an event. Let Λ be a proper subset of Λ_0, $\Lambda \subset \Lambda_0$. If Λ and Λ_0 are two subsets with the property that the occurrence of Λ_0 implies the occurrence of Λ, and if $P(\Lambda_0) = 0$, then Λ need neither be assigned a probability nor can it be called an event. However, if a probability is assigned to Λ, then necessarily it has to have a measure 0 for consistency. We denote subsets of this type with zero probability as *null sets*. Let $\bar{\mathfrak{F}}$ be the σ-field generated by $\mathfrak{F}$ and the null sets. By the Extension Proposition 1.4.1, the probability measure P on $\mathfrak{F}$ can be uniquely extended to $\bar{P}$ on $\bar{\mathfrak{F}}$. This is called *completion of the probability measure P*. The corresponding probability space $(\Omega, \bar{\mathfrak{F}}, \bar{P})$ is called the *complete probability space*, and the process of getting $\bar{P}$ from P is known as completion. We shall hereafter assume that the probability space $(\Omega, \mathfrak{F}, P)$ is complete.

In Example 1.4.1 if the σ-finite measure μ is completed, then we have the Lebesgue measure (Halmos, 18, p. 62).]

Product Spaces

We now define the concept of product spaces and product measures. If $\omega_1 \in \Omega_1$ and $\omega_2 \in \Omega_2$, then the set of all pairs (ω_1, ω_2) is called the *Cartesian product* of Ω_1 and Ω_2 (notation $\Omega_1 \times \Omega_2$). Let $(\Omega_1, \mathcal{F}_1)$ and $(\Omega_2, \mathcal{F}_2)$ be two measurable spaces and let sets A_1 and A_2 belong to the σ-fields $\mathcal{F}_1$ and $\mathcal{F}_2$, respectively. Then the set $\{(\omega_1, \omega_2)\colon \ \omega_1 \in A_1, \ \omega_2 \in A_2\}$ is a *measurable rectangle* $A_1 \times A_2$. However, the class $\{A_1 \times A_2\colon \ A_1 \in \mathcal{F}_1, A_2 \in \mathcal{F}_2\}$ may not be a σ-field. We will call the minimum σ-field generated by this class the *product* σ-field (notation $\mathcal{F}_1 \otimes \mathcal{F}_2$). We have now established the product measurable space $(\Omega_1 \times \Omega_2, \mathcal{F}_1 \otimes \mathcal{F}_2)$ as the Cartesian product of two measurable spaces $(\Omega_1, \mathcal{F}_1)$ and $(\Omega_2, \mathcal{F}_2)$. We want to define a σ-finite measure on the product measurable space. Let $(\Omega_1, \mathcal{F}_1, \mu_1)$ and $(\Omega_2, \mathcal{F}_2, \mu_2)$ be two σ-finite measure spaces. The *product measure* λ is a set function defined on the product σ-field $\mathcal{F}_1 \otimes \mathcal{F}_2$. It is a σ-finite measure such that for every measurable rectangle $A_1 \times A_2$, $(A_1 \in \mathcal{F}_1, A_2 \in \mathcal{F}_2)$

$$\lambda(A_1 \times A_2) = \mu_1(A_1) \times \mu_2(A_2)$$

Next we establish the concept of *ω-sections*. Let $(\Omega_1 \times \Omega_2, \mathcal{F}_1 \otimes \mathcal{F}_2)$ be a product measure space. Let B be a set in $\Omega_1 \times \Omega_2$. The ω_1-section of B, denoted by B_{ω_1}, is defined as

$$B_{\omega_1} = \{\omega_2\colon \ (\omega_1, \omega_2) \in B\}$$

and the ω_2-section of B, denoted by B_{ω_2}, is defined as

$$B_{\omega_2} = \{\omega_1\colon \ (\omega_1, \omega_2) \in B\}$$

As an example, if B is the rectangle $A_1 \times A_2$, then $B_{\omega_1} = A_2$ and $B_{\omega_2} = A_1$.

We now state Fubini's Theorem, which relates the integrals on a product space to integrals on component spaces.

Theorem 1.4.1 Fubini's Theorem (Halmos, 18, p. 148)

Let $(\Omega_1, \mathcal{F}_1, \mu_1)$ and $(\Omega_2, \mathcal{F}_2, \mu_2)$ be two σ-finite measure spaces and let λ be a product measure $\mu_1 \times \mu_2$ on the product σ-field $\mathcal{F}_1 \otimes \mathcal{F}_2$. Let h be an integrable function on $\Omega_1 \times \Omega_2$. Then:

1. Almost every ω-section of h is integrable.
2. If functions f_1 and f_2 are defined by

$$f_1(\omega_1) = \int_{\Omega_2} h(\omega_1, \omega_2)\, d\mu_2(\omega_2); \qquad f_2(\omega_2) = \int_{\Omega_1} h(\omega_1, \omega_2)\, d\mu_1(\omega_1)$$

and f_1 and f_2 are integrable, then

$$\int_{\Omega_1 \times \Omega_2} h\, d\lambda = \int_{\Omega_1} f_1\, d\mu_1 = \int_{\Omega_2} f_2\, d\mu_2$$

In Section 1.2 we discussed the algebra of sets. Since events are sets, we can also have a sequence of events $\{A_n\}$ where we can define $\sup_n A_n$,

$\inf_n A_n$, $\limsup_n A_n$, and $\liminf_n A_n$. We now discuss the convergence of the probability of a sequence of events.

Lemma 1.4.1 Sequential Monotone Continuity

Let $\{A_n\}$ be a monotone decreasing sequence in $\mathcal{F}$ such that $A_{n+1} \subset A_n$, and let $\lim_{n\to\infty} A_n = \varnothing$. Then

$$\lim_{n\to\infty} P(A_n) = 0 \tag{1.4.2}$$

The probability measure is said to satisfy the sequential monotone continuity at $\varnothing$.

Proposition 1.4.2 Sequential Continuity

Let $\{A_n\}$ be a convergent sequence of events in $\mathcal{F}$, with $\lim_n A_n = A$. Then

$$\lim_{n\to\infty} P(A_n) = P\Big(\lim_{n\to\infty} A_n\Big) = P(A) \tag{1.4.3}$$

The probability measure is sequentially continuous.

Proof

1. If $A = \varnothing$, then this is exactly Lemma 1.4.1.
2. If A is a nonempty set and $\{A_n\}$ is a monotone sequence, $A_n \downarrow A$, (Figure 1.4.1),

$$P(A_n) = P(A_n - A + A) = P(A_n - A) + P(A)$$

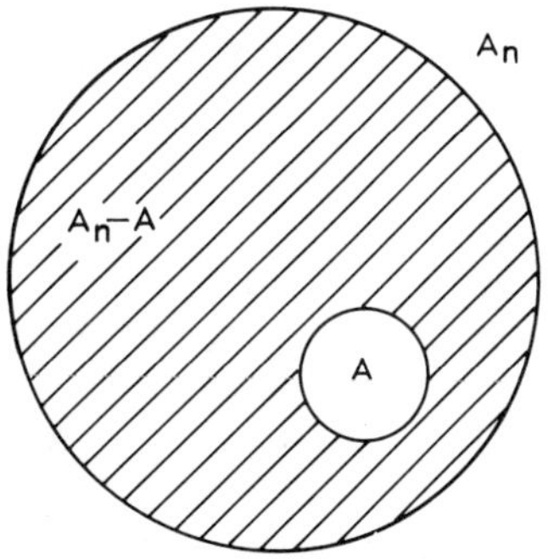

FIGURE 1.4.1

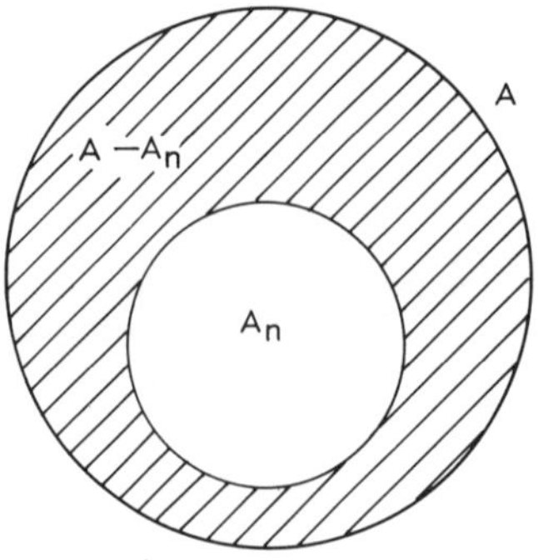

FIGURE 1.4.2

since $(A_n - A)$ and A are disjoint. If $A_n \uparrow A$ (Fig. 1.4.2),

$$P(A_n) = P(A - A + A_n) = P(A) - P(A - A_n)$$

In either case $\lim_n(A_n - A)$ or $\lim_n(A - A_n)$ decreases to $\varnothing$, and by Lemma 1.4.1 the results follow.

3. If $\{A_n\}$ is not a monotone sequence, then $\{B_n = \sup_{k \geq n} A_k\}$ and $\{C_n = \inf_{k \geq n} A_k\}$ are monotone decreasing and increasing sequences, respectively, from eqs. 1.2.8 and 1.2.9. Therefore $B_n \supset A_n \supset C_n$ and $B_n \downarrow A$ and $C_n \uparrow A$. □

The Borel–Cantelli lemma is used to prove properties which are true with probability 1. Proposition 1.4.2 is used to prove this important lemma.

Proposition 1.4.3 Borel – Cantelli Lemma

1. If $\sum_{n=1}^{\infty} P(A_n) < \infty$ for an arbitrary sequence of events $\{A_n\}$, then $P(\limsup_n A_n) = 0$.
2. If $\sum_{n=1}^{\infty} P(A_n) = \infty$ and sets $A_1, A_2, \ldots$ are independent $[P(A_{i_1} \cap A_{i_2} \cap \cdots \cap A_{i_k}) = P(A_{i_1})P(A_{i_2}) \cdots P(A_{i_k})$ for any different $i_1, i_2, \ldots, i_k]$, then $P(\limsup_n A_n) = 1$.

Proof. From the fact that probability of intersection $\leq$ probability of union, and from Proposition 1.4.2, we have

1. $$P(\limsup_n A_n) \leq P \lim \bigcup_{k=n}^{\infty} A_k$$
$$= \lim_{n \to \infty} P\left(\bigcup_{k=n}^{\infty} A_k\right) \leq \lim_{n \to \infty} \sum_{k=n}^{\infty} P(A_k)$$
since $\sum_{k=1}^{\infty} P(A_k) < \infty \Rightarrow \lim_{n \to \infty} \sum_{k=n}^{\infty} P(A_k) = 0$, implying $P(\limsup A_n) = 0$.

2. Now suppose that the A_k are independent:

$$
\begin{aligned}
1 - P(\limsup_n A_n) &= 1 - \text{Prob(occurrence of } \omega\text{-points in infinitely many } A_n) \\
&= \text{Prob(nonoccurrence of points after the } n\text{th event for } n \to \infty) \\
&= \lim_{n\to\infty} P\left(\bigcap_{k=n}^{\infty} A_k^c\right) = \lim_{n\to\infty} \prod_{k=n}^{\infty} (1 - P(A_k))
\end{aligned}
$$

since the A_k are independent.

Since $\sum_{n=1}^{\infty} P(A_n) = \infty$, the infinite product $\prod_{k=n}^{\infty}(1 - P(A_k)) = 0$. Therefore $1 - P(\limsup_n A_n) = 0 \Rightarrow P(\limsup_n A_n) = 1$. □

1.5 RANDOM VARIABLES

An important class of functions are measurable functions which are different from the measure functions μ. Whereas measure functions are set functions, measurable functions are invariably point functions.

Definition 1.5.1 Measurable Function

Let $(\Omega_1, \mathcal{F}_1)$ and $(\Omega_2, \mathcal{F}_2)$ be two measurable spaces. Let g be a function with domain $E_1 \subset \Omega_1$ and range $E_2 \subset \Omega_2$

$$g\colon\ \Omega_1 \to \Omega_2$$

g is called an $\mathcal{F}_1$-measurable function or an $\mathcal{F}_1$-measurable mapping if for every $E_2 \in \mathcal{F}_2$

$$g^{-1}(E_2) = \{\omega\colon\ g(\omega) \in E_2\} \triangleq E_1 \tag{1.5.1}$$

is in the σ-field $\mathcal{F}_1$.

If g is measurable with respect to the σ-field $\mathcal{F}$ of sets that are P-measurable, then we might also say that g is P-measurable if there is no confusion.

The set E_1 given by $g^{-1}(E_2)$ is called the *inverse image* or inverse mapping of E_2, and it is a measurable set. Inverse mappings preserve all set relations, as shown by the following proposition.

Proposition 1.5.1 Inverse Mappings

Let g be a measurable mapping from $(\Omega_1, \mathcal{F}_1) \to (\Omega_2, \mathcal{F}_2)$. If $\mathcal{A}$ is a nonempty class of subsets of Ω_2, then

$$\sigma(g^{-1}(\mathcal{A})) = g^{-1}(\sigma(\mathcal{A})) \tag{1.5.2}$$

Proof. Since $g^{-1}(\Omega_2) = \Omega_1$, $g^{-1}(A^c) = (g^{-1}(A))^c$ for $A \in \mathcal{F}_2$ and $g^{-1}(\bigcup_n A_n) = \bigcup_n g^{-1}(A_n)$, and hence $g^{-1}(\sigma(A))$ is a σ-field. Since $g^{-1}(\mathcal{A}) \subset g^{-1}(\sigma(\mathcal{A}))$, we have

$$\sigma(g^{-1}(\mathcal{A})) \subset g^{-1}(\sigma(A))$$

To obtain the reverse inclusion, let $\mathcal{B}$ denote a collection of all subsets E_2 of Ω_2, such that

$$\mathcal{B} = \{E_2\colon \ g^{-1}(E_2) \in \sigma(g^{-1}(\mathcal{A}))\}$$

It can be shown that $\mathcal{B}$ is a σ-field and that $\mathcal{A} \subset \mathcal{B}$. Hence $\sigma\{\mathcal{A}\} \subset \mathcal{B}$, implying that

$$g^{-1}\sigma(\mathcal{A}) \subset g^{-1}(\mathcal{B}) \subset \sigma(g^{-1}(\mathcal{A})) \qquad \square$$

Any measurable function g can be given as the difference of two nonnegative measurable functions g^+ and g^-,

$$g = g^+ - g^- \tag{1.5.3}$$

An important class of functions is that of a real-valued function X which maps $\Omega \to R$. If $\mathcal{R}$ is the Borel field of subsets of R and if $\mathcal{F}$ is the σ-field of subsets of Ω, then if for any $A \in \mathcal{R}$, $X^{-1}(A) \in \mathcal{F}$, then X is an $\mathcal{F}$-measurable function according to the definition of measurability. If now a probability measure P is defined on the measurable space $(\Omega, \mathcal{F})$, then X is a P-measurable function (actually measurable on the σ-field $\mathcal{F}$ of P-measurable sets) and is called a random variable.

Definition 1.5.2 Random Variable

Let $(\Omega, \mathcal{F})$ be a measurable space and $(R, \mathcal{R})$ another measurable space consisting of the real line R and the σ-field of Borel sets $\mathcal{R}$. Let the probability measure P be defined on $(\Omega, \mathcal{F})$. The measurable mapping X from $(\Omega, \mathcal{F})$ into $(R, \mathcal{R})$ is called a real-valued *random variable*.

We shall always assume a real-valued random variable unless otherwise specified.

Naturally, the probability measure P induces a probability measure P_X in the space $(R, \mathcal{R})$. If now $E_2 \in \mathcal{R}$, then

$$P_X(E_2) = P(X^{-1}(E_2)) = P(E_1) = P\{\omega\colon \ X(\omega) \in E_2\} \tag{1.5.4}$$

Equation 1.5.4 relates the probability measure P_X in $(R, \mathcal{R})$ to the probability measure P in $(\Omega, \mathcal{F})$. Instead of writing $P\{\omega\colon \ X(\omega) \in E_2\}$, we shall have the abbreviated notation $P\{X \in E_2\}$.

If Ω is a metric topological space, then $\mathcal{F}$ is the σ-field of all Borel sets of Ω. Then a function g mapping $\Omega \to R$ is a *Borel function* if for every $E_2 \in \mathcal{R}$, $g^{-1}(E_2)$ is a Borel set of Ω. Since Borel sets of Ω are measurable by assumption, every Borel function is $\mathcal{F}$-measurable.

Properties of Real-Valued Random Variables

1. Let X and Y be two real-valued random variables. Then $f \vee g$, $f \wedge g$, $f + g$ are random variables.
2. Let $\{X_n,\ n = 1, 2, \ldots, N\}$ be a convergent sequence of real-valued random variables converging to a limit X. Then X is also a random variable.
3. Let $\{X_n,\ n = 1, 2, \ldots, N\}$ be a convergent sequence of real-valued random variables. Then the set on which $\{X_n\}$ converges is measurable.

If g is a measurable mapping from $(\Omega, \mathcal{F}_1) \to (\Omega_2, \mathcal{F}_2)$ and h is another measurable mapping from $(\Omega_2, \mathcal{F}_2) \to (\Omega_3, \mathcal{F}_3)$, then $h(g(\omega))$ is a composition of the functions g and h and is a measurable mapping from $(\Omega_1, \mathcal{F}_1) \to (\Omega_3, \mathcal{F}_3)$. The inverse mapping $(hg)^{-1}$ is from the subsets of Ω_3 into the subsets of Ω_1, such that for any $B \subset \Omega_3$,

$$
\begin{aligned}
(hg)^{-1}(B) &= \{\omega:\ h(g(\omega)) \in B\} \\
&= \{\omega:\ g(\omega) \in h^{-1}(B)\} \\
&= g^{-1}(h^{-1}(B))
\end{aligned}
$$

or

$$(hg)^{-1} = g^{-1}h^{-1}$$

Indicator Functions

Definition 1.5.3 Indicator Functions

An *indicator* function is a real-valued function defined on the sample space Ω taking either of the two values 1 or 0, depending upon whether or not the ω-point is in the event A:

$$I_A(\omega) = \begin{cases} 1 & \omega \in A \\ 0 & \omega \notin A \quad \text{or} \quad \omega \in \Omega - A \end{cases} \tag{1.5.5}$$

Obviously the indicator function is a random variable since it is a measurable mapping of the sample space into the real line.

As the indicator function is the simplest nontrivial function, we shall enumrate some of the properties. We shall use the quantities cup $(\vee)$ and cap $(\wedge)$

defined by

$$a \vee b = \max(a, b)$$
$$a \wedge b = \min(a, b) \tag{1.5.6}$$

1. $A \subset B \Leftrightarrow I_A \leq I_B$
2. $I_A = I_A^2 = \cdots = I_A^n$
3. $I_\Omega = 1$ (1.5.7)
4. $I_{A \cap B} = I_A \cdot I_B = I_A \wedge I_B$
5. $I_{A \cup B} = I_A + I_B - I_A \wedge I_B = I_A \vee I_B$
6. $I_{A^c} = 1 - I_A$

Definition 1.5.4 Simple Function

Let $\{A_i,\ i = 1, 2, \ldots, n\}$ be a partition of the sample space Ω. A *simple* function $g(\omega)$ can be written in the form

$$g(\omega) = \sum_{k=1}^{n} g_k I_{A_k}(\omega) \tag{1.5.8}$$

where the g_k are distinct real numbers and $I_{A_k}(\omega)$ is the indicator function of the set A_k.

Simple functions can be used to characterize measurable functions as given by the following proposition.

Proposition 1.5.2

A function defined on Ω is measurable if and only if it is a limit of a sequence of simple functions.

This can be proven by noting that if g is measurable, so are g^+ and g^-, and by showing that either of these two functions is the limit of an increasing sequence of nonnegative simple functions. In establishing theorems we will frequently use the technique of proving them for simple functions and extend the result to arbitrary measurable functions using the above characterization.

Since a random variable is a measurable function, a simple random variable can be given in the form

$$X(\omega) = \sum_{k=1}^{n} x_k I_{A_k}(\omega) \tag{1.5.9}$$

where $\{A_k\}$ is the partition of the sample space Ω and the x_k are real numbers.

Distribution Functions

Definition 1.5.5 Distribution Function

A function F from $R \to R$ is called a *distribution* function if it is increasing and right continuous. It is a probability distribution if in addition $\lim_{x \to -\infty} F(x) = 0$ and $\lim_{x \to \infty} F(x) = 1$.

Right continuous functions are those functions for which $F(x) = \lim_{\epsilon \downarrow 0} F(x + \epsilon)$. Similarly *left continuous* functions are those functions for which $F(x) = \lim_{\epsilon \uparrow 0} F(x - \epsilon)$.

We now show how the concept of distribution function is related to the concept of measure. Let the measure space be $(\Omega, \mathcal{F}, \mu)$, where $\Omega = R$ the real line, $\mathcal{F}$ is the σ-field of Borel sets on the real line, and μ is a finite measure. Let k be any point in R. We define a function F_k as

$$F_k(x) = \begin{cases} -\mu(x, k] & x < k \\ 0 & x = k \\ \mu(k, x] & x > k \end{cases} \tag{1.5.10}$$

Clearly

$$F_k(b) - F_k(a) = \mu(a, b] \qquad \text{for } a \leq b \tag{1.5.11}$$

and since μ is a measure with $\mu(a, b] \geq 0$ the function is increasing. Further

$$\lim_{b \downarrow a+} [F_k(b) - F_k(a)] = \lim_{b \downarrow a+} \mu(a, b] = \mu(\varnothing) = 0$$

and therefore F_k is right continuous, and as a consequence F_k is a distribution function determined by the measure μ.

Since μ is a finite measure, the functions F_k are all bounded. Then the function $F_{-\infty}(x)$ defined on R by

$$F_{-\infty}(x) = \mu(-\infty, x] = \mu\{\xi: \ \xi \leq x\} \tag{1.5.12}$$

is also a distribution function determined by μ and will be denoted by $F(x)$. If now μ is the probability measure P, then $F(x)$ is the probability distribution determined by the probability measure P, and eq. 1.5.12 assumes the form

$$F(x) = P(-\infty, x] = P\{\xi: \ \xi \leq x\} \tag{1.5.13}$$

with the property

$$F(-\infty) = \lim_{x \to -\infty} F(x) = 0$$

$$F(\infty) = \lim_{x \to \infty} F(x) = 1 \tag{1.5.14}$$

Thus a measure determines the distribution function, and it can be shown that a distribution function determines the measure. Therefore we can use the terms distribution function and measure interchangeably.

For a random variable X we denote the probability distribution function by

$$F(x) = P\{\omega: \ X(\omega) \leq x\} = P\{X \leq x\} \tag{1.5.15}$$

If the probability distribution function is differentiable, then we obtain the probability density function $f(x)$

$$f(x) = \frac{dF(x)}{dx} \tag{1.5.16}$$

Example 1.5.1

A set consisting of a single point is measurable. Thus

$$\mu\{b\} = \lim_{k \to \infty} \mu(b - 1/k, b] = F(b) - F(b-)$$

If F is continuous at b, then the measure of the set of a single point is zero. If there is a jump at point b, then the measure of the set of the single point is the amount of jump.

1.6 EXPECTATION OF RANDOM VARIABLES

Let $(\Omega, \mathcal{F}, P)$ be a probability space. The *expectation* of a random variable X is usually defined by the Stieltjes integral

$$EX = \int_{-\infty}^{\infty} x \, dF(x) \tag{1.6.1}$$

where $F(x)$ is the probability distribution function as given by eq. 1.5.15. If at least one of the two integrals $\int_0^\infty x \, dF(x)$ or $\int_{-\infty}^0 x \, dF(x)$ is less than ∞, then the integral is well defined. This definition is not convenient for our purposes since the probability measure does not enter in the expression explicitly. As already seen, since distribution function and measure can be used interchangeably, we can interpret the expectation as a measure theoretic concept by the integral of the random variable X over the sample space Ω with respect to the probability measure P, as given by the following definition.

Definition 1.6.1 Expectation

Let $(\Omega, \mathcal{F}, P)$ be a probability space, and let X be a real random variable. The expectation of X is defined by

$$EX = \int_\Omega X(\omega) \, dP(\omega) \qquad \text{or} \qquad \int_\Omega X \, dP \tag{1.6.2}$$

We now have to define the integral, which we will do by stages. First we take a simple random variable of the form

$$X = \sum_{k=1}^{n} x_k I_{A_k} \tag{1.6.3}$$

and define

$$EX = \sum_{k=1}^{n} x_k P(A_k) \tag{1.6.4}$$

Before extending this definition to arbitrary random variables, we enumerate the properties of the expectation operator for simple random variables from eq. 1.6.4.

Properties of Expectation Operator

1. Linearity: $E(aX + bY) = aEX + bEY$ for constants a and b.
2. Homogeneity: $E(cX) = cEX$ for constant c. (1.6.5)
3. Order preservation: $X \geq Y$ implies $EX \geq EY$.

It can be shown that if $\{X_n\}$ is a monotone sequence of simple random variables converging to a simple random variable X, then

$$\lim_{n\to\infty} EX_n = E \lim_{n\to\infty} X_n = EX \qquad \text{(monotone convergence)}$$

Next we consider the case of a nonnegative random variable $X \geq 0$. From Proposition 1.5.2 we can construct an increasing sequence $\{X_n\}$ of nonnegative simple random variables converging to X. Since $\{X_n\}$ is an increasing sequence, $EX_n \leq EX_{n+1}$, and hence $\{EX_n\}$ is an increasing sequence of nonnegative numbers converging to a limit which may be $+\infty$. It can be shown that if there are two sequences $\{X_n\}$ and $\{Y_n\}$ converging to the same limit X, then

$$\lim_{n\to\infty} EX_n = \lim_{n\to\infty} EY_n \tag{1.6.6}$$

We can thus define

$$EX = \lim_{n\to\infty} EX_n \tag{1.6.7}$$

and this limit is unique.

For an arbitrary random variable X we can associate two nonnegative random variables X^+ and X^- as in eq. 1.5.3, defined by

$$\begin{aligned} X^+ &= XI_{\{x \geq 0\}} \\ X^- &= XI_{\{x < 0\}} \end{aligned} \tag{1.6.8}$$

such that

$$X = X^{+} - X^{-} \tag{1.6.9}$$

Since both X^{+} and X^{-} are nonnegative, their expectation is well defined as in eq. 1.6.7. Therefore we can define

$$EX = EX^{+} - EX^{-} \tag{1.6.10}$$

provided that at least one of the expectations, EX^{+} or EX^{-}, is not ∞.

Thus the expectation operator given by eq. 1.6.2 is very well defined. It can be verified that the expectation operator for any random variable also satisfies all three properties of eq. 1.6.5.

A random variable X is *integrable* if $E|X| < \infty$, that is, both EX^{+} and EX^{-} are $< \infty$.

Next we give propositions without proof on passage to the limit of random variables under the expectation operator.

Proposition 1.6.1 Monotone Convergence

Let $\{X_n\}$ be a monotone sequence of random variables converging to X with X integrable. Then

$$EX = \lim_{n\to\infty} EX_n \tag{1.6.11}$$

Here EX may be finite or infinite.

Proposition 1.6.2 Fatou's Lemma

Let $\{X_n\}$ be a sequence of random variables and X an integrable random variable such that $X_n(\omega) \geq X(\omega)$ for all n and ω (bounded from below). Then

$$E \liminf_n X_n \leq \liminf_n EX_n$$

and if $X(\omega)$ is such that $X_n(\omega) < X$ for all n and ω (bounded from above), then

$$\limsup_n EX_n \leq E \limsup_n X_n \tag{1.6.12}$$

Proposition 1.6.3 Dominated Convergence

Let $\{X_n\}$ be a sequence of random variables converging to X. If there exists an integrable random variable Y such that $|X_n(\omega)| \leq Y(\omega)$ for all n and ω, then

$$EX = \lim_{n\to\infty} EX_n \tag{1.6.13}$$

The sequence $\{X_n\}$ is dominated by the integrable random variable Y.

Independence

The concept of independence is basic to probability theory. There is no parallel for independence in measure theory.

Definition 1.6.2 Independence

1. Let $(\Omega, \mathfrak{F}, P)$ be a probability space and let subsets $A, B \in \mathfrak{F}$. The events A and B are *independent* (notation $A \perp\!\!\!\perp B$) if

$$P(A \cap B) = P(A)P(B) \tag{1.6.14}$$

2. n events $A_1, A_2, \ldots, A_n$ are independent if for any subset $\{k_1, k_2, \ldots, k_r\}$, where $r = 1, 2, \ldots, n$,

$$P\left(\bigcap_{i=1}^{r} A_{k_i}\right) = \prod_{i=1}^{r} P(A_{k_i}) \tag{1.6.15}$$

Pairwise independence is not sufficient for N events to be independent. Thus if there are N events,

$$\binom{N}{2} + \binom{N}{3} + \cdots + \binom{N}{N} = 2^N - N - 1$$

equations such as eq. 1.6.15 have to be satisfied to show independence.

Example 1.6.1

If subsets A, B, C of a sample space Ω are $\mathfrak{F}$-measurable, then they are independent if

$$P(A \cap B) = P(A)P(B) \qquad P(B \cap C) = P(B)P(C)$$

$$P(A \cap C) = P(A)P(C) \qquad P(A \cap B \cap C) = P(A)P(B)P(C)$$

Independence can also be defined in terms of σ-fields as given below.

Definition 1.6.3 Independence of σ-Fields

Let $(\Omega, \mathfrak{F}, P)$ be a probability space and let $\{\mathfrak{F}_i, i = 1, 2, \ldots, n\}$ be sub-σ-fields of $\mathfrak{F}$. These sub-σ-fields are independent if for all $A_1 \in \mathfrak{F}_1, A_2 \in \mathfrak{F}_2, \ldots, A_n \in \mathfrak{F}_n$ the events $A_1, A_2, \ldots, A_n$ are independent.

We can also define the independence of random variables X and Y.

Definition 1.6.4 Independence of Random Variables

Let $(\Omega, \mathcal{F}, P)$ be a probability space and let X and Y be two integrable random variables with values in $(R, \mathcal{R})$. If the random variables X and Y are independent, then

$$E(XY) = EXEY \tag{1.6.16}$$

The converse of the above is not true. However, the following proposition holds.

Proposition 1.6.4 Independence of Random Variables

Let $(\Omega, \mathcal{F}, P)$ be a probability space and let X and Y be two integrable random variables with values in $(R, \mathcal{R})$. The random variables X and Y are independent if and only if

$$E[f(X)g(Y)] = E[f(X)]E[g(Y)] \tag{1.6.17}$$

for every choice of f, g: $R \to R$ bounded and measurable.
Equation 1.6.16 is a weaker condition of eq. 1.6.17.

Example 1.6.2

Let us consider the six permutations of $1, 2, 3$ and the three triples $(1, 1, 1)$, $(2, 2, 2)$, and $(3, 3, 3)$ as points in the sample space. We shall assign a probability of $\frac{1}{9}$ to each of these points. Let A_k, $k = 1, 2, 3$, be the event that the kth place is occupied by 1. Obviously $P(A_k) = \frac{1}{3}$, $k = 1, 2, 3$, and

$$P(A_1 \cap A_2) = P(A_1 \cap A_3) = P(A_2 \cap A_3) = \tfrac{1}{9}$$

Hence the three events A_1, A_2, A_3 are pairwise independent. However, $P(A_1 \cap A_2 \cap A_3) = \frac{1}{9} \neq P(A_1)P(A_2)P(A_3) = \frac{1}{27}$. Hence the events A_1, A_2, A_3 are not independent.

From Definition 1.6.2 we can express the independence of events A and B by means of indicator functions. Since $EI_A = P(A)$ and $EI_B = P(B)$,

$$E(I_A I_B) = P(A \cap B) = P(A)P(B) = EI_A EI_B \tag{1.6.18}$$

1.7 CONDITIONING

We shall define conditional probability before going into the discussion of conditional expectation.

Definition 1.7.1 Conditional Probability

Let $(\Omega, \mathfrak{F}, P)$ be a probability space and let A and B be events in the probability space with $P(A) \neq 0$. The *conditional* probability of the event B given that A has occurred is defined by

$$P(B|A) = \frac{P(B \cap A)}{P(A)} \tag{1.7.1}$$

Let us give the physical concept of conditional probability. Let A be an arbitrary but fixed subset of Ω belonging to the field $\mathfrak{F}$. Suppose we construct the following class of events:

$$A \cap \mathfrak{F} = \{A \cap B: \quad B \in \mathfrak{F}\} = \mathfrak{F}_A \tag{1.7.2}$$

Clearly the class $\mathfrak{F}_A$ is a σ-field of subsets of A. Hence we have now constructed a measurable space $(A, \mathfrak{F}_A)$ from $(\Omega, \mathfrak{F})$. However, the probability measure P defined on $(A, \mathfrak{F}_A)$ may not be normed since $P(A)$ is not unity in general. We can therefore define another probability measure P_A by

$$P_A(B) = \frac{P(A \cap B)}{P(A)} \tag{1.7.3}$$

on the σ-field $\mathfrak{F}_A$ with the condition $P(A) > 0$. The measure space $(A, \mathfrak{F}_A, P_A)$ is now a probability space. The set function P_A defined on $\mathfrak{F}_A$ is called the *conditional probability measure* given A. Conditional probability measures, in addition to satisfying the Kolmogorov axioms, eq. 1.4.1, have the following properties:

1. P_A is also a probability measure on $(\Omega, \mathfrak{F})$ since $P_A(\Omega) = 1$. If B_i are disjoint,

$$P_A\left(\sum_i B_i\right) = \frac{P(A \cap \Sigma_i B_i)}{P(A)} = \sum_i \frac{P(A \cap B_i)}{P(A)} = \sum_i P_A(B_i)$$

with the result that $(\Omega, \mathfrak{F}, P_A)$ is also a probability space.

2. If events A and B are independent, then

$$P(B|A) = P(B)$$

which means that the occurrence of A gives no information as to the occurrence of B.

Before defining conditional expectation we shall try to get a physical picture of what it is in light of the above discussion on conditional probabilities. Let X

be a random variable defined on $(\Omega, \mathscr{F}, P)$ and let EX be well defined, namely, if $X = X^+ - X^-$, then either of EX^+ or EX^- is $< \infty$. Let $\mathscr{F}_1$ be a sub-σ-field of $\mathscr{F}$. The conditional expectation of X relative to the σ-field $\mathscr{F}_1$ is an $\mathscr{F}_1$-measurable random variable obtained by averaging X over the atoms of $\mathscr{F}_1$.

Definition 1.7.2 Conditional Expectation

Let $(\Omega, \mathscr{F}, P)$ be a probability space, let $\mathscr{F}_1$ be a sub-σ-field of $\mathscr{F}$, and let X be an integrable real-valued random variable. The conditional expectation of X relative to $\mathscr{F}_1$ is an integrable $\mathscr{F}_1$-measurable random variable $E(X|\mathscr{F}_1)$ or $E^{\mathscr{F}_1}X$, such that for every $A \in \mathscr{F}_1$,

$$\int_A E(X|\mathscr{F}_1)\, dP = \int_A E^{\mathscr{F}_1}X\, dP = \int_A X\, dP \tag{1.7.4}$$

By using the indicator function I_A, eq. 1.7.4 can be expressed in an alternative form by

$$E\left(I_A E^{\mathscr{F}_1}X\right) = E(I_A X) \qquad A \in \mathscr{F}_1 \tag{1.7.5}$$

Radon–Nikodym Theorem

The existence of the conditional expectation is guaranteed by the Radon–Nikodym theorem. We define the absolute continuity of measures before stating the theorem.

Definition 1.7.3 Absolute Continuity of Signed Measures (Halmos, 18, p. 124)

Let $(\Omega, \mathscr{F})$ be a measurable space and let μ and ν be signed measures on $\mathscr{F}$. We say that ν is *absolutely continuous* with respect to μ (notation $\nu \ll \mu$) if for every measurable set $A \in \mathscr{F}$, $\nu(A) = 0$, for which $\mu(A) = 0$.

The statements $\nu \ll \mu$, $\nu^+ \ll \mu$, $\nu^- \ll \mu$, and $|\nu| \ll |\mu|$ are all equivalent. What the definition conveys is that if $\nu \ll \mu$, then ν is small whenever μ is small. If $\nu \ll \mu$ and $\mu \ll \nu$, then ν and μ are *mutually* absolutely continuous and denoted by $\nu \equiv \mu$.

Proposition 1.7.1 Radon–Nikodym Theorem (Halmos, 18, p. 129)

Let $(\Omega, \mathscr{F}, \mu)$ be a σ-finite measure space and let a σ-finite signed measure ν on $\mathscr{F}$ be absolutely continuous with respect to μ ($\nu \ll \mu$). Then there exists a finite real-valued $\mathscr{F}$-measurable function ψ on Ω such that for every $A \in \mathscr{F}$,

$$\nu(A) = \int_A \psi(\omega)\, d\mu(\omega) = \int_A \psi\, d\mu \tag{1.7.6}$$

Further the function ψ is unique up to sets of μ-measure 0.

For a proof see Halmos (18).

The function ψ is called the *density of the signed measure* ν with respect to μ, and it is also called the *Radon–Nikodym derivative* of the signed measure ν,

$$\psi(\omega) = \frac{d\nu}{d\mu}(\omega) \tag{1.7.7}$$

Next we show the existence of the conditional expectation $E^{\mathcal{F}_1}X$. X is an integrable variable on $(\Omega, \mathcal{F}, P)$ and $\mathcal{F}_1$ is a sub-σ-field of $\mathcal{F}$. Let $X = X^+ - X^-$, and by the integrability condition EX^+ and EX^- are finite. Let any event A be $\mathcal{F}_1$-measurable. Now define a signed measure ν on $(\Omega, \mathcal{F}_1)$ by

$$\nu(A) = EI_A X \qquad A \in \mathcal{F}$$

If $P(A) = 0$, then

$$\nu(A) = \int_A X\,dP = 0 \tag{1.7.8}$$

and the signed measure $\nu \ll P$. Therefore by the Radon–Nikodym theorem there exists a unique function ψ such that for all $A \in \mathcal{F}_1$,

$$\nu(A) = \int_A \psi\,dP = \int_A E^{\mathcal{F}_1}X\,dP \tag{1.7.9}$$

We denote ψ by $E^{\mathcal{F}_1}X$ and call it the conditional expectation of X given the σ-field $\mathcal{F}_1$. Therefore the conditional expectation exists and is unique. Combining eqs. 1.7.8 and 1.7.9 gives rise to eq. 1.7.4 of Definition 1.7.2 for the conditional expectation.

Conditional expectation plays a key role in the definition of martingales, which are a collection of random variables. Clearly both conditional expectation and conditional probability are random variables. We next enumerate some important properties of conditional expectations.

Properties of Conditional Expectations. Let $(\Omega, \mathcal{F}, P)$ be a probability space and X, Y, Z are integrable random variables defined on the probability space. Further, let $\mathcal{F}_1$ and $\mathcal{F}_2$ be sub-σ-fields of $\mathcal{F}$.

1. For constants a, b, c and for any $\mathcal{F}_1 \subset \mathcal{F}$,

$$E^{\mathcal{F}_1}(aX + bY + cZ) = aE^{\mathcal{F}_1}X + bE^{\mathcal{F}_1}Y + cE^{\mathcal{F}_1}Z \tag{1.7.10}$$

This expresses the linearity of the conditional expectation.

2. $X \leq Y \Rightarrow E^{\mathcal{F}_1}X \leq E^{\mathcal{F}_1}Y$ (1.7.11)

3. The random variable $E^{\mathcal{F}_1}X$ is clearly $\mathcal{F}_1$-measurable and if X is also $\mathcal{F}_1$-measurable, then

$$E^{\mathcal{F}_1}X = X \tag{1.7.12}$$

This is a repetition of the definition of conditional expectation.

4. If $\mathcal{F}_1 \subset \mathcal{F}_2 \subset \mathcal{F}$, then

$$E^{\mathcal{F}_1}E^{\mathcal{F}_2}X = E^{\mathcal{F}_2}E^{\mathcal{F}_1}X = E^{\mathcal{F}_1}X \tag{1.7.13}$$

Given $\mathcal{F}_1 \subset \mathcal{F}_2$ and by property 3, since $E^{\mathcal{F}_1}X$ is $\mathcal{F}_1$-measurable, it is also $\mathcal{F}_2$-measurable. Hence $E^{\mathcal{F}_2}(E^{\mathcal{F}_1}X) = E^{\mathcal{F}_1}X$. We have to show that $E^{\mathcal{F}_1}E^{\mathcal{F}_2}X = E^{\mathcal{F}_1}X$. Let A be $\mathcal{F}_1$-measurable, and it is also $\mathcal{F}_2$-measurable. The indicator function I_A is also $\mathcal{F}_1$- and hence $\mathcal{F}_2$-measurable. From eq. 1.7.5, for every $A \in \mathcal{F}_1$,

$$E\left(I_A E^{\mathcal{F}_1}E^{\mathcal{F}_2}X\right) = E\left(I_A E^{\mathcal{F}_2}X\right) = E(I_A X) = E\left(I_A E^{\mathcal{F}_1}X\right)$$

which proves eq. 1.7.13 completely. As a consequence of the above it can be shown that

$$EE^{\mathcal{F}_1}X = EX \tag{1.7.14}$$

5. Let X be an $\mathcal{F}_1$-measurable random variable and let the product XY be integrable. Then

$$E^{\mathcal{F}_1}XY = XE^{\mathcal{F}_1}Y \tag{1.7.15}$$

Let A be an event in $\mathcal{F}_1$ and let $X = I_A$. Then from eq. 1.7.5, for every $B \in \mathcal{F}_1$,

$$E\left(I_B E^{\mathcal{F}_1}XY\right) = E(I_B I_A Y) = E(I_{B\cap A}Y) \qquad \text{from eq. 1.5.7}$$

$$E\left(I_B X E^{\mathcal{F}_1}Y\right) = E\left(I_B I_A E^{\mathcal{F}_1}Y\right) = E(I_{B\cap A}Y)$$

and eq. 1.7.15 follows when X is an indicator function. By the linearity property, eq. 1.7.15 is true for simple functions. Again by virtue of linearity we need to prove for the general case only when X and Y are nonnegative, since any function can be given by the difference of two nonnegative functions. For a nonnegative X we can always find a sequence of nonnegative simple functions $\{X_n\}$ converging to X. Using limiting arguments, we can show that eq. 1.7.15 is true in this case also.

6. If X is independent of the σ-field $\mathcal{F}_1$, then

$$E^{\mathcal{F}_1}X = EX \tag{1.7.16}$$

By eq. 1.7.5 for any A measurable in $\mathcal{F}_1$,

$$E\left(I_A E^{\mathcal{F}_1}X\right) = E(I_A X) = (EI_A)(EX)$$

by independence. On the other hand, since EX is a constant,

$$E(I_A EX) = (EI_A)(EX)$$

Hence by the uniqueness of $E^{\mathcal{F}_1}X$ eq. 1.7.16 follows.

7. If A is an atom of $\mathcal{F}_1$ and $P(A) > 0$, then the value of the conditional expectation $E^{\mathcal{F}_1}X$ on an atom $A \in \mathcal{F}_1$ is given by

$$(E^{\mathcal{F}_1}X)_A = \frac{1}{P(A)}\int_A X\,dP \tag{1.7.17}$$

Since A is an atom of $\mathcal{F}_1$, $E^{\mathcal{F}_1}X$ must be a constant on A. Again from eq. 1.7.5,

$$E(I_A E^{\mathcal{F}_1}X) = E(I_A X)$$

Because $E^{\mathcal{F}_1}X$ is constant on A, we can also write

$$E(I_A E^{\mathcal{F}_1}X) = (EI_A)(E^{\mathcal{F}_1}X)_A$$

Hence

$$(E^{\mathcal{F}_1}X)_A = \frac{E(I_A X)}{E(I_A)} = \frac{\int_A X\,dP}{P(A)}$$

Conditional expectations also satisfy convergence properties similar to monotone convergence (eq. 1.6.11), Fatou's lemma (eq. 1.6.12), and dominated convergence (eq. 1.6.13).

Remark. Conditional expectation is really a smoothing operator. Unlike the expectation operator which smooths a random variable to a constant, conditional expectation smooths the random variable, retaining some of the characteristics. However, if we further smooth the conditional expectation, we do get a constant.

1.8 CONVERGENCE OF RANDOM VARIABLES

We have already discussed the convergence of random variables under the expectation operator. Next we discuss the convergence of sequences of random variables where the probability measure plays an important role. The *pointwise convergence* of any sequence $\{X_n\}$ to a limit X is defined as follows.

Definition 1.8.1 Pointwise Convergence (Whittaker and Watson, 58, p. 13)

A sequence $\{X_n\}$ converges to a limit X if and only if for any $\epsilon > 0$, however small, we can find an integer n_0 such that

$$|X_n - X| < \epsilon$$

for every $n > n_0$.

If we now consider a sequence of random variables

$$\{X_1, X_2, \ldots, X_n, \ldots\}$$

and define a pointwise convergence to another random variable X as in Definition 1.8.1, then we must have for every ω-point in Ω the sequence of numbers

$$X_1(\omega),\ X_2(\omega), \ldots, X_n(\omega)$$

converging to $X(\omega)$. This type of convergence is called *everywhere convergence* and is very highly restrictive. It is entirely possible that the sequence may converge for ω-points belonging to a subset of Ω. Consequently, convergence concepts using probability measure are of much greater interest. We now discuss these convergence concepts.

Definition 1.8.2 Almost Sure Convergence

A sequence of random variables $\{X_n\}$ *converges almost surely* (a.s.), or *almost certainly*, or *strongly*, to X if for every ω-point not belonging to the null event A,

$$\lim_{n\to\infty} |X_n(\omega) - X(\omega)| = 0 \tag{1.8.1}$$

This type of convergence is known as convergence with probability 1 and is denoted by

$$X_n(\omega) \underset{n\to\infty}{\overset{\text{a.s.}}{\to}} X(\omega) \qquad \text{or} \qquad X(\omega) = \lim_{n\to\infty} X_n(\omega)\ (\text{a.s.})$$

If the limit X is not known a priori, then we can define a mutual convergence almost surely. The sequence X_n converges *mutually almost surely* if

$$\sup_{m\geq n} |X_m - X_n| \underset{n\to\infty}{\overset{\text{a.s.}}{\to}} 0$$

Both definitions are equivalent.

Definition 1.8.3 Convergence in Probability

A sequence of random variables $\{X_n\}$ *converges in probability* to X if for every $\epsilon > 0$, however small,

$$\lim_{n\to\infty} P(|X_n - X| \geq \epsilon) = 0 \tag{1.8.2}$$

or, equivalently,

$$\lim_{n\to\infty} P(|X_n - X| < \epsilon) = 1$$

It is denoted by

$$X_n(\omega) \overset{\text{l.i.p.}}{\underset{n\to\infty}{\to}} X(\omega) \qquad \text{or} \qquad X(\omega) = \underset{n\to\infty}{\text{l.i.p.}}\, X_n(\omega)$$

We can also define mutual convergence in probability as

$$\lim_{n\to\infty} \sup_{m\geq n} P(|X_m - X_n| \geq \epsilon) \to 0$$

The concept of convergence in probability plays an important role in the consistency of estimators and the weak law of large numbers. We give next some results concerning this concept.

1. If a sequence of random variables $\{X_n\}$ converges almost surely to X, then it converges in probability to the same limit. The converse is not true. However, the following is true.
2. If $\{X_n\}$ converges in probability to X, then there exists a subsequence $\{X_{nk}\}$ of $\{X_n\}$ which converges almost surely to the same limit.
3. $\{X_n\}$ converges in probability if and only if it converges mutually in probability.

Definition 1.8.4 Convergence in the Mean

A sequence of random variables $\{X_n\}$ *converges in the pth mean* ($p > 0$) to X if

$$\lim_{n\to\infty} E|X_n - X|^p \to 0 \tag{1.8.3}$$

It is usually written as

$$X_n(\omega) \overset{\text{l.i.p.m.}}{\underset{n\to\infty}{\to}} X(\omega) \qquad \text{or} \qquad X(\omega) = \underset{n\to\infty}{\text{l.i.p.m.}}\, X_n(\omega)$$

We can also define mutual convergence in the pth mean as

$$\lim_{n\to\infty} \sup_{m\geq n} E|X_m - X_n|^p \to 0$$

An important convergence concept is the *mean-square convergence* in which $p = 2$. The mean-square convergence is written as

$$\lim_{n\to\infty} E|X_n - X|^2 \to 0$$

or, equivalently, by the *mean-square mutual convergence*

$$\lim_{n\to\infty} \sup_{m\geq n} E|X_m - X_n|^2 \to 0 \tag{1.8.4}$$

These are also known as the limit in the *quadratic mean* and denoted by

$$X_n(\omega) \underset{n\to\infty}{\overset{\text{l.i.q.m.}}{\rightarrow}} X(\omega) \qquad \text{or} \qquad X(\omega) = \underset{n\to\infty}{\text{l.i.q.m.}}\, X_n(\omega)$$

Even though convergence in the pth mean is stronger than convergence in probability, it neither implies nor implied by almost sure convergence. We can state some results concerning convergence in the pth mean.

1. If a sequence of random variables $\{X_n\}$ converges in the pth mean, then it converges in probability to the same limit.
2. $\{X_n\}$ converges in the pth mean if and only if it converges mutually in the pth mean.

1.9 MAIN INEQUALITIES OF EXPECTATIONS

Throughout this book we will be using a number of inequalities, and we list them here for ready reference. In the following inequalities X and Y are random variables defined on the probability space $(\Omega, \mathcal{F}, P)$.

Hölder's Inequality. If p and q are real numbers greater than 1 with $1/p + 1/q = 1$ and if the random variables X, Y and $|X|^p$, $|Y|^q$ are integrable, then

$$E|XY| \leq [E|X|^p]^{1/p}[E|Y|^q]^{1/q} \tag{1.9.1}$$

Let x be a positive number and consider the function $\phi(x) = x^p/p + x^{-q}/q$. This function has a minimum at $x = 1$, and at this minimum value $\phi(1) = 1$ by assumption. Let us now substitute $x = b^{1/q}/a^{1/p}$ with $a, b > 0$. Then

$$\begin{aligned}\phi(x) &= (ap)^{-1}b^{p/q} + (bq)^{-1}a^{q/p} \geq 1 \\ &= p^{-1}b^{(p+q)/q} + q^{-1}a^{(p+q)/p} \geq ab\end{aligned}$$

Since $(p+q)/pq = 1$, we have $(p+q)/q = p$ and $(p+q)/p = q$, and we have

$$ab \leq \frac{b^p}{p} + \frac{a^q}{q}$$

We now substitute

$$b = \frac{|X|}{[E|X|^p]^{1/p}} \qquad \text{and} \qquad a = \frac{|Y|}{[E|Y|^q]^{1/q}}$$

and taking expectations we obtain

$$\frac{E|XY|}{[E|X|^p]^{1/p}[E|Y|^q]^{1/q}} \le \frac{1}{p} + \frac{1}{q} = 1$$

and Hölder's inequality follows.

Schwartz's Inequality. In Hölder's inequality if we substitute $p = q = 2$, we obtain

$$E|XY| \le \sqrt{E|X|^2 E|Y|^2} \tag{1.9.2}$$

if X, Y and $|X|^2$, $|Y|^2$ are integrable.

Minkowski's Inequality. If p is a real number with $p \ge 1$ and if random variables X, Y and $|X|^p$, $|Y|^p$ are integrable, then

$$[E|X+Y|^p]^{1/p} \le [E|X|^p]^{1/p} + [E|Y|^p]^{1/p} \tag{1.9.3}$$

If $p = 1$, the result follows from the triangle inequality. We shall prove the result for $p > 1$.

$$\begin{aligned} E|X+Y|^p &= E[|X+Y||X+Y|]^{p-1} \\ &\le [E|X||X+Y|]^{p-1} + E[|Y||X+Y|]^{p-1} \end{aligned}$$

By Hölder's inequality, using $1/q = 1 - 1/p$, we have

$$E|X+Y|^p \le [E|X|^p]^{1/p}[E|X+Y|^p]^{1-1/p} + [E|Y|^p]^{1/p}[E|X+Y|^p]^{1-1/p}$$

Dividing throughout by $[E|X+Y|^p]^{1-1/p}$, we have the desired result.

As already seen, if $p = 1$, we have the triangle inequality

$$E|X+Y| \le E|X| + E|Y| \tag{1.9.4}$$

If $p = 2$, we have

$$[E|X+Y|^2]^{1/2} \le [E|X|^2]^{1/2} + [E|Y|^2]^{1/2} \tag{1.9.5}$$

Jensen's Inequality. If ϕ is a continuous convex function and if both X and $\phi(X)$ are integrable, then

$$\phi(EX) \le E\phi(X) \tag{1.9.6}$$

Since ϕ is a convex function, we can construct a chord $a_i + b_i x$ such that

$$a_i + b_i x \le \phi(x)$$

and

$$\sup_x (a_i + b_i x) = \phi(x)$$

Hence

$$a_i + b_i X \leq \phi(X)$$

and

$$a_i + b_i EX \leq E[\phi(X)]$$

or

$$\sup(a_i + b_i EX) = \phi(EX) \leq E[\phi(X)]$$

Jensen's inequality will have wide application in martingale theory.

All the above inequalities also hold if the expectation operator is replaced by the conditional expectation operator $E^{\mathscr{F}}$. For example, Jensen's inequality can be written for the conditional expectation operator by

$$\phi(E^{\mathscr{F}}X) \leq E^{\mathscr{F}}[\phi(X)] \tag{1.9.7}$$

Generalized Chebyshev Inequality. Let ϕ be a nonnegative Borel function which is even and monotonically increasing in R^+. Let X and $\phi(X)$ be integrable random variables. Then

$$P[|X| \geq a] \leq \frac{E\phi(X)}{\phi(a)} \tag{1.9.8}$$

Let the event A be $\{|X| \geq a\}$. Then

$$E[\phi(X)] = \int_A \phi(X)\, dP + \int_{A^c} \phi(X)\, dP \geq \int_A \phi(X)\, dP$$

Since $\phi(X)$ is increasing and even, $\phi(a) \leq \phi(X)$ and

$$E[\phi(X)] \geq \int_A \phi(X)\, dP \geq \phi(a) \int_A dP = \phi(a) P\{|X| > a\}$$

Equation 1.9.8 follows immediately.

If $\phi(x) = |x|^r$, then we obtain Markov's inequality

$$P[|X| \geq a] \leq \frac{E|X|^r}{a^r} \tag{1.9.9}$$

and if $r = 2$ in Markov's inequality, then we obtain the Chebyshev inequality

$$P[|X| \geq a] \leq \frac{EX^2}{a^2} \tag{1.9.10}$$

Problems

1. If $B = \limsup_n A_n$ and $C = \liminf_n A_n$, show that

$$B^c = \liminf_n A_n^c, \qquad C^c = \limsup_n A_n^c$$

2. If A_n is equal to B or C depending upon whether n is odd or even, show that

$$\limsup_n A_n = B \cup C, \qquad \liminf_n A_n = B \cap C$$

Under what conditions do $\lim_n A_n$ exist?

3. Find $\limsup_n A_{2n}$ and $\liminf_n A_{2n}$ for the following sequence:

$$A_{2n} = \left[0, \frac{1}{2n}\right], \quad A_{2n+1} = \left(-1, \frac{1}{2n+1}\right)$$

Is the sequence $\{A_{2n}\}$ convergent?

4. The minimal σ-field of the class $\mathcal{A}$ can be obtained as follows.
   a. First find $\mathcal{A}_1 = \{\Omega, \varnothing, A_i \in \mathcal{A} \text{ or } A_i^c \in \mathcal{A}, i = 1, 2, \ldots\}$.
   b. Obtain the class $\mathcal{A}_2 = \bigcap_{k=1}^{\infty} B_k$ where $\{B_k \in \mathcal{A}_1\}$. Show that $\mathcal{A}_2$ is closed under intersections but not complementations.
   c. Obtain $\mathcal{F} = \{$finite union of pairwise disjoint subsets belonging to $\mathcal{A}_2\}$. Show that $\mathcal{F}$ is a σ-field and is a minimum field containing $\mathcal{A}$.

5. Show that if $\{A_i^c \in \mathcal{F}, i = 1, 2, \ldots\}$ and $\bigcup_{i=1}^{\infty} A_i \in \mathcal{F}$, then $\bigcap_{i=1}^{\infty} A_i \in \mathcal{F}$.

6. Consider the class $\mathcal{A}$ of all intervals of the form $(-\infty, x)$, $x \in R$. Let $\mathcal{B}$ be the class of all intervals of the form (a, b), $a < b$ and $a, b \in R$. Show that $\sigma(\mathcal{A}) = \sigma(\mathcal{B})$.

7. Prove that the sum of two measures on the same σ-field is a measure. Prove also that the sum of a complete measure and any other measure is a measure.

8. Let $\Omega = \{\omega_1, \omega_2, \omega_3, \omega_4\}$ and let $P\{\omega_1\} = \frac{1}{12}$, $P\{\omega_2\} = \frac{1}{6}$, $P\{\omega_3\} = \frac{1}{3}$, and $P\{\omega_4\} = \frac{5}{12}$. Let $A_n = \{\omega_1, \omega_3\}$ if n is odd and $\{\omega_2, \omega_4\}$ if n is even. Find $P\{\liminf_n A_n\}$, $P\{\limsup_n A_n\}$, $\liminf_n P(A_n)$, and $\limsup_n P(A_n)$ and compare.

9. Prove that a function defined on Ω is measurable if and only if it is a limit of a sequence of simple functions.

10. Prove that if $\{X_n, n = 1, 2, \ldots, N\}$ is a convergent sequence of real-valued random variables, then the set on which $\{X_n\}$ converges is measurable.

11. Prove that if $\{X_n, n = 1, 2, \ldots\}$ is a sequence of real-valued random variables, then $\sup_n X_n$, $\inf_n X_n$, $\limsup_n X_n$, and $\liminf_n X_n$ are all measurable.

12. If g is mapping from $R \to R$, find g^+ and g^-.

13. Show that

$$\mu(a, b) = F(b-) - F(a)$$

$$\mu[a, b) = F(b-) - F(a-)$$

$$\mu[a, b] = F(b) - F(a-)$$

$$\mu(a, b] = F(b) - F(a)$$

14. Prove that if $\{X_n\}$ and $\{Y_n\}$ are two increasing sequences of nonnegative simple random variables converging to the same limit X, then

$$\lim_{n\to\infty} EX_n = \lim_{n\to\infty} EY_n$$

15. Prove Proposition 1.6.2, Fatou's lemma.

16. Let X be a random variable defined on $(\Omega, \mathcal{F}, P)$ with the distribution function $F_X(x)$. Let f be any arbitrary Borel function. Then $f(X(\omega))$ is a random variable defined on $(\Omega, \mathcal{F}, P)$ and $f(X)$ is a random variable defined on $(R, \mathcal{R}, P_X)$. Show that

$$\int_\Omega f(X(\omega))\, dP(\omega) = \int_R f(X)\, dP_X(x)$$

17. Let Ω be the part of a real line $(-3, 2)$. Taking $(\Omega, \mathcal{F}, \mu)$ to be the measure space (μ is the Lebesgue measure), evaluate

$$\int_A X\, d\mu$$

where $A = [-1, 1)$ and

$$X(\omega) = \begin{cases} \frac{1}{2} & \omega \in (-3, -1) \\ \frac{1}{3} & \omega = -1 \\ \frac{1}{6} & \omega \in (0, 1] \\ 1 & \omega \in (1, 2) \end{cases}$$

18. The joint probability density function of random variables X_1, X_2, X_3 is given by

$$f(x_1, x_2, x_3) = \begin{cases} \frac{1}{2} + 4x_1x_2x_3 & 0 < x_1, x_2, x_3 \leq 1 \\ 0 & \text{otherwise} \end{cases}$$

Find whether X_1, X_2, X_3 are pairwise independent or independent.

19. Let $\Omega = \{1, 2, 3, 4\}$ and $\mathcal{F} = \{\varnothing, \Omega, \{1, 3\}, \{2, 4\}\}$ with $P\{1, 3\} = \frac{2}{3}$ and $P\{2, 4\} = \frac{1}{3}$. Define random variables X_1 and X_2 by

$$X_1(k) = k \qquad k = 1, 2, 3, 4$$

$$X_2(k) = \begin{cases} 1 & k = 1, 3 \\ 0 & k = 2, 4 \end{cases}$$

If $\mathcal{F}_X = \sigma\{X_1, X_2\}$, find a whether a conditional probability given $\mathcal{F}_X$ can be defined on $\mathcal{F}$.

20. Let Ω consist of three disjoint sets A, B, C with $A + B + C = \Omega$. Define $P(A) = \frac{1}{2}$, $P(B) = \frac{1}{6}$, and $P(C) = \frac{1}{3}$. $\mathcal{F}$ is the σ-field induced by A, B, C. Define a random variable on $(\Omega, \mathcal{F})$ by $X = I_A + 2I_B + 3I_C$. Let $\mathcal{F}_1 = \{\varnothing, \Omega, A \cup B, C\}$. Find the conditional expectation of X given $\mathcal{F}_1, (E^{\mathcal{F}_1}X)$.

21. Let $\{X_n\}$ be a sequence of random variables with

$$P(X_n = 2^n) = 2^{-n}$$

$$P(X_n = -2^n) = 2^{-n}$$

$$P(X_n = 0) = 1 - 2^{-n+1}$$

Show that $X_n \underset{n\to\infty}{\overset{\text{a.s.}}{\to}} 0$ but not in the pth mean.

22. Let $\{X_n\}$ be a sequence of independent random variables with

$$P(X_n = 0) = 1 - n^{-1}$$

$$P\left(X_n = n^{1/2p}\right) = n^{-1}$$

Show that X_n converges in the pth mean but not almost surely.

23. Give examples of Hölder, Minkowski, and Jensen inequalities.

24. State and prove the Hölder and Minkowski inequalities for finite and infinite sums.

2 STOCHASTIC PROCESSES

2.1 DEFINITION OF STOCHASTIC PROCESSES

Let $(\Omega, \mathfrak{F}, P)$ be a probability space. Let T be an arbitrary indexed parameter set called the *time set*. T can be the real line R, the positive real line R^+, the set of positive integers N, or any semiclosed interval in R or R^+. Unless otherwise specified, we shall assume that T is a semiclosed time interval in R^+. Sometimes we will explicitly state that T is in R^+.

Definition 2.1.1 Stochastic Process

Let $(\Omega, \mathfrak{F}, P)$ be a complete probability space and let T be any time set. Let $(R, \mathfrak{R})$ be a measurable space, where R is the real line and $\mathfrak{R}$ is the σ-field of Borel sets on the real line. A stochastic process $\{X_t, t \in T\}$ is a family of random variables defined on the probability space $(\Omega, \mathfrak{F}, P)$ and taking values in the measurable space $(R, \mathfrak{R})$.

The probability space $(\Omega, \mathfrak{F}, P)$ is called the *base space* and the measurable space $(R, \mathfrak{R})$ the *state space*. For each $t \in T$, the $\mathfrak{F}$-measurable random variable X_t is called the *state* of the process at time t. For each $\omega \in \Omega$ the map $t \to X_t(\omega)$ defined on T and taking values in R is called a *sample function*.

If the time set T is N, then the stochastic process $\{X_t, t \in T\}$ becomes $\{X_n, n \in N\}$ and is called a *discrete* stochastic process. If the time set T is R or R^+, then the stochastic process is a *continuous* one.

Let $T_n = \{t_1, t_2, \ldots, t_n\}$ be a finite set of values from the time set T. The joint distribution function F_{T_n} of the family of random variables

$\{X_{t_1}, X_{t_2}, \ldots, X_{t_n}\}$ is defined by

$$F_{T_n} = P\{X_{t_1} \in A_1, X_{t_2} \in A_2, \ldots, X_{t_n} \in A_n\} \qquad \{A_1, A_2, \ldots, A_n\} \in \mathfrak{R} \tag{2.1.1}$$

The family $\{F_{T_n}\}$ as T_n ranges over all finite sets in T is called the *finite dimensional distribution* of the process.

In practice we are not given a priori the probability space $(\Omega, \mathfrak{F}, P)$ and a family of random variables defined on it. What we observe is a natural phenomenon whose evolution is governed by chance. Observations are made on this phenomenon at time instants $\{t_1, t_2, \ldots, t_n\}$, and the family of distribution functions $\{F_{T_n}\}$ of the type of eq. 2.1.1 is obtained. The question now arises as to whether we can find a stochastic process $\{X_t, t \in T\}$ having these finite dimensional distributions $\{F_{T_n}\}$. One obvious condition should be the following. If T_n and T_m are two ordered finite subsets of T such that $T_m \subset T_n \subset T$, then F_{T_m} should be equal to F_{T_n} with the $n - m$ sets $\{A_{m+1}, \ldots, A_n\}$ being the entire set R:

$$F_{T_m} = P\{X_{t_1} \in A_1, X_{t_2} \in A_2, \ldots, X_{t_m} \in A_m, X_{t_{m+1}} \in R, \ldots, X_{t_n} \in R\} \tag{2.1.2}$$

For example, if $T_m = \{t_1\}$ and $T_n = \{t_1, t_2\}$, then

$$F_{t_1}(x_1) = F_{t_1 t_2}(x_1, \infty)$$

Condition 2.1.2 is known as the compatibility condition.

The answer to the question posed earlier is given in the following proposition stated without proof (Wong, 63, p. 39).

Proposition 2.1.1

Let $\{F_{T_n}\}$ be a compatible family of finite dimensional distribution functions with all finite $T_n \subset T$. Then we can always construct a probability space $(\Omega, \mathfrak{F}, P)$ and a stochastic process $\{X_t, t \in T\}$ such that the stochastic process has the given finite dimensional distribution.

2.2 SEPARABILITY AND MEASURABILITY

Let us first motivate the concepts of separability and measurability by means of examples.

Example 2.2.1

Let $\Omega = [0, 1]$, $\mathfrak{F} = \sigma$-field of Borel sets on $[0, 1]$, let P be the Lebesgue measure, and $T = [0, 1]$. Let us define two stochastic processes $\{X_t, t \in T\}$

and $\{Y_t, t \in T\}$ by

$$X_t(\omega) = 0 \qquad \text{for } t \in T, \omega \in \Omega$$

$$Y_t(\omega) = \begin{cases} 1 & \omega = t \\ 0 & \omega \neq t \end{cases}$$

For both processes $\{X_t\}$ and $\{Y_t\}$, $P\{X_t = 0\} = P\{Y_t = 0\} = 1$, and both processes have the same finite dimensional distribution in the sense that

$$P\{X_{t_1} \leq x_1, X_{t_2} \leq x_2, \dots, X_{t_n} \leq x_n\} = P\{Y_{t_1} \leq y_1, Y_{t_2} \leq y_2, \dots, Y_{t_n} \leq y_n\}$$

for all t_n, x_n and y_n. If we now consider X_t and Y_t as random variables, then X_t and Y_t are different, but they have the same law. Note also that

$$\sup_{t \in T} X_t(\omega) = 0 \qquad \text{for all } \omega \in \Omega$$

$$\sup_{t \in T} Y_t(\omega) = 1 \qquad \text{for all } \omega \in \Omega$$

Thus the finite dimensional distribution of a stochastic process does not determine the distribution of every function of the process without further conditions or criteria which involve all time points *simultaneously*.

Example 2.2.2

Let us now take the stochastic process $\{X_t, t \in T\}$ as defined in Example 2.2.1, where $T = [0, 1]$ and $\Omega = [0, 1]$. If now S is a countably infinite set in $0 \leq t \leq 1$, for example, $S = \{1/k, k = 1, 2, 3, \dots\}$, then clearly

$$P\{X_t(\omega) = 0, t \in S\} = 1$$

However, if we want to assert that

$$P\{X_t(\omega) = 0, t \in T\} = 1$$

then it may not be possible to do so without additional criteria such as separability.

Example 2.2.3

Let $\{X_n, n \in N\}$ be a discrete stochastic process. Then

$$\left\{\sup_n |X_n(\omega)| > \epsilon\right\} = \bigcup_{n=1}^{\infty} \{|X_n(\omega)| > \epsilon\}$$

Each set $\{X_n(\omega) > \epsilon\}$ is measurable, and since the union of measurable sets is also measurable, we can assert that the ω-set $\{\sup_n |X_n(\omega)| > \epsilon\}$ is measurable. However, if T is an interval, then for the set

$$\sup_{t \in T} \{|X_t(\omega)| > \epsilon\} = \bigcup_{t \in T} \{|X_t(\omega)| > \epsilon\}$$

we cannot say anything about its measurability since the union is of an uncountable number of sets. The same argument applies to $\inf_{t\in T}\{|X_t(\omega)| < \epsilon\}$ and to other limiting operations.

The above examples illustrate that in addition to finite dimensional distributions some other concepts such as *separability* and *measurability* (Doob, 14, pp. 51–71) have to be introduced.

Definition 2.2.1 Separable Process

Let $\{X_t, t \in T\}$ be a stochastic process defined on $(\Omega, \mathfrak{F}, P)$ with time set T and values in R. Let K be any closed subset in R, and let I be an open interval in T. Then the process $\{X_t, t \in T\}$ is *separable*, relative to the class of all closed sets K in R, if there exist a countable subset $S \subset T$ and an ω-set Λ of probability 0 such that the two ω-sets

$$\{\omega:\ X_t(\omega) \in K, t \in I \cap T\}, \qquad \{\omega:\ X_t(\omega) \in K, t \in I \cap S\}$$

differ by Λ.

The countable set $S \subset T$ is called a *separating set* or *separant*. What the definition implies is that if $\{X_t, t \in T\}$ is separable, then every set of the form $\{\omega:\ X_t(\omega) \in K,\ t \in I \cap T\}$ differs from the event $\{\omega:\ X_t(\omega) \in K,$ $t \in I \cap S\}$ by the null set Λ and can be made an event by completing the underlying probability space.

Going back to Example 2.2.2, if $\{t_i\}$ is any sequence of values in [0, 1], then

$$P\{X_{t_i}(\omega) = 0, i \geq 0\} = 1$$

Therefore, if we can find a separating set $S \subset I$, then the process $\{X_t, t \in T\}$ is separable and we can assert

$$P\{X_t(\omega) = 0, t \in T\} = 1$$

and indeed $\{t_i\}$ is a separating set.

In Example 2.2.1, in the process Y_t defined by

$$Y_t(\omega) = \begin{cases} 1 & \omega = t, \quad t \in T \\ 0 & \omega \neq t \end{cases}$$

we cannot assert that $P\{Y_t = 0, t \in T\} = 1$ because we cannot find a separating set.

In Example 2.2.3, if the process $\{X_t, t \in T\}$ is separable, then for any open interval $I \subset T$, $\{|X_t(\omega)| > \epsilon, t \in I \cap S\}$ implies that $\{X_t(\omega) > \epsilon, t \in I \cap T\}$. Therefore

$$\sup_{t\in I\cap S}\{|X_t(\omega)| > \epsilon\} \geq \sup_{t\in I\cap T}\{|X_t(\omega)| > \epsilon\}$$

Since $S \subset T$, the reverse inequality holds, leading to the equality

$$\sup_{t \in I \cap S} \{|X_t(\omega)| > \epsilon\} = \sup_{t \in I \cap T} \{|X_t(\omega)| > \epsilon\}$$

for all $\omega \notin \Lambda$.

The function $\sup_{t \in I \cap S}\{|X_t(\omega)| > \epsilon\}$ is a random variable since S is countable. Hence $\sup_{t \in I \cap T}\{|X_t(\omega)| > \epsilon\}$ is a random variable almost everywhere except possibly on Λ, and if the underlying probability space is complete, then it is a random variable.

Since a stochastic process is a mathematical model of a natural phenomenon, the relationship between two stochastic processes $\{X_t, t \in T\}$ and $\{Y_t, t \in T\}$ representing the same phenomenon is given in Definitions 2.2.2, 2.2.3, and 2.2.4.

Definition 2.2.2 Equivalence

Let two stochastic processes $\{X_t\}$ and $\{Y_t\}$ having the same time set T and taking values on the same state space $(R, \mathscr{R})$ be defined on two different probability spaces $(\Omega, \mathscr{F}, P)$ and $(\Omega_1, \mathscr{F}_1, P_1)$, respectively. Then the processes $\{X_t, t \in T\}$ and $\{Y_t, t \in T\}$ are called *equivalent* if the finite dimensional distributions

$$P\{X_{t_1} \in A_1, X_{t_2} \in A_2, \ldots, X_{t_n} \in A_n\} = P_1\{Y_{t_1} \in A_1, Y_{t_2} \in A_2, \ldots, Y_{t_n} \in A_n\} \tag{2.2.1}$$

for every finite time sequence $\{t_n\}$ and $\{A_i, i = 1, 2, \ldots, n\} \in \mathscr{R}$.

If the two processes $\{X_t\}$ and $\{Y_t\}$ have the same time law and take values on the same state space, then they are equivalent and $\{Y_t\}$ is also called a *version* of $\{X_t\}$.

Example 2.2.4

In Example 2.2.1 the two processes $\{X_t, t \in T\}$ and $\{Y_t, t \in T\}$ have the same time law and $P\{Y_t = X_t\} = 1$. We can say that the process $\{X_t\}$ is equivalent to the process $\{Y_t\}$. However, the sample paths of $\{X_t\}$ are continuous whereas the sample paths of $\{Y_t\}$ are almost discontinuous. The set of all ω such that $\{Y_t(\omega) = X_t(\omega)\}$ is empty for all $\omega \in \Omega$. Hence $P\{\omega: \;\; Y_t(\omega) = X_t(\omega)\} = 0$ for all $\omega \in \Omega$.

Considering the above factors in Example 2.2.4, the following definitions make the relationship between two stochastic processes more precise.

Definition 2.2.3 Modification

Let $\{X_t, t \in T\}$ and $\{Y_t, t \in T\}$ be two stochastic processes defined on the same probability space $(\Omega, \mathfrak{F}, P)$ taking values in the same state space $(R, \mathfrak{R})$. Then $\{Y_t, t \in T\}$ is a *modification* of the processes $\{X_t, t \in T\}$ if $P\{X_t = Y_t\} = 1$ for all $t \in T$.

Example 2.2.5

Using Definition 2.2.3, the process $\{X_t, t \in T\}$ in Examples 2.2.1 and 2.2.4 is a modification of $\{Y_t, t \in T\}$. However, the difference between the two processes is brought forth by the following very precise definition.

Definition 2.2.4 Indistinguishability

The processes $\{X_t, t \in T\}$ and $\{Y_t, t \in T\}$ of Definition 2.2.3 are indistinguishable with respect to the probability measure P if for almost all $\omega \in \Omega$, $P\{\omega\colon\ X_t(\omega) = Y_t(\omega)\} = 1$.

In other words, the processes $\{X_t\}$ and $\{Y_t\}$ are indistinguishable if and only if the set $\{t, \omega\colon\ X_t(\omega) \neq Y_t(\omega)\}$ is a null set. If two processes are indistinguishable, their sample paths coincide almost everywhere.

Example 2.2.6

Referring to Examples 2.2.1 and 2.2.4, the process $\{X_t\}$ is a modification of $\{Y_t\}$ and their sample paths do not coincide almost everywhere. Hence $\{X_t\}$ and $\{Y_t\}$ are not indistinguishable.

The following proposition given without proof connects any stochastic process with another separable stochastic process.

Proposition 2.2.1 (Doob, 14, p. 57; Meyer, 41)

If the probability space $(\Omega, \mathfrak{F}, P)$ is complete, then every stochastic process $\{X_t, t \in T\}$ on $(\Omega, \mathfrak{F}, P)$ admits of a separable modification on the same probability space.

Example 2.2.7

Again in Example 2.2.1 the process $\{X_t\}$ is a separable modification of the nonseparable process $\{Y_t\}$. Further discussions on separability are given at the beginning of Section 2.3.

Next we shall turn our attention to the concepts of measurability. In Example 2.2.3 the set $\sup_{t \in T}\{|X_t(\omega)| > \epsilon\}$ may not be a random variable due to uncountable set operations. Similarly in integrals of the type $\int_a^b X_t(\omega)\,dt$, even if almost all sample functions of the stochastic process $\{X_t, t \in T\}$ are Lebesgue integrable, the resulting integral may not be a random variable. What we need here is that the process $X_t(\omega)$ should define a measurable mapping of a pair of variables (t, ω) taking values on some state space $(R, \mathfrak{R})$. Here the t-measure is taken as the Lebesgue measure and the ω-measure as the given probability measure P. The product of these two measures assumed independent defines a (t, ω) measure. We have taken the Lebesgue measure on time rather than any other Borel measure because we are interested in defining integrals of the type $\int_a^b X_t(\omega)\,dt$ as a Lebesgue integral of sample functions. We have the following definition for measurability.

Definition 2.2.5 Measurability (Doob, 14, p. 60)

A stochastic process $\{X_t, t \in T\}$ defined on a probability space $(\Omega, \mathfrak{F}, P)$ with a time set T is a *measurable process* if for all Lebesgue measurable sets B belonging to the σ-field $\mathfrak{L}(T)$ generated by Lebesgue measurable sets the mapping $(t, \omega) \to X_t(\omega)$ is measurable on $T \times \Omega$ with respect to the product σ-field $\mathfrak{L} \otimes \mathfrak{F}$, that is,

$$\{(t, \omega):\quad X_t(\omega) \in B\} \in \mathfrak{L} \otimes \mathfrak{F} \tag{2.2.2}$$

Since every stochastic process has a separable modification according to Proposition 2.2.1, separability is not a restriction on finite dimensional distributions, whereas measurability generally imposes restrictions. For example, if the time set T has a positive Lebesgue measure, the measurability of the process imposes restrictions on the finite dimensional distributions.

The following theorem by Doob (14) justifies all integrals of the sample functions of a stochastic process defined on a complete probability space $(\Omega, \mathfrak{F}, P)$.

Theorem 2.2.1 (Doob, 14, p. 62)

Let $\{X_t, t \in T\}$ be a measurable stochastic process with respect to the product σ-field $\mathfrak{L} \otimes \mathfrak{F}$. Then

1. Almost all sample functions of this process are Lebesgue measurable functions of $t \in T$.
2. If $EX_t(\omega)$ exists for all $t \in T$, then it also defines a Lebesgue measurable function of $t \in T$.
3. If A is a Lebesgue measurable time set in T and if $\int_A E|X_t|\,dt < \infty$, then almost all sample functions $X_t(\omega)$ are Lebesgue integrable on the set A, that is,

$$\int_A |X_t(\omega)|\,dt < \infty \qquad \text{for almost all } \omega$$

Since the value of an absolutely convergent integral is independent of the order of integration, we have

$$\int_A EX_t(\omega)\,dt = E\int_A X_t(\omega)\,dt \tag{2.2.3}$$

Next we define additional terminology connected with stochastic processes. We continue to assume that the time set T is the positive real line R^+ unless otherwise specified. Extensions to other time sets can be established easily.

Definition 2.2.6 Increasing σ-Field or Filtration σ-Field

Let $(\Omega, \mathcal{F})$ be a complete measurable space and let $\{\mathcal{F}_t, t \in T, T = R^+\}$ be a family of sub-σ-fields of $\mathcal{F}$ such that for $s \le t$, $\mathcal{F}_s \subset \mathcal{F}_t$. Then $\{\mathcal{F}_t\}$ is called an *increasing family* of sub-σ-fields on $(\Omega, \mathcal{F})$ or the *filtration* σ-field of $(\Omega, \mathcal{F})$.

$\mathcal{F}_t$ is called the σ-field of events prior to t. If $\{X_t, t \in T\}$ is a stochastic process defined on $(\Omega, \mathcal{F}, P)$ then clearly $\mathcal{F}_t$ given by

$$\mathcal{F}_t = \sigma\{X_s, s \le t, t \in T\} \tag{2.2.4}$$

is increasing.

Since the probability space $(\Omega, \mathcal{F}, P)$ is complete, the σ-field $\mathcal{F}$ contains all subsets of Ω having probability measure zero. We shall assume here that the filtration σ-field $\{\mathcal{F}_t, t \in T\}$ also contains all the sets from $\mathcal{F}$ having probability measure zero.

We now define continuity concepts for the filtration σ-field $\{\mathcal{F}_t, t \in T\}$.

Definition 2.2.7 Continuity

The filtration σ-field $\{\mathcal{F}_t, t \in T, T = R^+\}$ is right continuous if

$$\mathcal{F}_t = \mathcal{F}_{t+} = \bigcap_{\tau > t} \mathcal{F}_\tau \qquad \text{for all } t \in T \tag{2.2.5a}$$

and left continuous if

$$\mathcal{F}_t = \mathcal{F}_{t-} = \sigma\Big\{\bigcup_{\tau < t} \mathcal{F}_\tau\Big\} = \bigvee_{\tau < t} \mathcal{F}_\tau \qquad \text{for all } t \in T \tag{2.2.5b}$$

Remark. If the time set T is a set of positive integers N, then $\mathcal{F}_{n+}$ and $\mathcal{F}_{n-}$ are interpreted as $\mathcal{F}_{n+1}$ and $\mathcal{F}_{n-1}$ for all $n \in N$.

Definition 2.2.8 Adaptation of $\{X_t\}$

Let $\{X_t, t \in T, T = R^+\}$ be a stochastic process defined on a probability space $(\Omega, \mathcal{F}, P)$ and let $\{\mathcal{F}_t, t \in T, T = R^+\}$ be a filtration σ-field. The process $\{X_t\}$

is *adapted* to the family $\{\mathfrak{F}_t\}$ if X_t is $\mathfrak{F}_t$-measurable for every $t \in T$. Or

$$E^{\mathfrak{F}_t} X_t = X_t \qquad t \in T$$

$\mathfrak{F}_t$-adapted random processes are also $\mathfrak{F}_t$-measurable and nonanticipative with respect to the σ-field $\mathfrak{F}_t$.

Example 2.2.8

If $\mathfrak{F}_t$ is the σ-field generated by $\{X_s, s \leq t\}$, then clearly the process $\{X_t, t \in T\}$ is adapted to the family $\{\mathfrak{F}_t, t \in T\}$, which is called the *natural family* or *natural filtration* of the process $\{X_t\}$.

Now we give a physical meaning to the filtration σ-field which plays a key role in the theory of estimation. If t represents the present time and each event a physical phenomenon, say, the temperature of a place, then the sub-σ-field $\mathfrak{F}_t$ consists of all physical phenomena that have occurred before the present time t. The $\mathfrak{F}_t$-measurable random variables, for example, the temperature of a place, are those phenomena that depend only on the evolution before the present time t. The temperature of a place yesterday is adapted, but the temperature of a place tomorrow is not adapted. Whereas the former depends on the past history, the latter depends on the future evolution. However, both may have the same probability law. The introduction of the filtration σ-field is a natural consequence of the distinction between the uncertainty of the future and the knowledge of the past.

The introduction of the filtration σ-field makes the concept of measurability of a stochastic process $\{X_t, t \in T\}$ more precise.

Definition 2.2.9 Progressive Measurability

Let $(\Omega, \mathfrak{F}, P)$ be a complete probability space and let $\{\mathfrak{F}_t, t \in T, T = R^+\}$ be a filtration σ-field of it. Let $\{X_t, t \in T, T = R^+\}$ be a stochastic process defined on this space with values in $(R, \mathfrak{R})$. The process $\{X_t, t \in T\}$ is *progressively measurable* if for any $t \in T$, the mapping $(\tau, \omega) \to X_\tau(\omega)$, $\tau \leq t$, of $[0, t] \times \Omega$ into R is measurable with respect to the product σ-field $\mathfrak{L}([0, t]) \otimes \mathfrak{F}_t$ where $\mathfrak{L}([0, t])$ is the σ-field of Lebesgue measurable sets B on $[0, t]$. Or

$$\{(\omega, \tau \leq t):\ X_\tau(\omega) \in B\} \in \mathfrak{L}([0, t]) \otimes \mathfrak{F}_t \tag{2.2.6}$$

Remark. Any progressively measurable process $\{X_t, t \in T\}$ is both measurable and adapted to the filtration σ-field $\{\mathfrak{F}_t, t \in T\}$.

Fubini's theorem gives us the measurability of the expectation $EX_t(\omega)$ of a measurable stochastic process. In the spirit of this theorem we make the following assumption regarding conditional expectation. Let $\{X_t, t \in T, T = R^+\}$ be a stochastic process defined on a probability space $(\Omega, \mathfrak{F}, P)$ with $E|X_t(\omega)| < \infty$. Let $\{\mathfrak{F}_t, t \in T\}$ be a filtration σ-field with $\{X_t\}$ not necessarily adapted to $\mathfrak{F}_t$. Then the conditional expectation $E^{\mathfrak{F}_t}X_t$ is either $\mathfrak{F}_t$-measurable, or an $\mathfrak{F}_t$-measurable modification can be constructed. Hence we shall assume throughout the book that the conditional expectation $E^{\mathfrak{F}_t}X_t$ is adapted to the family $\{\mathfrak{F}_t\}$.

As we shall be dealing with second-order processes, we next define second-order processes and allied concepts.

Definition 2.2.10 Second-Order Process

A *second*-order stochastic process $\{X_t, t \in T\}$ is a process which satisfies $E|X_t|^2 < \infty$ for every $t \in T$. It is also called an L^2-process.

The *mean*, *autocovariance* and *autocorrelation* functions of a second-order process are defined by

$$\begin{aligned} \mu(t) &= EX_t \\ C_X(t, s) &= E[X_t - \mu(t)][X(s) - \mu(s)]^* \\ R_X(t, s) &= EX_t X_s^* \end{aligned} \tag{2.2.7}$$

where the asterisk denotes the complex conjugate.

The matrix Γ formed by setting $\Gamma_{ij} = C_X(t_i, t_j)$ defined on the square $T \times T$ is a nonnegative definite function.

2.3 CONTINUITY CONCEPTS

The sample paths of a stochastic process are due to chance phenomena, and the regularity of these paths is of concern to us. The first question we have to answer is whether they are continuous at a point or continuous in an interval. In stochastic processes many well-behaved processes may have jumps, and an ill-behaved process may be continuous. Nevertheless, continuity plays a role in the properties of a stochastic process, and hence we define different types of continuity just as we defined different types of convergence.

Definition 2.3.1 Continuous in Probability

A stochastic process $\{X_t, t \in T\}$ is *continuous in probability at a point* $t \in T$ if for every $\epsilon > 0$,

$$\lim_{s \to t} P\{|X_s - X_t| \geq \epsilon\} \to 0 \tag{2.3.1}$$

If $\{X_t, t \in T\}$ is continuous in probability at every point $t \in T$, then we say, that it is *continuous in probability on T* or simply continuous in probability.

We saw in Proposition 2.2.1 that for every stochastic process there is a separable modification. In general, the separating set as given in Definition 2.2.1 is quite complicated. However, if a continuity condition is satisfied by the finite dimensional distributions, we have a simpler separating set as given by the following proposition.

Proposition 2.3.1

Let $\{X_t, t \in T\}$ be any separable stochastic process continuous in probability defined on a complete probability space $(\Omega, \mathcal{F}, P)$. Then every countable dense set in T is a separating set.

What the proposition conveys is that if a stochastic process $\{X_t, t \in T\}$ is separable and continuous in probability, then the probability of an event involving an uncountable X_t can be calculated by choosing a countable number of partitions of T and letting the number of partitions become arbitrarily fine. This will be illustrated by the following example.

Example 2.3.1

We assume that the stochastic process $\{X_t, t \in T\}$ is both separable and continuous in probability. We have to determine $P\{X_t \geq 0, t \in T, T = [0,1]\}$. Clearly this probability is given by the probability of the uncountable intersection $\cap_{t \in T}\{\omega\colon\ X_t(\omega) \geq 0\}$. To calculate the pobability, we assume that the countably dense set S is the partition of T given by

$$S = \left\{\frac{k}{2^n}, 0 \leq k \leq 2^n, n = 0, 1, 2, \ldots\right\}$$

Then

$$P\{X_t \geq 0, t \in T\} = P\left(\bigcap_{t \in T} \omega\colon\ X_t(\omega) \geq 0\right)$$

$$= P\left(\bigcap_{n=0}^{\infty} \omega\colon\ X_{k/2^n}(\omega) \geq 0, 0 \leq k \leq 2^n\right)$$

If we define $A_n = \{\omega\colon\ X_{k/2^n}(\omega) \geq 0, 0 \leq k \leq 2^n\}$, then the sequence $\{A_n\}$ is a decreasing sequence, and since the probability measure is sequentially continuous, the limit exists and we can write

$$P\{X_t \geq 0, t \in T\} = \lim_{n \to \infty} P\left\{\omega\colon\ X_{k/2^n}(\omega) \geq 0, 0 \leq k \leq 2^n\right\}$$

The continuity condition also gives a sufficient condition for a separable and measurable modification of any stochastic process to exist (Doob, 14, p. 61).

Proposition 2.3.2

If $\{X_t, t \in T\}$ is any stochastic process continuous in probability defined on a complete probability space $(\Omega, \mathfrak{F}, P)$, then it admits a separable and measurable modification.

Separability and measurability may not be automatically implied if a process $\{X_t, t \in T\}$ is continuous in probability. However, we can always construct a separable and measurable modification with the separating set being a countably dense set.

Definition 2.3.2 *p*th Mean Continuity

A stochastic process $\{X_t, t \in T\}$ defined on a probability space $(\Omega, \mathfrak{F}, P)$ is continuous in the pth mean at $t \in T$ if

$$\lim_{s \to t} E|X_s - X_t|^p \to 0 \tag{2.3.2}$$

If it is continuous in the pth mean at every $t \in T$, then it is a pth mean continuous process.

If $p = 2$, we have a quadratic mean continuous process defined by

$$\lim_{s \to t} E|X_s - X_t|^2 \to 0 \tag{2.3.3}$$

The quadratic mean continuity of a second-order process is tied to the continuity of the mean and the autocovariance functions as given by the following proposition.

Proposition 2.3.3

Let $\{X_t, t \in T\}$ be a real stochastic process defined on the probability space $(\Omega, \mathfrak{F}, P)$ with $E|X_t|^2 < \infty$ for all $t \in T$, and let $\mu_X(t)$ and $C_X(t, s) = E[X(t) - \mu(t)][X(s) - \mu(s)]$ represent the mean and the autocovariance functions, respectively, of the process. Then the process is continuous in the quadratic mean at $t \in T$ if and only if

1. $\mu_X(t) = EX_t$ is continuous at t.
2. $C_X(t, s)$ is continuous at the diagonal point $t = s$.

Proof. The proof is quite simple. Expanding eq. 2.3.3,

$$E|X_s - X_t|^2 = C_X(s,s) - 2C_X(s,t) + C_X(t,t) - [\mu_X(s) - \mu_X(t)]^2$$

Since $C_X(t, s)$ is continuous at $s = t$ and $\mu_X(t)$ is continuous at t, the right-hand side terms go to zero as $s \to t$, and thus

$$\lim_{s \to t} E|X_s - X_t|^2 \to 0$$

Conversely,

$$C_X(\tau, s) - C_X(t,t) = EX_\tau X_s - \mu_\tau \mu_s - EX_t^2 + \mu_t^2$$

$$= E(X_s - X_t)X_\tau + E(X_\tau - X_t)X_t - \mu_\tau\mu_s + \mu_t^2$$

By Schwartz's inequality we have

$$C_X(\tau, s) - C_X(t,t) \le \left(E|X_s - X_t|^2 EX_\tau^2\right)^{1/2} + \left(E|X_\tau - X_t|^2 EX_t^2\right)^{1/2}$$

$$-\mu_\tau\mu_s + \mu_t^2$$

Because the process $\{X_t\}$ is quadratic mean continuous, the left-hand side of the inequality goes to zero as $\tau, s \to t$, and the continuity of $C_X(t, s)$ at $s = t$ and EX_t can be deduced. □

From Chebyshev's inequality

$$P(|X_s - X_t| \ge \epsilon) \le \frac{E(X_s - X_t)^2}{\epsilon^2} \qquad \epsilon > 0$$

we deduce that, as $s \to t$, the right-hand side goes to zero by quadratic mean continuity, thereby implying continuity in probability.

The two continuity concepts defined above can be decided on the basis of finite dimensional distributions of the process. We now define continuity concepts where separability plays an important role.

Definition 2.3.3 Almost Sure Continuity

Let $\{X_t,\ t \in T\}$ be a separable stochastic process defined on a complete probability space $(\Omega, \mathfrak{F}, P)$. The process is *almost surely* (a.s.) *continuous* at a point $t \in T$ if

$$P\left\{\omega\colon \lim_{s \to t} |X_s(\omega) - X_t(\omega)| = 0\right\} = 1 \qquad (2.3.4)$$

If it is almost surely continuous at every point $t \in T$, then it is an almost surely continuous process.

Almost sure continuity at a point $t \in T$ can be interpreted in a different way. If we now define an $\mathcal{F}$-measurable set

$$\Lambda_t = \left\{\text{set of all trajectories of } X_t \text{ discontinuous at } t,\ X_t \neq \lim_{s \to t} X_s\right\}$$

then almost sure continuity at a point t implies that Λ_t is a null set, that is, $P(\Lambda_t) = 0$. Almost sure continuity of a process implies only that the probability of countable union of Λ_t for $t \in T$ is zero. By its very definition almost sure continuity implies continuity in probability.

Even though almost sure continuity implies that the countable union of Λ_t is also a null set, it is not necessary that the uncountable union of Λ_t be a null set, as given by the following example.

Example 2.3.2

Let $(\Omega, \mathcal{F}, P)$ be the probability space with $\Omega = [0,1]$. Let $\{X_t\}$ be the stochastic process defined on $T = [0,1]$ and Ω by

$$X_{t_i}(\omega) = \begin{cases} 0 & t_i < \omega \\ 1 & t_i \geq \omega \end{cases}$$

Clearly all the trajectories of this process are continuous except at the point $t_i = \omega$. Hence the set $N_{t_i} = \{t_i\}$ is a null set, and the countable union $\cup_{i=1}^{\infty}\{t_i\}$ is also a null set. However, the uncountable union $\cup_{t_i \in T}\{t_i\}$ is equal to Ω and is not a null set.

We may deduce from the examples given above that the three concepts of continuity defined may not be adequate to cover all cases. It is shown in Section 2.4 that at any point t the Poisson process is continuous in probability, continuous in the quadratic mean using Proposition 2.3.3, and continuous almost surely using Example 2.3.2. However, the graph of a Poisson process is anything but continuous, and hence a much stronger criterion of continuity is required, as given in the following definition.

Definition 2.3.4 Almost Surely Sample Continuous

Let $\{X_t,\ t \in T\}$ be a separable stochastic process defined on a complete probability space $(\Omega, \mathcal{F}, P)$. The process is *almost surely sample continuous* if

$$P\left[\bigcup_{t \in T}\left\{\omega\colon\ \lim_{s \to t} X_s(\omega) - X_t(\omega) \neq 0\right\}\right] = 0 \qquad (2.3.5)$$

What the definition conveys is that if a stochastic process $\{X_t, t \in T\}$ is almost surely sample continuous, then there is a representation of X_t whose sample function will be continuous at t with probability 1.

Clearly almost sure continuity at every $t \in T$ does not imply almost sure sample continuity. The former is concerned with the countable union of null sets and the latter with the uncountable union of null sets. Even though the Poisson process satisfies the three criteria of continuity, it is not almost surely sample continuous. However, almost sure sample continuity implies almost sure continuity at every $t \in T$, which in turn implies continuity in probability.

It is difficult to determine the sample continuity of a process from the definition. To this end the Kolmogorov condition as given by the following proposition, without proof, is used to verify sample continuity.

Proposition 2.3.4 Kolmogorov Condition

Let $\{X_t, t \in T\}$ be a separable stochastic process defined on a complete probability space $(\Omega, \mathfrak{F}, P)$. Let T be a closed interval in R^+. If there exist three strictly positive constants α, β, and C such that for all $t \in T$

$$E|X_{t+h} - X_t|^\alpha \leq Ch^{1+\beta} \tag{2.3.6}$$

then

$$\lim_{h \to 0} \sup_{\substack{s,t \in T \\ |s-t|<h}} |X_s - X_t| \overset{\text{a.s.}}{\to} 0$$

and almost every sample function is uniformly continuous on T.

2.4 CLASSES OF STOCHASTIC PROCESSES

In this section we shall consider several types of stochastic processes frequently encountered in this book and discuss their properties.

Stationary Processes and Ergodicity

Definition 2.4.1 Stationary Process

Let $\{X_t, t \in T\}$ be a stochastic process with time set T defined on a probability space $(\Omega, \mathfrak{F}, P)$ taking values in the state space $(R, \mathfrak{R})$. Let $T_n = \{t_1, t_2 \ldots t_n\}$ be any finite set of values belonging to T. Then the process is *strictly stationary* or *stationary* if for any real Δt the joint distribution of the sequence $\{X(t_1), X(t_2), \ldots, X(t_n)\}$ is the same as the joint distribution of $\{X(t_1 + \Delta t), X(t_2 + \Delta t), \ldots, X(t_n + \Delta t)\}$ for any positive integer n.

In other words, the finite dimensional distributions given by eq. 2.1.1 can be expressed for a strictly stationary process as

$$P\{X_{t_1} \in A_1, X_{t_2} \in A_2, \ldots, X_{t_n} \in A_n\}$$

$$= P\{X_{t_1+\Delta t} \in A_1, X_{t_2+\Delta t} \in A_2, \ldots, X_{t_n+\Delta t} \in A_n\} \qquad (2.4.1)$$

for $A_i \in \mathcal{R}$, $i = 1, 2, \ldots, n$, and therefore they depend only on the time difference Δt and not on $\{t_1, t_2, \ldots, t_n\}$.

In many applications this is too strict a definition, and hence we define now stationarity for a wider class of processes.

Definition 2.4.2 Wide Sense Stationary

A real stochastic process X_t, $t \in T$, is *wide sense stationary* or *covariance stationary* if

1. $EX_t^2 < \infty$.
2. $\mu_X = EX_t$ a constant. (2.4.2)
3. $C_X(t-s) = E(X_t - \mu)(X_s - \mu)$ depends only on the time difference $t - s$ and not on either t or s.

By the very nature of the definition, strict sense stationarity implies wide sense stationarity, but the converse is not true.

Example 2.4.1

Let us consider a stochastic process consisting of a sequence $\{X_1, X_2, \ldots\}$ of independent identically distributed random variables with mean μ and variance σ^2. The autocovariance $\sigma_x(h) = \sigma^2\delta_h$, where h is the lag and δ_h is the Kronecker delta. Clearly this process is wide sense stationary according to the definition.

Example 2.4.2

Let us consider another process given by $Y_1 = Y_2 = \cdots = Y$ with mean μ and variance σ^2. Here $C_X(h) = \sigma^2$ for all h. This process is also wide sense stationary.

The processes $\{X_n\}$ and $\{Y_n\}$ of Examples 2.4.1 and 2.4.2 are two extreme cases of stationary processes. The sample mean of the process $\{X_n\}$ given by $\hat{\mu}_X = (1/n)(X_1 + X_2 + \cdots + X_n)$ converges to the true value μ as $n \to \infty$.

However, the sample mean of the process $\{Y_n\}$ given by $\hat{\mu}_Y = (1/n)(Y_1 + Y_2 + \cdots + Y_n)$ does not converge to anything as $n \to \infty$. There is as much randomness in the nth sample mean as there is in the first observation Y_1.

On the other hand, knowledge of X_i gives no information on X_{i+1}, but knowledge of Y_i precisely determines Y_{i+1}. $\{X_n\}$ is unpredictable, and $\{Y_n\}$ is predictable.

The behavior of sample averages obtained from a process converging to some parameter of the process is termed *ergodic.* If a stationary process is ergodic, we can draw inferences by observing a single sample path for a sufficiently long time rather than observing separate independent sample paths. The conditions under which a stationary process can be considered ergodic is given by the following proposition.

Proposition 2.4.1 Ergodic Theorem

Let $\{X_t, t \in T\}$ be a separable and measurable stationary process defined on a complete probability space $(\Omega, \mathfrak{F}, P)$ taking values on $(R, \mathfrak{R})$, and let g be any measurable function such that $E|g(X_0)| < \infty$. Then the process is ergodic if and only if

$$\lim_{T\to\infty} \frac{1}{T}\int_{-T/2}^{T/2} g(X_t)\,dt = Eg(X_0) \tag{2.4.3}$$

In the two processes given in Examples 2.4.1 and 2.4.2 the process $\{X_n\}$ is ergodic, whereas $\{Y_n\}$ is not.

We shall have more to say about wide sense stationary processes in Chapter 5.

Gaussian Processes

Many physically occurring random phenomena can be modeled by Gaussian processes. This is because the finite dimensional distributions are fairly simple to manipulate, the first two moments completely characterizing the process, and uncorrelatedness implying independence. The Brownian motion process, which is discussed in later chapters, is a Gaussian process playing a key role in the modeling of many physical phenomena. The concept of white noise derived from the Brownian motion process is widely used to model noise processes in engineering problems.

Definition 2.4.3 Gaussian Random Variable

Let X be a random variable with $EX^2 < \infty$, and let $\mu = EX$ and $\sigma^2 = E(X - \mu)^2$. Then the random variable X is *Gaussian* if the probability distribution function

$$F_X(a) = P\{X \le a\} = \int_{-\infty}^{a} \frac{1}{\sqrt{2\pi\sigma^2}} \exp\left[-\frac{(x-\mu)^2}{2\sigma^2}\right] dx \qquad (2.4.4)$$

Remarks

1. σ^2 can have a value 0, in which case the random variable $X = \mu$ with probability 1 and we have a degenerate Gaussian random variable.

2. The probability density function of X in the nondegenerate case is given by

$$f_X(x) = \frac{1}{\sqrt{2\pi\sigma^2}} \exp\left[-\frac{(x-\mu)^2}{2\sigma^2}\right] \qquad 0 < \sigma^2 < \infty \qquad (2.4.5)$$

3. The characteristic function of a Gaussian random variable is given by

$$\Phi(u) = Ee^{juX} = \exp(ju\mu - \tfrac{1}{2}u^2\sigma^2) \qquad (2.4.6)$$

Definition 2.4.4

A second-order stochastic process $\{X_t, t \in T\}$ is a *Gaussian process* if for every finite collection $\{t_1, t_2, \ldots, t_n\} \subset T$ and every finite linear combination of random variables $X_{t_1}, X_{t_2}, \ldots, X_{t_n}$, the random variable X given by

$$X = \sum_{i=1}^{n} \alpha_i X_{t_i} \qquad \alpha_i \text{ constant} \qquad (2.4.7)$$

is Gaussian for any n.

However, this may not be sufficient. The following remark gives necessary and sufficient conditions for a stochastic process to be Gaussian.

Remark. A stochastic process $\{X_t, t \in T\}$ is Gaussian if and only if for every finite collection $\{t_1, t_2, \ldots, t_n\} \subset T$, the joint characteristic function $\Phi(\mathbf{u})$ is given by

$$\Phi(\mathbf{u}) = E\exp(j\mathbf{u}^T\mathbf{X}) = \exp(j\mathbf{u}^T\boldsymbol{\mu} - \tfrac{1}{2}\mathbf{u}^T\boldsymbol{\Gamma}\mathbf{u}) \qquad (2.4.8)$$

where

$$\mathbf{u}^T = (u_1, u_2, \ldots, u_n), \qquad \mathbf{X}^T = (X_{t_1}, X_{t_2}, \ldots, X_{t_n}),$$

$$\boldsymbol{\mu}^T = (EX_{t_1}, EX_{t_2}, \ldots, EX_{t_n}),$$

and $\boldsymbol{\Gamma}$ is the covariance matrix with components $\Gamma_{ij} = C_X(t_i, t_j)$. The covariance matrix is in general nonnegative definite and symmetric. However, in the nondegenerate case the matrix $\boldsymbol{\Gamma}$ is positive definite and hence $|\boldsymbol{\Gamma}| = \det \boldsymbol{\Gamma} > 0$, in which case the joint probability density function for the collection $(X_{t_1}, X_{t_2}, \ldots, X_{t_n})$ can be given by

$$f_X(x_1, t_1; x_2, t_2; \ldots; x_n, t_n) = \frac{1}{(2\pi)^{n/2}|\boldsymbol{\Gamma}|^{1/2}} \exp\left[-\tfrac{1}{2}(\mathbf{X} - \boldsymbol{\mu})^T \boldsymbol{\Gamma}^{-1} (\mathbf{X} - \boldsymbol{\mu}) \right] \tag{2.4.9}$$

Equations 2.4.8 and 2.4.9 show that all finite dimensional distributions of a Gaussian process are completely determined if its mean $\mu(t)$ and the covariance function $C_X(t, s)$ are given.

Markov Processes (Doob, 14, pp. 80–91)

Markov processes are an important class of processes where the probability of the future evolution of a stochastic process $\{X_t, t \in T\}$ when its present state is known exactly, does not change with the additional knowledge of the past behavior. The following definition reflects the character of a Markov process.

Definition 2.4.5 Markov Process

A stochastic process $\{X_t, t \in T\}$ defined on a probability space $(\Omega, \mathfrak{F}, P)$ is a *Markov process* if for any increasing collection $(t_1, t_2, \ldots, t_n) \in T$,

$$\begin{aligned} P\{X_{t_n} \le x_n | X_{t_1} = x_1, X_{t_2} = x_2, \ldots, X_{t_{n-1}} = x_{n-1}\} \\ = P\{X_{t_n} \le x_n | X_{t_n - 1} = x_{n-1}\} \end{aligned} \tag{2.4.10}$$

with probability 1.

This property of a Markov process is similar to that of linear systems where the future state depends only on the present state and not on the past history.

The Markov property can be restated in a more precise form by the following definition.

Definition 2.4.6

Let $(\Omega, \mathfrak{F}, P)$ be a probability space and let $\{X_t, t \in T\}$ be a stochastic process defined on it. Let $\mathfrak{F}_t$ be the σ-field generated by $\{X_s, s \le t\}$. Let $\mathfrak{F}_t^c$ be the σ-field generated by $\{X_s, s > t\}$, and let $A \in \mathfrak{F}_t$ and $B \in \mathfrak{F}_t^c$. The process $\{X_t, t \in T\}$ is a Markov process with respect to the family $\{\mathfrak{F}_t, t \in T\}$ if

$$P(A \cap B | \mathfrak{F}_t) = P(A | \mathfrak{F}_t) P(B | \mathfrak{F}_t) \tag{2.4.11}$$

If the finite dimensional distribution defined by

$$F_X(x_1, t_1; x_2, t_2; \ldots; x_n, t_n) = P\{X_{t_1} \le x_1; X_{t_2} \le x_2; \ldots; X_{t_n} \le x_n\}$$

is differentiable, then the finite dimensional density function can be expressed as

$$f_X(x_1, t_1; x_2, t_2; \ldots; x_n, t_n) = f_X(x_n, t_n | x_1, t_1; x_2, t_2; \ldots; x_{n-1}, t_{n-1}) \times f_X(x_1, t_1; x_2, t_2; \ldots; x_{n-1}, t_{n-1})$$

and using the Markov property,

$$f_X(x_1, t_1; x_2, t_2; \ldots; x_n, t_n) = f_X(x_n, t_n | x_{n-1}, t_{n-1}) \times f_X(x_1, t_1; x_2, t_2; \ldots; x_{n-1}, t_{n-1})$$

Using the Markov property repeatedly for lower order density functions, we can write

$$f_X(x_1, t_1; x_2, t_2; \ldots; x_n, t_n) = f_X(x_1, t_1) \prod_{\nu=2}^{n} f_X(x_\nu, t_\nu | x_{\nu-1}, t_{\nu-1}) \tag{2.4.12}$$

Hence all finite dimensional densities of a Markov process are completely determined by two-dimensional densities. The term $f_X(x_\nu, t_\nu | x_{\nu-1}, t_{\nu-1})$ is called the *transition probability density*.

In a manner similar to eq. 2.4.12 the n-dimensional distribution can also be expressed as

$$F_X(x_1, t_1; x_2, t_2; \ldots; x_n, t_n) = \int_{-\infty}^{x_1} \int_{-\infty}^{x_2} \cdots \int_{-\infty}^{x_{n-1}} F_X(x_n, t_n | \xi_{n-1}, t_{n-1})\, dF_X(\xi_{n-1}, t_{n-1} | \xi_{n-2}, t_{n-2}) \cdots dF_X(\xi_2, t_2 | \xi_1, t_1)\, dF_X(\xi_1, t_1) \tag{2.4.13}$$

Thus the finite dimensional distribution of a Markov process can be expressed in terms of the one-dimensional distribution $F_X(x, t)$ and the conditional distribution $F_X(x, t | \xi, s)$, $t > s$, both of which are obtainable from the two-dimensional distribution $F_X(\xi, s; x, t)$.

What we have shown above is that all finite dimensional distributions of a Markov process can be expressed in terms of two-dimensional distributions. In order to construct a finite dimensional distribution from any two-dimensional distribution, the following consistency conditions have to be satisfied.

1. $$F(x, t) = \int_{-\infty}^{\infty} F(x, t|\xi, s)\, dF(\xi, s) \tag{2.4.14a}$$

This is an obvious condition which relates any second-order distribution to a first-order distribution.

2. For $t_0 < s < t$,

$$F(x, t|x_0, t_0) = \int_{-\infty}^{\infty} F(x, t|\xi, s)\, dF(\xi, s|x_0, t_0) \tag{2.4.14b}$$

Equation 2.4.14b is called the Chapman–Kolmogorov equation. The corresponding equation for the density function is given by

$$f(x, t|x_0, t_0) = \int_{\xi} f(x, t|\xi, s) f(\xi, s|x_0, t_0)\, d\xi \tag{2.4.15}$$

where ξ, s represents the intermediate state (Figure 2.4.1).

We have been discussing Markov processes in terms of conditional distribution. Next we discuss the Markov property in terms of conditional expectations. To this end we have the following proposition.

Proposition 2.4.2 (Doob, 14, p. 81)

Let $\{X_t, t \in T\}$ be a stochastic process defined on a probability space $(\Omega, \mathfrak{F}, P)$. Let g be any Borel function with $\sup_x |g(x)| < \infty$, and let $\{t_1 < t_2 < \cdots < t_n\}$ be any collection $T_n \subset T$. The process $\{X_t, t \in T\}$ is Markov if

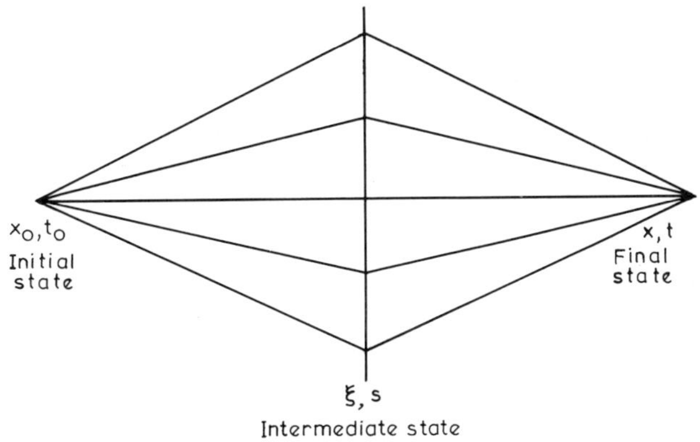

FIGURE 2.4.1

and only if

$$E\{g(X_{t_n})|X_{t_1}, X_{t_2},\ldots,X_{t_{n-1}}\} = E\{g(X_{t_n})|X_{t_{n-1}}\} \tag{2.4.16}$$

We now express some conditions for a Markov process in terms of conditional expectations. Let $\{X_t, t \in T\}$ be a Markov process defined on a probability space $(\Omega, \mathfrak{F}, P)$. Let $\mathfrak{F}_t$ be the σ-field generated by $\{X_s, s \le t, t \in T\}$ and $\mathfrak{F}_t^c$ the σ-field generated by $\{X_s, s > t, t \in T\}$. Let a random variable Y be $\mathfrak{F}_t$-measurable and another one Z, be $\mathfrak{F}_t^c$-measurable. The following conditions hold up to probabilty measure zero.

1. Given the present information the future and the past are conditionally independent

$$E(ZY|X_t) = E(Z|X_t)E(Y|Z_t) \tag{2.4.17}$$

This is a restatement of eq. 2.4.11 in terms of conditional expectations.

2. The future, conditioned on the past history up to the present, is equal to the future, given the present,

$$E^{\mathfrak{F}_t}Z = E(Z|\mathfrak{F}_t) = E(Z|X_t) \tag{2.4.18}$$

3. If $t_0 < t$,

$$E(Z|X_{t_0}) = E\left[E(Z|X_t)|X_{t_0}\right] \tag{2.4.19}$$

Equation 2.4.19 is the restatement of the Chapman-Kolmogorov property in terms of conditional expectations.

Independent Increment Process

Definition 2.4.7

A stochastic process $\{X_t, t \in T\}$ defined on the probability space $(\Omega, \mathfrak{F}, P)$ is an *independent increment* process if for any collection $\{t_1, t_2,\ldots,t_n\} \subset T$ satisfying $t_1 < t_2 < \cdots < t_n$ the increments of the process X_{t_1}, $(X_{t_2} - X_{t_1}), (X_{t_3} - X_{t_2}),\ldots,(X_{t_n} - X_{t_{n-1}})$ are a sequence of independent random variables.

If the time set is discrete, $T = N = (0, 1, \ldots)$, then an independent increment process reduces to a sequence of independent random variables $Y_0 = X_0$, $Y_i = X_i - X_{i-1}$, $i = 1, 2, \ldots$. The independent increment process is a special case of a Markov process.

If the distribution of the increments $(X_t - X_s)$, $t < s$, depends only on the time difference $t - s$, then the process is a *stationary independent increment* process. A stationary independent increment process is not a stationary process as shown below.

If the stationary independent increment process given by $\{X_t, t \in T, T = [0, \infty)\}$ has a finite mean, then

1. $EX_t = \mu_0 + \mu_1 t$ (2.4.20a)
   where $\mu_0 = EX_0$ and $\mu_1 = EX_1 - \mu_0$.
2. $\sigma_{X_t}^2 = \sigma_0^2 + \sigma_1^2 t$ (2.4.20b)
   where $\sigma_0^2 = E(X_0 - \mu_0)^2$ and $\sigma_1^2 = E(X_1 - \mu_1)^2 - \sigma_0^2$.

We show next that the result holds for EX_t. Assume that $g(t) = E(X_t - X_0)$. Then for any t and τ,

$$
\begin{aligned}
g(t+\tau) &= E(X_{t+\tau} - X_0) \\
&= E(X_{t+\tau} - X_\tau + X_\tau - X_0) \\
&= E(X_t - X_0) + E(X_\tau - X_0) \quad \text{using stationary increment property} \\
&= g(t) + g(\tau)
\end{aligned}
$$

Differentiating both sides independently with respect to t and τ, we obtain

$$g'(t+\tau) = g'(t) \qquad g'(t+\tau) = g'(\tau)$$

Thus we have $g'(t) = g'(\tau)$, and at $\tau = 1$, $g'(t) = g'(1) = k_1$. Solution of the differential equation $g'(t) = k_1$ yields $g(t) = k_1 t + k_2$, and since $g(0+0) = 2g(0)$ implies $g(0) = 0$, we have $g(t) = k_1(t)$. Substituting $t = 1$ yields $g(1) = k_1$, and hence we have the solution $g(t) = g(1) \cdot t$. Substituting $g(t) = E(X_t - X_0)$,

$$E(X_t - X_0) = E(X_1 - X_0) \cdot t$$

or

$$EX_t = \mu_0 + \mu_1 t$$

In a similar manner it can be shown that the result holds good for $\sigma_{X_t}^2$ also.

With the property described above a process with stationary independent increments is a nonstationary process, because both the mean and the variance depend upon time.

Examples of stationary independent increment processes are the Poisson process and the Brownian motion process. These are perhaps the most studied of all stochastic processes. We discuss these processes more exhaustively in later chapters.

Similar to the independent increment process, we can define uncorrelated increment and orthogonal increment processes.

Definition 2.4.8 Uncorrelated and Orthogonal Increment Processes

Let $\{X_t, t \in T\}$ be a stochastic process defined on a probability space $(\Omega, \mathfrak{F}, P)$. Let $E|X_t - X_s|^2 < \infty$ for $s, t \in T$. If $s_1 < t_1 \leq s_2 < t_2$, then $\{X_t, t \in T\}$ is

1. a process with *uncorrelated increments* if

$$E(X_{t_2} - X_{s_2})(X_{t_1} - X_{s_1}) = E(X_{t_2} - X_{s_2})E(X_{t_1} - X_{s_1}) \quad (2.4.21)$$

2. a process with *orthogonal increments* if

$$E(X_{t_2} - X_{s_2})(X_{t_1} - X_{s_1}) = 0 \quad (2.4.22)$$

Clearly independent increment process implies uncorrelated increment process, but the converse is not true. If $\{X_t\}$ is a process with uncorrelated increments, then $Y_t = X_t - EX_t$ is a process with uncorrelated and orthogonal increments. If a Gaussian process with $EX_t = 0$ for all $t \in T$ has uncorrelated or orthogonal increments, then it has independent increments.

Orthogonal increment processes play a key role in the study of spectral processes.

Poisson Process

Next we define the Poisson process formally.

Definition 2.4.9 Poisson Process

The stochastic process $\{N_t, t \in T, T = R^+\}$ defined on a probability space $(\Omega, \mathfrak{F}, P)$ is a *Poisson process* if

1. $N_0 = 0$.
2. For almost all ω, the sample functions $N_t(\omega)$ are monotone functions increasing in isolated jumps of unit magnitude.
3. For every pair $s < t$, the increment $(N_t - N_s)$ is integral valued with distribution

$$P\{N_t - N_s = k\} = e^{-\lambda(t \quad s)} \frac{\lambda^k (t-s)^k}{k!} \quad (2.4.23)$$

where $\lambda > 0$ is a parameter associated with the Poisson process and is called the *density parameter*.

4. For every collection $\{t_1 < t_2 < \cdots < t_n\} \subset T$ and Borel sets $A_1, A_2, \ldots, A_n$,

$$P\{N_{t_1} \in A_1, N_{t_2} - N_{t_1} \in A_2, \ldots, N_{t_n} - N_{t_{n-1}} \in A_n\}$$

$$= P\{N_{t_1} \in A_1\} P\{N_{t_2} - N_{t_1} \in A_2\} \cdots P\{N_{t_n} - N_{t_{n-1}} \in A_n\} \quad (2.4.24)$$

In the definition given above we conclude that the increments N_{t_1}, $(N_{t_2} - N_{t_1}), \ldots, (N_{t_n} - N_{t_{n-1}})$ are independent random variables. If the density parameter $\lambda = 1$, then we have a standard Poisson process.

Properties of Poisson Processes

1. The mean and autocovariance of the Poisson process are

$$EN_t = \lambda t$$

$$C_N(t, s) = \lambda(t \wedge s) \quad (2.4.25)$$

2. If each jump is considered an event, then the probability that no event occurs in the time interval τ is $P\{N_{t+\tau} - N_t = 0\} = e^{-\lambda\tau}$.

3. Let τ_1 be the time to the first event, and let τ_k be the time between the $(k-1)$th and the kth event. Then the random variables $(\tau_1, \tau_2, \ldots)$ are mutually independent with the distribution function

$$P\{\tau_k(\omega) \le x\} = \begin{cases} 1 - e^{-\lambda x} & \lambda \ge 0 \\ 0 & \lambda < 0 \end{cases} \quad (2.4.26)$$

The time intervals $\tau_1, \tau_2, \ldots$ are called waiting times between events.

4. The Poisson process is continuous in the quadratic mean at any point t. This follows immediately from Proposition 2.3.3 because both EN_t and $C_N(t, s)$ are continuous at $t = s$.

5. The Poisson process is almost surely continuous at any point t, as shown by

$$P\left\{\omega: \lim_{\epsilon \to 0} |N_{t+\epsilon}(\omega) - N_t(\omega)| = 0\right\} = \lim_{\epsilon \to 0} e^{-\lambda\epsilon} = 1 \quad (2.4.27)$$

6. However, the probability of continuity at *all* points in an interval T is less than 1 and it is not almost surely sample continuous.

2.5 BROWNIAN MOTION

Next we define a Brownian motion process assuming that the time set $T = R^+$ or any interval $[0, a]$, $a > 0$.

Definition 2.5.1 Brownian Motion

Let $(\Omega, \mathfrak{F}, P)$ be a complete probability space. The stochastic process $\{W_t, t \in T\}$ defined on $(\Omega, \mathfrak{F}, P)$ is a *Brownian motion process* with parameter σ^2 if

1. $W_0(\omega) = 0$ (a.s.)
2. $\{W_t\}$ is a stationary independent increment process.
3. For every s and t, $s \leq t$, belonging to T the increments $W_t - W_s$ are Gaussian distributed with mean zero and variance $\sigma^2(t - s)$.
4. For almost all $\omega \in \Omega$ the sample functions $t \to W_t(\omega)$ are uniformly continuous in the interval T.

With the definition given above we shall now derive the autocovariance function $C_W(t, s)$.
With $t > s$.

$$C_W(t, s) = EW_tW_s = E(W_t - W_s + W_s)W_s$$

$$= E(W_t - W_s)W_s + EW_s^2$$

$$= EW_s^2 \qquad \text{from 2}$$

$$= \sigma^2 s \qquad \text{from 3}$$

Similarly, for $t < s$, $C_W(t, s) = \sigma^2 t$. Hence $C_W(t, s) = \sigma^2(t \wedge s)$.
We can also give an alternate definition in the following form.

Definition 2.5.2

The stochastic process $\{W_t, t \in T\}$ defined on a complete probability space $(\Omega, \mathfrak{F}, P)$ is a Brownian motion process with parameter σ^2 if

1. $W_0(\omega) = 0$ (a.s.)
2. $\{W_t, t \in T\}$ is an almost surely sample continuous Gaussian process.
3. $EW_t = 0$.
4. $C_W(t, s) = EW_tW_s = \sigma^2 \min(t, s) = \sigma^2(t \wedge s)$ (2.5.1)

The Brownian motion process with $\sigma^2 = 1$ is called a standard Brownian motion.

Conditions 3 and 4 characterize any stationary independent increment process and along with condition 2 the process becomes a Brownian motion process. We now show that these conditions yield a stationary independent increment process.

For $0 = t_0 < t_1 < t_2 < \cdots < t_n \in T$ the covariance matrix Γ from condition 4 is $\sigma^2 \min(t_k, t_l)$, that is,

$$\Gamma = \sigma^2 \begin{bmatrix} t_1 & t_1 & t_1 & \cdots & t_1 \\ t_1 & t_2 & t_2 & \cdots & t_2 \\ t_1 & t_2 & t_3 & \cdots & t_3 \\ \vdots & & & & \vdots \\ t_1 & t_2 & t_3 & \cdots & t_n \end{bmatrix}$$

It can be shown that this matrix is positive definite. Hence the finite dimensional density function can be written from eq. 2.4.9 as

$$f_W(w_1, t_1; w_2, t_2; \ldots; w_n, t_n) = \frac{1}{(2\pi)^{n/2} |\Gamma|^{1/2}} \exp\left(-\frac{1}{2}\mathbf{w}^T \Gamma^{-1} \mathbf{w}\right)$$

With $|\Gamma| = \sigma^{2n} t_1 (t_2 - t_1) \cdots (t_n - t_{n-1})$ it can be shown by induction that

$$f_W(w_1, t_1; w_2, t_2; \ldots; w_n, t_n) = \prod_{\nu=1}^{n} \frac{1}{\sqrt{2\pi(t_\nu - t_{\nu-1})\sigma^2}} \exp\left[-\frac{1}{2}\frac{(w_\nu - w_{\nu-1})^2}{\sigma^2 (t_\nu - t_{\nu-1})}\right]$$

where $t_0 = 0 = w_0$. The preceding equation shows that $\{W_{t_1}, (W_{t_2} - W_{t_1}) \cdots W_{t_n} - W_{t_{n-1}}\}$ is a collection of independent random variables for every increasing $\{t_0, t_1, \ldots, t_n\}$ and the density depends only on the time difference $(t_\nu - t_{\nu-1})$. Hence the Brownian motion process is a process of stationary independent increments.

The existence of a Brownian motion process on a suitable probability space can be accomplished by constructing such a process. Let T be the interval $[0, 1]$, and let Ω be equal to R^∞, a countable product of real lines. Let $\mathcal{B}(R^\infty)$ be the σ-field generated by Borel sets in R^∞, and let P be the countable product of Gaussian measures, and let $\mathcal{F}$ be the completion of $\mathcal{B}(R^\infty)$ with respect to the P-measure. Thus we have defined the probability space $(\Omega, \mathcal{F}, P)$ on which the Brownian motion process will be defined.

Let us take a Haar family of functions known to be a complete orthonormal set in $L^2[0,1]$. They are defined by

$$\phi_1(t) = 1 \qquad 0 \le t \le 1$$

$$\phi_2(t) = \begin{cases} 1 & 0 \le t \le \frac{1}{2} \\ -1 & \frac{1}{2} \le t \le 1 \end{cases}$$

$$\phi_{2^n+1}(t) = \begin{cases} 2^{n/2} & 0 \le t \le 2^{-(n+1)} \\ -2^{n/2} & 2^{-(n+1)} \le t \le 2^{-n} \\ 0 & \text{otherwise} \end{cases}$$

$$\phi_{2^n+1+k} = \phi_{2^n+1}\left(t - \frac{k}{2^n}\right) \qquad k = 1, 2, 3, \ldots, 2^n - 1$$

We define now the integral of the Haar functions as

$$\Phi_k(t) = \int_0^t \phi_k(\tau)\, d\tau$$

The maximum value of $\Phi_{2^n+1+k}(t)$ is given by

$$\max_{0 \le t \le 1} \Phi_{2^n+1+k}(t) = \left(\tfrac{1}{2}\right)^{(n+2)/2} \qquad n = 0, 1, \ldots, \quad 1 \le k \le 2^n - 1$$

Let us now take a sequence $\{X_1, X_2, \ldots\}$ of mutually independent Gaussian random variables on the probability space $(\Omega, \mathfrak{F}, P)$ with zero mean and unit variance. We define the quantity $Y_n = \max_{1 \le k \le 2^n - 1} |X_k|$. We form the product $X_n \Phi_n(t)$ and the sum

$$W(t) = \sum_{n=1}^{\infty} X_n \Phi_n(t)$$

Then whenever $\sum_{n=0}^{\infty} Y_n \left(\frac{1}{2}\right)^{n/2} < \infty$, W_t is a continuous function representing a realization of a standard Brownian motion process. The proof (Kallianpur, 29, p. 13) is left as an exercise.

It is not necessary that we should take the Haar family for constructing a Brownian motion process. In fact any complete orthonormal set in the interval T can be used for $\phi_k(t)$, and the series $W_t = \sum_{n=1}^{\infty} X_n \Phi_n(t)$ will represent a Brownian motion process in the interval T. The choice of the Haar family makes the proof easier.

Next we derive the joint density of the collection $W_{t_1}, W_{t_2}, \ldots, W_{t_n}$ for $\{t_1 < t_2 < \cdots < t_n\} \subset T$ from Definition 2.5.1. Since $\{W_t, t \in T\}$ is also a

Markov process, we can write from eq. 2.4.12

$$f_W(x_1, t_1; x_2, t_2; \ldots; x_n, t_n) = f_W(x_1, t_1) \prod_{\nu=2}^{n} f_W(x_\nu, t_\nu | x_{\nu-1}, t_{\nu-1}) \tag{2.5.2}$$

In eq. 2.5.2 the term $f_W(x_\nu, t_\nu | x_{\nu-1}, t_{\nu-1})$ defined by

$$f_W(x_\nu, t_\nu | x_{\nu-1}, t_{\nu-1})\, dx = P\{x_\nu < W_{t_\nu} \le x_\nu + dx | W_{t_{\nu-1}} = x_{\nu-1}\}$$

is the transition probability density and is usually written as

$$f_W(x_{\nu-1}, t_{\nu-1}; x_\nu, t_\nu)$$

Using the independent increment nature of the process $\{W_t\}$,

$$f_W(x_\nu, t_\nu | x_{\nu-1}, t_{\nu-1}) = f_W(x_\nu - x_{\nu-1}, t_\nu - t_{\nu-1}) \tag{2.5.3}$$

Substituting eq. 2.5.3 into eq. 2.5.2,

$$f_W(x_1, t_1; x_2, t_2; \ldots; x_n, t_n) = f_W(x_1, t_1) \prod_{\nu=2}^{n} f_W(x_\nu - x_{\nu-1}, t_\nu - t_{\nu-1}) \tag{2.5.4}$$

where

$$f_W(x_1, t_1) = \frac{1}{\sqrt{2\pi\sigma^2 t_1}} \exp\left(-\frac{x_1^2}{2\sigma^2 t_1}\right) \tag{2.5.5}$$

$$f_W(x_\nu - x_{\nu-1}, t_\nu - t_{\nu-1}) = \frac{1}{\sqrt{2\pi\sigma^2(t_\nu - t_{\nu-1})}} \exp\left[-\frac{(x_\nu - x_{\nu-1})^2}{2\sigma^2(t_\nu - t_{\nu-1})}\right] \tag{2.5.6}$$

With $s < t$ the transition probability density

$$f(x, s; y, t) = \frac{1}{\sqrt{2\pi\sigma^2(t-s)}} \exp\left[-\frac{(y-x)^2}{2\sigma^2(t-s)}\right] \tag{2.5.7}$$

satisfies a simplified form of Kolmogorov forward and backward equations:

$$\frac{\partial f(x, s; y, t)}{\partial t} = \frac{1}{2} \frac{\partial^2 f(x, s; y, t)}{\partial y^2} \qquad t > s \qquad (2.5.8)$$

$$\frac{\partial f(x, s; y, t)}{\partial s} = \frac{1}{2} \frac{\partial^2 f(x, s; y, t)}{\partial x^2} \qquad s < t \qquad (2.5.9)$$

The forward equation, eq. 2.5.8, is called the Fokker–Planck equation.

Now we study some of the properties of Brownian motion processes.

Continuity of Paths. We first show that $\{W_t, t \in T\}$ is continuous in probability. From Chebyshev's inequality, for all $t \in T$,

$$P\{|W_{t+h} - W_t| > \epsilon\} \leq \frac{\text{var}(W_{t+h} - W_t)}{\epsilon^2} \qquad \epsilon > 0$$

From Definition 2.5.1 the variance of $(W_{t+h} - W_t)$ is $\sigma^2 h$. Hence

$$P\{|W_{t+h} - W_t| > \epsilon\} \leq \frac{\sigma^2 h}{\epsilon^2} \qquad \epsilon > 0$$

which tends to zero as h tends to zero, thus implying continuity in probability.

Quadratic mean continuity can be established from Proposition 2.3.3 by noting that the mean value is zero and the autocovariance function $C_W(t, s) = \sigma^2 \min(t, s)$ is continuous at every $t = s$.

From Proposition 2.3.2 any process continuous in probability admits of a separable and measurable moification. Hence every Brownian motion process has a separable and measurable modification. The almost sure sample continuity of a separable Brownian motion process $\{W_t, t \in T\}$ can be established by the Kolmogorov condition of Proposition 2.3.4. From eq. 2.5.6 the probability density function is given by

$$f_{|W_{t+h} - W_t|}(x) = \frac{1}{\sqrt{2\pi\sigma^2 h}} \exp\left(-\frac{x^2}{2\sigma^2 h}\right)$$

Hence

$$E(W_{t+h} - W_t)^4 = 3\sigma^4 h^2$$

which verifies the Kolomorogov condition with $\alpha = 4$, $C = 3$, and $\beta = 1$. Thus every separable Brownian motion process is almost surely sample continuous. However, the sample paths are highly irregular in nature, and in fact they are of unbounded variation and differentiable nowhere with probability 1 as we see presently.

Differentiability and Bounded Variation. First we show that $\{W_t, t \in T\}$ is differentiable nowhere with probability 1. To show this result, it is enough if we show that for each fixed $t_0 \in T$ and for any $\epsilon > 0$,

$$P\left\{\sup_{t_0<t\le t_0+h} \frac{W_t - W_{t_0}}{t - t_0} \ge \epsilon\right\}$$

goes to 1 when $h \to 0$. Now

$$\begin{aligned} P\left\{\sup_{t_0<t\le t_0+h} \frac{W_t - W_{t_0}}{t - t_0} \ge \epsilon\right\} &\ge P\left\{\max_{t_0<t\le t_0+h} \left(W_t - W_{t_0}\right) \ge \epsilon h\right\} \\ &= 2P\left\{\left(W_{t_0+h} - W_{t_0}\right) \ge \epsilon h\right\} \\ &= 2P\left\{\frac{W_{t_0+h} - W_{t_0}}{\sqrt{h}} \ge \epsilon\sqrt{h}\right\} \end{aligned}$$

According to Definition 2.5.1, for every t_0 the random variable $(W_{t_0+h} - W_{t_0})/\sqrt{h}$ is Gaussian distributed with mean zero and variance σ^2 independent of h. Hence as $h \to 0$,

$$2P\left\{\frac{W_{t_0+h} - W_{t_0}}{\sqrt{h}} \ge 0\right\} = 1$$

thus showing the nondifferentiability of the process $\{W_t, t \in T\}$.

Next we show that $\{W_t, t \in T\}$ is of unbounded variation. Let g_t be any continuous function in a closed interval $[a, b] \subset R^+$. For any partition of $[a, b]$ such that $a = t_0^{(n)} < t_1^{(n)} < \cdots < t_{N(n)}^{(n)} = b$ we have

$$\sum_{\nu=0}^{N(n)-1} \left(g_{t_{\nu+1}^{(n)}} - g_{t_\nu^{(n)}}\right)^2 \le \max_{\nu \le N(n)-1} |g_{t_{\nu+1}^{(n)}} - g_{t_\nu^{(n)}}| \sum_{\nu=0}^{N(n)-1} |g_{t_{\nu+1}^{(n)}} - g_{t_\nu^{(n)}}|$$

If the summation on the right of the inequality is *bounded* independently of the choice of $N(n)$ and t_ν, then the function g_t is of bounded variation and the sum on the left will go to zero when $\max_{\nu \le N(n)-1}(t_{\nu+1}^{(n)} - t_\nu^{(n)}) \to 0$. However, we show that $\sum_{\nu=0}^{N(n)-1}(W_{t_{\nu+1}^{(n)}} - W_{t_\nu^{(n)}})^2$ does not go to zero as $\max_{\nu \le N(n)-1}(t_{\nu+1}^{(n)} - t_\nu^{(n)}) \to 0$ by the following proposition and hence the process $\{W_t, t \in T\}$ is almost surely not of bounded variation.

Proposition 2.5.1

Let $[a, b]$ be a closed subinterval of T. Let T_n be a sequence of partitions of $[a, b]$ such that

$$T_n = \left\{a = t_0^{(n)} < t_1^{(n)} < \cdots < t_{N(n)}^{(n)} = b, n = 1, 2, \ldots\right\}$$

and let

$$\Delta_n = \max_{\nu \le N(n)-1} \left(t_{\nu+1}^{(n)} - t_\nu^{(n)} \right) \to 0 \qquad \text{as } n \to \infty$$

Let $\{W_t, t \in T\}$ be a standard Brownian motion ($\sigma^2 = 1$) defined on a complete probability space $(\Omega, \mathcal{F}, P)$. Then in any interval $[a, b] \subset T$

1. $$\underset{n\to\infty}{\text{l.i.q.m.}} \sum_{\nu=0}^{N(n)-1} \left(W_{t_{\nu+1}^{(n)}} - W_{t_\nu^{(n)}} \right)^2 = b - a \tag{2.5.10}$$
2. If $\sum_{n=1}^{\infty} \Delta_n < \infty$, then the convergence to $b - a$ is in the almost sure sense.

Proof

1. Let

$$S_n = \sum_{\nu=0}^{N(n)-1} \left(W_{t_{\nu+1}^{(n)}} - W_{t_\nu^{(n)}} \right)^2 - (b - a)$$

However,

$$b - a = \sum_{\nu=0}^{N(n)-1} \left(t_{\nu+1}^{(n)} - t_\nu^{(n)} \right)$$

and hence

$$S_n = \sum_{\nu=0}^{N(n)-1} \left[\left(W_{t_{\nu+1}^{(n)}} - W_{t_\nu^{(n)}} \right)^2 - \left(t_{\nu+1}^{(n)} - t_\nu^{(n)} \right) \right]$$

From Definition 2.5.1 $E(W_{t_{\nu+1}^{(n)}} - W_{t_\nu^{(n)}})^2 = t_{\nu+1}^{(n)} - t_\nu^{(n)}$, and therefore the process S_n is an independent increment process with zero mean. Hence the variance of the process S_n is given by

$$ES_n^2 = \sum_{\nu=0}^{N(n)-1} E\Big[\left(W_{t_{\nu+1}^{(n)}} - W_{t_\nu^{(n)}} \right)^4 - 2\left(t_{\nu+1}^{(n)} \cdot t_\nu^{(n)} \right)\left(W_{t_{\nu+1}^{(n)}} - W_{t_\nu^{(n)}} \right) + \left(t_{\nu+1}^{(n)} - t_\nu^{(n)} \right)^2 \Big] \tag{2.5.11}$$

Since $W_{t_{\nu+1}^{(n)}} - W_{t_\nu^{(n)}}$ is Gaussian distributed with mean zero and variance $t_{\nu+1}^{(n)} - t_\nu^{(n)}$, we have

$$E\left(W_{t_{\nu+1}^{(n)}} - W_{t_\nu^{(n)}} \right)^4 = 3\left(t_{\nu+1}^{(n)} - t_\nu^{(n)} \right) \tag{2.5.12}$$

Substituting eq. 2.5.12 into eq. 2.5.11,

$$ES_n^2 = \sum_{\nu=0}^{N(n)-1} 2\left(t_{\nu+1}^{(n)} - t_\nu^{(n)}\right)^2 \le \sum_{\nu=0}^{N(n)-1} 2\Delta_n\left(t_{\nu+1}^{(n)} - t_\nu^{(n)}\right)$$

Hence

$$ES_n^2 \le 2\Delta_n(b-a)$$

and as $n \to \infty$, $\Delta_n \to 0$ by assumption, and $ES_n^2 \to 0$, assuring us of quadratic mean convergence.

2. By Chebyshev's inequality,

$$P\{|S_n| \ge \epsilon\} \le \frac{\operatorname{var} S_n}{\epsilon^2} = \frac{ES_n^2}{\epsilon^2} = \frac{2\Delta_n(b-a)}{\epsilon^2}$$

Hence

$$\sum_{n=1}^{\infty} P\{|S_n| \ge \epsilon\} \le \frac{2(b-a)}{\epsilon^2} \sum_{n=1}^{\infty} \Delta_n < \infty$$

since $\sum_{n=1}^{\infty} \Delta_n < \infty$ by assumption.

As a result of the Borel–Cantelli lemma, if $\sum_{n=1}^{\infty} P(S_n) < \infty$, then

$$\lim_{n\to\infty} \sum_{k \ge n}^{\infty} P(S_k) = 0$$

Since $|S_n| > \epsilon$ only a finite number of times with probability 1, we have almost sure convergence. □

From this proposition we have established the unbounded variation of the sample paths of the Brownian motion and also intuitively the result $(dW_t)^2 \sim dt$. The consequences of this result are far-reaching. For example, if we have a function of the Brownian motion process $g(W_t)$, then

$$\begin{aligned} dg(W_t) &= g(W_{t+dt}) - g(W_t) \\ &= \frac{dg}{dw} dW_t + \frac{1}{2}\frac{d^2g}{dw^2} dW_t^2 \\ &= \frac{dg}{dw} dW_t + \frac{1}{2}\frac{d^2g}{dw^2} dt \end{aligned}$$

Thus the function $g(W_t)$ does not obey the ordinary laws of calculus. We shall expand on this theme in later chapters.

Martingale Property. Let $\{W_t, t \in T\}$ be a separable Brownian motion defined on $(\Omega, \mathcal{F}, P)$. Let $\mathcal{F}_t = \sigma\{W_\tau, \tau \leq t,\ t \in T\}$ and $\mathcal{F}_s = \sigma\{W_\tau, \tau \leq s, s \in T\}$. Then we have the following result:

$$E^{\mathcal{F}_s} W_t = W_s \qquad s \leq t \tag{2.5.13}$$

We prove this result by writing

$$\begin{aligned} E^{\mathcal{F}_s} W_t &= E^{\mathcal{F}_s}(W_s + W_t - W_s) \\ &= E^{\mathcal{F}_s} W_s + E^{\mathcal{F}_s}(W_t - W_s) \end{aligned}$$

The first term, $E^{\mathcal{F}_s} W_s$, in the right-hand side of the above equation is $\mathcal{F}_s$-measurable and hence equals W_s. Because of independent increments, $W_t - W_s$ is independent of $\mathcal{F}_s$, $s < t$. Hence $E^{\mathcal{F}_s}(W_t - W_s) = E(W_t - W_s) = 0$.

This property of the Brownian motion process, known as the martingale property, is an exceedingly important one. We discuss martingales in the next chapter.

Problems

1. Show that the stochastic process

$$Y_t(\omega) = \begin{cases} 1 & \omega = t, \quad t \in [0,1] \quad \omega \in \Omega = [0,1] \\ 0 & \omega \neq t \end{cases}$$

is not separable.

2. Let the processes $\{Y_t, t \in T\}$ be a modification of the process $\{X_t, t \in T\}$ and let the sample functions of both be right continuous. Then show that they are indistinguishable.

3. If the time set of a stochastic process $\{X_t, t \in T\}$ has a positive Lebesgue measure, construct an example to illustrate how measurability poses restrictions on the finite dimensional distributions.

4. Let $\{X_t, t \in T\}$ be a stochastic process defined on $(\Omega, \mathcal{F}, P)$ with values in $(R, \mathcal{R})$ having right continuous (left continuous) sample paths adapted to the filtration $\{\mathcal{F}_t, t \in T\}$. Show that $\{X_t, t \in T\}$ is progressively measurable.

5. Using techniques other than that presented in this chapter, show that the Poisson process is
   a. Continuous in probability.
   b. Mean square continuous.
   c. Almost surely continuous.

6. Let $\{X_t, t \in T, T = [0,1]\}$ be a separable Gaussian process with zero mean. If

$$E(X_{t+h} - X_t)^2 = h^a \qquad a > 0$$

then show that the process is almost surely sample continuous, however small a might be.

7. $X_t = A\cos(ut + \Phi)$ is a stochastic process with A, Φ independent random variables and Φ being uniformly distributed in the range $[0, 2\pi]$. Find the conditions for

a. X_t to be wide sense stationary.

b. X_t^2 to be wide sense stationary.

c. Can X_t and X_t^2 be strictly stationary?

8. $\{X_n, n \in N\}$ is a discrete stochastic process with

$$X_i = X_{i-1} + v_i$$

where $\{v_i\}$ is a sequence of zero mean uncorrelated random variables with a positive variance σ^2. Show that the process $\{X_n, n \in N\}$ cannot be stationary.

9. If the process of Problem 8 can be modified to $X_i = \phi X_{i-1} + v_i$, with $|\phi| < 1$, then show that $\{X_n\}$ can be a wide sense stationary process.

10. Show that a necessary and sufficient condition for a second-order process to be Gaussian is for its joint characteristic function to be given by

$$E\exp(j\mathbf{u}^T\mathbf{X}) = \exp\left(j\mathbf{u}^T\boldsymbol{\mu} - \tfrac{1}{2}\mathbf{u}^T\boldsymbol{\Gamma}\mathbf{u}\right)$$

where

$$\mathbf{u}^T = \{u_1, u_2, \ldots, u_n\}, \quad \mathbf{X}^T = \{X_t, X_{t_2}, \ldots, X_{t_n}\},$$

$$\boldsymbol{\mu}^T = \{\mu_{t_1}, \mu_{t_2}, \ldots, \mu_{t_n}\}$$

and $\boldsymbol{\Gamma}$ is the covariance matrix.

11. Let $\{X_t, t \in T, T = (-\infty, \infty)\}$ be Gaussian process with $EX_t = 0$ and covariance $C_X(t, s) = \frac{1}{2}(|t| + |s| - |t - s|)$. Show that the two processes $\{X_t, -\infty < t \leq 0\}$ and $\{X_t, 0 \leq t < \infty\}$ are independent.

12. Construct a Markov process $\{X_t, t \in T, T = [0, \infty)\}$ with the following properties:

a. X_t takes only values $+1$ and -1.

b. $P\{X_t = 1\} = P\{X_t = -1\} = \frac{1}{2}$.

c. For $t \geq s$,

$$P\{X_t = X_s\} = p(t - s)$$

$$P\{X_t = -X_s\} = 1 - p(t - s)$$

with $p(t)$ continuous and $p(0) = 1$.

13. If $\{X_t, t \in T, T = [0, \infty)\}$ is a stationary independent increment process, then show that $\sigma_{X_t}^2 = \sigma_0^2 + \sigma_1^2 t$, where $\sigma_0^2 = E(X_0 - \mu_0)^2$ with $\mu_0 = EX_0$ and where $\sigma_1^2 = E(X_1 - \mu_1)^2 - \sigma_0^2$ with $\mu_1 = EX_1 - \mu_0$. Hence derive the variance of a Poisson process and a Brownian motion process.

14. Show that every discrete stochastic process $\{X_n, n \in N, N = 0, 1, \ldots\}$ with independent increments is a Markov process. Can this property be extended to $\{X_t, t \in T, T = (-\infty, \infty)\}$?

15. Show that under the conditions stated in Section 2.5 the series $W_t = \sum_{n=1}^{\infty} X_n \Phi_n(t)$ satisfies Definition 2.5.2 of the Brownian motion process.

16. Show that the probability density function $f(y, t; x, s)$

$$f(y, t; x, s) = \frac{1}{\sqrt{2\pi\tau}} \exp\left[-\frac{(y - x)^2}{2\tau}\right] \qquad \tau = t - s$$

satisfies the heat equation

$$\frac{\partial f}{\partial \tau} = \frac{1}{2} \frac{\partial^2 f}{\partial y^2}$$

17. $\{X_t, -\infty < t < \infty\}$ is a Gaussian process with zero mean and $EX_t X_s = e^{-|t-s|}$. If $\{W_t, 0 \leq t < \infty\}$ is a standard Brownian motion process, show that X_t can be expressed in the form $X_t = f(t) W_{g(t)/f(t)}$ and find the form for $f(t)$, $g(t)$.

18. $\{W_t, 0 \leq t < \infty\}$ is a standard Brownian motion process. Show that the conditional density of W_t, for $t_1 < t < t_2$, given that $W_{t_1} = x_1$ and $W_{t_2} = x_2$, that is, $f_W(x < W_t < x + dx | W_{t_1} = x_1, W_{t_2} = x_2)$ is a normal density with mean

$$x_1 + \frac{x_2 - x_1}{t_2 - t_1}(t - t_1)$$

and variance

$$\frac{(t_2 - t)(t - t_1)}{t_2 - t_1}$$

3 MARTINGALE PROCESSES

3.1 UNIFORM INTEGRABILITY

In Chapter 1 we enunciated convergence criteria for expectations. In the matter of justifying the interchange of limit and expectation as $n \to \infty$, uniform integrability criteria of random variables play an important role.

Definition 3.3.1 Uniform Integrability

A family of integrable random variables $\{X_n, n \in N\}$ defined on a probability space $(\Omega, \mathcal{F}, P)$ is *uniformly integrable* if

$$\sup_{n \in N} \int_{|X_n| > a} |X_n| \, dP \to 0 \tag{3.1.1}$$

as $a \to \infty$.

As a consequence of the definition we have the following proposition.

Proposition 3.1.1 Uniform Integrability

Let $\{X_n, n \in N\}$ be a family of integrable random variables defined on a probability space $(\Omega, \mathcal{F}, P)$. The family is uniformly integrable if and only if

1. $\sup_{n \in N} \int_{\Omega} |X_n| \, dP = \sup_{n \in N} E|X_n| < \infty$
2. For every $\epsilon > 0$ there exists a $\delta_\epsilon > 0$ such that for any $A \in \mathcal{F}$,

$$P(A) \le \delta_\epsilon \Rightarrow \sup_{n \in N} \int_A |X_n| \, dP \le \epsilon \tag{3.1.2}$$

Proof

Necessity

$$\int_{\Omega} |X_n|\, dP = \int_{|X_n|>a} |X_n|\, dP + \int_{|X_n|\le a} |X_n|\, dP \le \int_{|X_n|>a} |X_n|\, dP + a$$

By uniform integrability of $\{X_n\}$, the term $\int_{|X_n|>a} |X_n|\, dP \to 0$, and hence condition 1 is true.

Let $\epsilon > 0$ be given, and for any $A \in \mathcal{F}$,

$$\int_A |X_n|\, dP = \int_{A \in \{|X_n|>a\}} |X_n|\, dP + \int_{A \in \{|X_n| \le a\}} |X_n|\, dP$$

$$\le \int_{|X_n|>a} |X_n|\, dP + aP(A)$$

Let a be chosen such that

$$\int_{|X_n|>a} |X_n|\, dP < \frac{\epsilon}{2}$$

Then

$$\int_A |X_n|\, dP \le \frac{\epsilon}{2} + aP(A)$$

If we now choose $\delta_\epsilon = \epsilon/2a$, then condition 2 is satisfied.

Sufficiency. Assuming $a = E|X_n|/\delta$, we have by Chebyshev's inequality

$$P\{|X_n| > a\} \le \frac{E|X_n|}{a} \le \delta \qquad n \in N$$

Therefore by condition 2 we have

$$\int_{|X_n|>a} |X_n|\, dP \le \epsilon \qquad n \in N$$

thereby showing the uniform integrability of $\{X_n\}$. □

We give another set of necessary and sufficient conditions for $\{X_n, n \in N\}$ to be uniformly integrable.

Proposition 3.1.2 La Vallé Poussin

Let $\{X_n, n \in N\}$ be a family of integrable random variables defined on $(\Omega, \mathcal{F}, P)$. Let g be an increasing function mapping $R^+ \to R^+$. Then $\{X_n, n \in N\}$ is uniformly integrable if and only if

1. $\lim_{x \to \infty} \frac{g(x)}{x} \to \infty$
2. $\sup_{n \in N} Eg(|X_n|) < \infty$ (3.1.3)

Proof. Let $\epsilon > 0$ and let

$$\sup_{n \in N} \frac{Eg(|X_n|)}{\epsilon} = \lambda$$

Let $a > 0$ be so chosen that $g(x)/x \geq \lambda$ for $x \geq a$. Therefore we have for $|X_n| \geq a$,

$$\frac{g(|X_n|)}{\lambda} \geq |X_n|$$

As a consequence we have for each X_n,

$$\int_{|X_n|>a} |X_n| \, dP \leq \frac{1}{\lambda} \int_{|X_n|>a} g(|X_n|) \, dP \leq \frac{1}{\lambda} \sup_{n \in N} Eg(|X_n|) = \epsilon$$

and hence $\{X_n, n \in N\}$ is uniformly integrable. □

3.2 STOPPING TIMES OR MARKOV TIMES

In the study of martingales stopping times play a very important role. We now introduce the concept of a stopping time or Markov time by the following definition.

Definition 3.2.1 Stopping Time

Let $(\Omega, \mathcal{F}, P)$ be a complete probability space, and let $\{\mathcal{F}_t, t \in T\}$ with T the interval $[0, \infty)$ be the right continuous filtration σ-field defined on the measurable space $(\Omega, \mathcal{F})$. A random variable τ: $\Omega \to R^+ \cup \{\infty\}$, where R^+ is the positive real line $[0, \infty)$, is called a *stopping time* or *Markov time* relative to $\{\mathcal{F}_t, t \in T\}$ if the set

$$\{\omega: \ \tau(\omega) \leq t\} \in \mathcal{F}_t \qquad t \in T \tag{3.2.1}$$

In other words, the stopping time $\tau(\omega)$ is determined by the event $\{\tau \leq t\}$ being measurable with respect to the past history up to t. The right continuity of $\{\mathcal{F}_t, t \in T\}$ assures the measurability of the event $\{\tau = t\}$ with respect to $\mathcal{F}_t$. Note that any other random variable $V(\omega)$ defined on Ω generally is measurable with respect to the bigger σ-field $\mathcal{F}$, and hence $\{\omega: \ V(\omega) \leq t\}$ may not be $\mathcal{F}_t$-measurable and $V(\omega)$ is not a stopping time. A stopping time $\tau(\omega)$ is a nonanticipative function, whereas any other random variable $V(\omega)$ may anticipate the future.

Consider a right continuous process $\{X_t, t \in T\}$ with left-hand limits adapted to the right continuous filtration σ-field $\{\mathcal{F}_t, t \in T\}$ with values in $(R^+, \mathcal{R})$, where $\mathcal{R}$ is the σ-field of Borel sets on R^+. We give examples of stopping times.

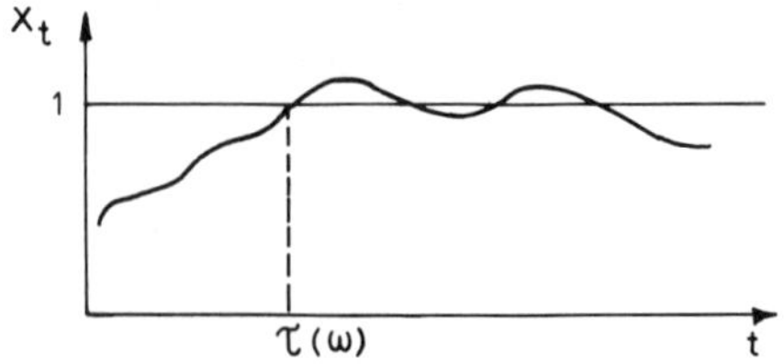

FIGURE 3.2.1

Example 3.2.1

Define

$$\tau(\omega) = \begin{cases} \inf\{t: \quad X_t \geq 1\} \\ \infty \text{ if the above set is empty} \end{cases}$$

$\tau(\omega)$ is the time at which the process $\{X_t, t \in T\}$ first crosses the level $+1$ (Figure 3.2.1). Hereafter we make the convention $\inf\{\varnothing\} = \infty$.

Example 3.2.2

$$\tau(\omega) = \inf\{t: \quad |X_t| \geq 1\}$$

$\tau(\omega)$ is the time at which the process $\{X_t, t \in T\}$ first crosses the level ± 1 (Figure 3.2.2).

Example 3.2.3

$$\tau(\omega) = \inf\{t: \quad \Delta X_t \geq 1\} \qquad \Delta X_t = X_t - X_{t-}, \quad X_{t-} = \lim_{s \uparrow t} X_s$$

$\tau(\omega)$ is the time at which the jump ΔX_t in the process $\{X_t, t \in T\}$ exceeds the level $+1$ for the first time (Figure 3.2.3).

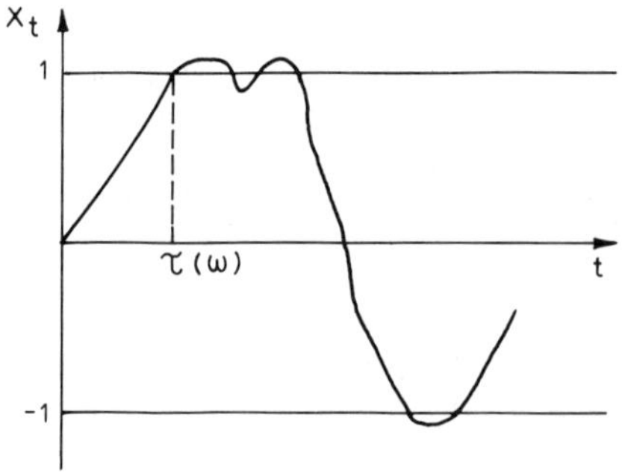

FIGURE 3.2.2

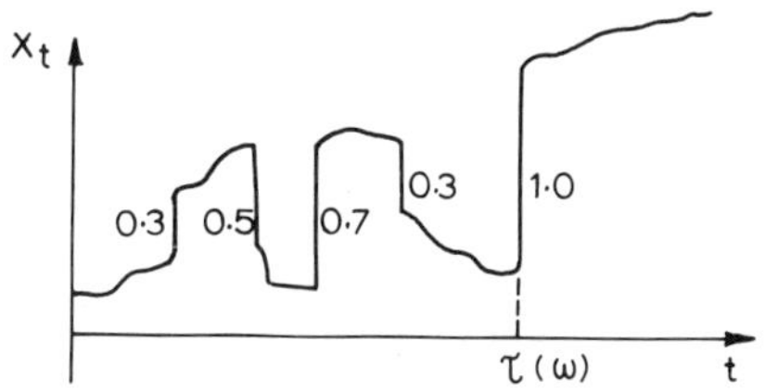

FIGURE 3.2.3

Example 3.2.4

Let B be a Borel set in $\mathcal{R}$ and let

$$\tau(\omega) = \inf\{t: \quad X_t(\omega) \in B\} \qquad B \in \mathcal{R}$$

then $\tau(\omega)$ is the time of first passage into the Borel set B.

Example 3.2.5

$$V(\omega) = \{\text{the last time before } t = 3, \text{ the process } X_t \text{ crossed the value } +1\}$$

$V(\omega)$ in general does not constitute a stopping time because it anticipates the future value 3.

Example 3.2.6

A trivial example of a stopping time is when $\tau = a$ a positive constant.

Definition 3.2.2

Let τ be a stopping time relative to the family of filtration σ-field $\{\mathcal{F}_t, t \in T\}$. We denote by $\mathcal{F}_\tau$ the class of events

$$\mathcal{F}_\tau = \{A \in \mathcal{F}_\infty: \quad A \cap \{\tau \le t\} \in \mathcal{F}_t, t \in T\} \tag{3.2.2}$$

where $\mathcal{F}_\infty$ is the σ-field generated by $\cup_{t \in T} \mathcal{F}_t$, $T = R^+$.

$\mathcal{F}_\tau$ is called the σ-field of events occurring before the stopping time τ.

Properties of Stopping Times

1. As already mentioned, if τ is a stopping time, then $\{\tau < t\} \in \mathcal{F}_t$ and if the family $\{\mathcal{F}_t, t \in T\}$ is right continuous, then $\{\tau \le t\} \in \mathcal{F}_t$. If $\{\tau < t\} \in \mathcal{F}_t$, then $\{\tau \le t\} \in \mathcal{F}_{t+\epsilon}$ for any $\epsilon > 0$, and hence $\{\tau \le t\} \in \mathcal{F}_{t+} = \mathcal{F}_t$.

2. If τ is a stopping time, then τ is $\mathfrak{F}_\tau$-measurable where $\mathfrak{F}_\tau$ is given by eq. 3.2.2. Let A be $\{\tau \leq s, s \in T\}$ in eq. 3.2.2. Then for all $s, t \in T$,

$$\{\tau \leq s\} \cap \{\tau \leq t\} = \{\tau \leq t \wedge s\} \in \mathfrak{F}_{t \wedge s} \subset \mathfrak{F}_t$$

Since the quantity $\{\tau \leq s\} \cap \{\tau \leq t\}$ is $\mathfrak{F}_t$-measurable, we infer from eq. 3.2.2 that τ is $\mathfrak{F}_\tau$-measurable.

3. If τ_1 and τ_2 are stopping times, then $\tau_1 \wedge \tau_2$, $\tau_1 \vee \tau_2$, $\tau_1 + \tau_2$, and all nonnegative constants are stopping times. The above results follow from the following relations:

$$\{\tau_1 \wedge \tau_2 > t\} = \{\tau_1 > t\} \cap \{\tau_2 > t\} \in \mathfrak{F}_t \qquad \text{for all } t \in T$$

$$\{\tau_1 \vee \tau_2 \leq t\} = \{\tau_1 \leq t\} \cap \{\tau_2 \leq t\} \in \mathfrak{F}_t \qquad \text{for all } t \in T$$

$$\{\tau_1 + \tau_2 \leq t\} = \{\tau_1 = 0, \tau_2 = t\} \cup \{\tau_1 = t, \tau_2 = 0\}$$

$$\cup \Big\{ \bigcup_{a+b<t} [\{\tau_1 < a\} \cap \{\tau_2 < b\}] \Big\} \qquad a \text{ and } b \text{ rationals} > 0$$

4. If τ_1 and τ_2 are two stopping times and if A is $\mathfrak{F}_{\tau_1}$-measurable, then

$$A \cap \{\tau_1 \leq \tau_2\} \in \mathfrak{F}_{\tau_2} \tag{3.2.3}$$

implying that if $\tau_1 \leq \tau_2$, then $\mathfrak{F}_{\tau_1} \subset \mathfrak{F}_{\tau_2}$. To show that $A \cap \{\tau_1 \leq \tau_2\}$ is $\mathfrak{F}_{\tau_2}$-measurable we have to verify that

$$A \cap \{\tau_1 \leq \tau_2\} \cap \{\tau_2 \leq t\} \in \mathfrak{F}_t \qquad t \in T$$

But the left-hand side can be written as

$$[A \cap \{\tau_1 \leq t\}] \cap \{\tau_1 \wedge t \leq \tau_2 \wedge t\} \cap \{\tau_2 \leq t\}$$

and each of the three events are $\mathfrak{F}_t$-measurable and the result follows.

5. If τ_1 and τ_2 are two stopping times, then each of the events $\{\tau_1 < \tau_2\}$, $\{\tau_1 > \tau_2\}$, and $\{\tau_1 = \tau_2\}$ belongs at the same time to the σ-fields $\mathfrak{F}_{\tau_1}$ and $\mathfrak{F}_{\tau_2}$, that is, they are $\mathfrak{F}_{\tau_1} \cap \mathfrak{F}_{\tau_2}$ measurable. From property 4, $\{\tau_1 \leq \tau_2\} \in \mathfrak{F}_{\tau_2}$. By complementation $\{\tau_1 > \tau_2\} \in \mathfrak{F}_{\tau_2}$. Now $\tau_1 \wedge \tau_2$ is also a stopping time which is $\mathfrak{F}_{\tau_1 \wedge \tau_2}$-measurable and hence $\mathfrak{F}_{\tau_2}$-measurable. Hence the events $\{\tau_1 \wedge \tau_2 = \tau_2\}$ $= \{\tau_1 = \tau_2\}$ and $\{\tau_1 \wedge \tau_2 < \tau_2\} = \{\tau_1 < \tau_2\}$ belong to $\mathfrak{F}_{\tau_2}$. Since τ_1 and τ_2 play a symmetric role, they can be shown to belong to $\mathfrak{F}_{\tau_1}$ also.

6. If $\{\tau_n, n \in N\}$ is a sequence of stopping times, then $\sup_n \tau_n$ is also a stopping time. If in addition the family $\{\mathfrak{F}_t, t \in T\}$ is right continuous, then $\inf_n \tau_n$, $\limsup_n \tau_n$, and $\liminf_n \tau_n$ are also stopping times. The results for $\sup_n \tau_n$

and $\inf_n \tau_n$ follow from

$$\{\sup_n \tau_n \leq t\} = \bigcup_n \{\tau_n \leq t\} \in \mathcal{F}_t$$

$$\{\inf_n \tau_n < t\} = \bigcap_n \{\tau_n < t\} \in \mathcal{F}_t$$

The cases of $\limsup_n \tau_n$ and $\liminf_n \tau_n$ follow from

$$\begin{aligned}\{\limsup_n \tau_n < t\} &= \left\{\inf_{n\geq 1} \sup_{k\geq n} \tau_k < t\right\} \\ &= \bigcup_{m=1}^{\infty} \bigcap_{n=1}^{\infty} \bigcup_{k=n}^{\infty} \left\{\tau_k < t - \frac{1}{m}\right\}\end{aligned}$$

and

$$\begin{aligned}\{\liminf_n \tau_n < t\} &= \left\{\sup_{n\geq 1} \inf_{k\geq n} \tau_k < t\right\} \\ &= \bigcup_{m=1}^{\infty} \bigcup_{n=1}^{\infty} \bigcap_{k=n}^{\infty} \left\{\tau_k > t + \frac{1}{m}\right\}\end{aligned}$$

In many situations the problem of approximating a stopping time τ from above by a discrete sequence of stopping times $\{\tau_n\}$ arises, and we give the following proposition.

Proposition 3.2.1 Approximation of τ from above

Let τ be a $\mathcal{F}_\tau$-measurable stopping time with respect to the right continuous filtration σ-field $\{\mathcal{F}_t, t \in T, T = R^+\}$. Then there exists a sequence of decreasing stopping times $\{\tau_n, n \geq 1\}$ with respect to $\{\mathcal{F}_t\}$ approaching τ from above such that

1. $\tau_n(\omega) \geq \tau(\omega)$.
2. For each ω, $\tau_n(\omega) \downarrow \tau(\omega)$ as $n \to \infty$.
3. The range of τ_n is a discrete subset of R^+ or possibly ∞.
4. Further if τ_n is $\mathcal{F}_{\tau_n}$-measurable, then

$$\mathcal{F}_\tau = \bigcap_n \mathcal{F}_{\tau_n}$$

Proof. We construct $\{\tau_n\}$ such that they are stopping times. Let

$$\tau_n(\omega) = \begin{cases} \dfrac{k}{2^n} & \dfrac{k-1}{2^n} \leq \tau(\omega) < \dfrac{k}{2^n}, \quad k = 1, 2, \ldots. \\ \infty & \tau(\omega) = \infty \end{cases}$$

Then for $t \geq 0$ and for each n,

$$\{\tau_n < t\} = \bigcup_{k/2^n \leq t} \left\{\tau_n = \frac{k}{2^n}\right\}$$

$$= \bigcup_{k/2^n \leq t} \left\{\frac{k-1}{2^n} \leq \tau(\omega) < \frac{k}{2^n}\right\} \in \mathcal{F}_t$$

Hence each τ_n is a stopping time, and by its very construction $\tau_n(\omega) \geq \tau(\omega)$, proving statement 1. For each ω and $\tau(\omega) < \infty$ we have

$$0 \leq \tau_n(\omega) - \tau(\omega) < \frac{1}{2^n} \Rightarrow \lim_{n \to \infty} \tau_n(\omega) = \tau(\omega)$$

thus proving statement 2. To obtain $\tau_{n+1}(\omega)$ we see that the number of partitions double, and hence $\tau_{n+1}(\omega)$ takes the value $(2k-1)/2^{n+1}$ or $2k/2^{n+1}$, depending upon the location of $\tau(\omega)$. Hence $\tau_{n+1}(\omega) \leq \tau_n(\omega)$, thus showing that $\{\tau_n(\omega)\}$ is a decreasing sequence. By the very definition of τ_n, statement 3 is obvious. For the final part we define $\mathcal{F}_{\tau_n}$ by

$$\mathcal{F}_{\tau_n} = \{A \in \mathcal{F}_\infty:\ A \cap \{\tau_n \leq t\} \in \mathcal{F}_t, t \in T, T = R^+\}$$

Thus τ_n is $\mathcal{F}_{\tau_n}$-measurable.

Since $\tau \leq \tau_n$, we have $\mathcal{F}_\tau \subset \cap_n \mathcal{F}_{\tau_n}$. To show the reverse inclusion let $B \in \cap_n \mathcal{F}_{\tau_n}$. Since the τ_n are stopping times, we have for all n and $t \in T$,

$$B \cap \{\tau_n < t\} \in \mathcal{F}_t$$

Since $\tau_n \downarrow \tau$ as $n \to \infty$,

$$B \cap \{\tau < t\} = \bigcup_n B \cap \{\tau_n < t\} \in \mathcal{F}_t$$

and if $\{\mathcal{F}_t\}$ is a right continuous family, then

$$B \cap \{\tau \leq t\} \in \mathcal{F}_t$$

This implies that $B \in \mathcal{F}_\tau$, and as a result $\cap_n \mathcal{F}_{\tau_n} \subset \mathcal{F}_\tau$. Hence the proposition. □

Remark. Even though a stopping time τ can be approximated from above by a discrete sequence $\{\tau_n\}$, it is not true that it can be approximated from below by a sequence $\{\tau_n\}$ such that $\tau_n < \tau$ a.s. and $\tau_n \uparrow \tau$.

Proposition 3.2.2 Measurability of X_τ

Let $\{X_t, t \in T\}$ be a progressively measurable stochastic process with respect to the right continuous filtration σ-field $\{\mathcal{F}_t, t \in T\}$ with values in $(R, \mathcal{R})$. Let

τ be a stopping time relative to $\{\mathfrak{F}_t, t \in T\}$ with values in $[0, \infty)$. Then the stopped process X_τ is $\mathfrak{F}_\tau$-measurable.

Proof. Since $\mathfrak{R}$ is a Borel field on the real line R, to prove the proposition we have to verify that for any Borel set $B \in \mathfrak{R}$, $\{X_\tau \in B\} \in \mathfrak{F}_\tau$. Or

$$\{X_\tau \in B\} \cap \{\tau \le t\} \in \mathfrak{F}_t \qquad t \in T$$

We define a random variable $\xi = t \wedge \tau$ and write

$$\begin{aligned}\{X_\tau \in B\} \cap \{\tau \le t\} &= \{X_\tau \in B\} \cap [\{\tau < t\} \cup \{\tau = t\}] \\ &= [\{X_\xi \in B\} \cap \{\xi < t\}] \cup [\{X_\tau \in B\} \cap \{\tau = t\}]\end{aligned}$$

Clearly the term $\{X_\xi \in B\} \cap \{\tau = t\}$ is $\mathfrak{F}_t$-measurable. We have to show that X_ξ is $\mathfrak{F}_t$-measurable. The mapping $\omega \to (\omega, \xi(\omega))$ is the measurable mapping of $(\Omega, \mathfrak{F}_t)$ into $([0, t] \times \Omega, \mathfrak{R}_{[0,t]} \otimes \mathfrak{F}_t)$, and the mapping $(\omega, \xi) \to X_\xi(\omega)$ is also a measurable mapping of the space $([0, t] \times \Omega, \mathfrak{R}_{[0,t]} \otimes \mathfrak{F}_t)$ into $(R, \mathfrak{R})$ because of progressive measurability of X_t. In other words,

$$(\Omega, \mathfrak{F}_t) \overset{(\omega, \xi(\omega))}{\to} ([0, t] \times \Omega, \mathfrak{R}_{[0,t]} \otimes \mathfrak{F}_t) \overset{X_\xi(\omega)}{\to} (R, \mathfrak{R})$$

Hence X_ξ is $\mathfrak{F}_t$-measurable. Thus $\{X_\tau \in B\} \cap \{\tau \le t\} \in \mathfrak{F}_t$. □

Under conditions stated in the previous proposition, the process X_τ is $\mathfrak{F}_\tau$-measurable. However, the process $X_{t \wedge \tau}$ is also $\mathfrak{F}_\tau$-measurable, as given by the following proposition stated without prof (Shiryaev, 51, p. 15).

Proposition 3.2.3 (Measurability of $X_{t \wedge \tau}$)

Let $\{X_t, t \in T\}$ be a measurable stochastic process with values in a measurable space $(R, \mathfrak{R})$. Let τ be a stopping time with respect to the right continuous natural filtration field $\{\mathfrak{F}_t, t \in T\}$ of $\{X_t, t \in T\}$ with values in $[0, \infty)$. Then $\mathfrak{F}_\tau$ is the smallest σ-field with which the stopped process $\{X_{t \wedge \tau}, t \in T\}$ can be measured:

$$\{\omega\colon \ X_{t \wedge \tau} \in B\} \in \mathfrak{F}_\tau \qquad t \in T, \quad B \in \mathfrak{R}$$

3.3 DISCRETE MARTINGALES AND SUBMARTINGALES

We saw in the previous chapter that the Brownian motion process satisfied the martingale property. We now discuss discrete martingales and then continuous parameter martingales. Throughout this section we assume that the time set T is a set of positive integers N.

Definition 3.3.1 Discrete Martingale

Let $(\Omega, \mathcal{F}, P)$ be a probability space, and let $\{\mathcal{F}_n, n \in N\}$ be an increasing family of sub-σ-fields of $\mathcal{F}$. The real-valued sequence $\{X_n, n \in N\}$ is a *discrete* $\mathcal{F}_n$*-martingale* if

$$
\begin{aligned}
&1.\quad E|X_n| < \infty. \\
&2.\quad \{X_n, n \in N\} \text{ is adapted to the family } \{\mathcal{F}_n, n \in N\}. \\
&3.\quad E^{\mathcal{F}_m} X_n = X_m \quad \text{(a.s.)} \qquad m \le n
\end{aligned}
\tag{3.3.1}
$$

We can give an intuitive meaning to the martingale property. A player tosses a fair coin and wins some money if heads come up and loses the same amount of money if tails come up. Let X_m denote the fortune of the player at the end of m tosses. What the martingale property conveys is that the player's fortune on the $(m+1)$th toss is on the average the player's current fortune, which is not affected by the previous history, thus capturing the notion that the game is fair. We can also think about the game being favorable to the player (submartingale) and unfavorable to the player (supermartingale).

In Definition 3.3.1, if the third condition is $E^{\mathcal{F}_m} X_n \ge X_m$ (a.s.), $m \le n$, then we have a *submartingale*, and if $E^{\mathcal{F}_m} X_n \le X_m$ (a.s.), $m \le n$, then we have a *supermartingale*. Since a negative supermartingale is a submartingale, all discussions about a submartingale will cover equally a supermartingale.

We now give several examples to demonstrate the martingale property.

Example 3.3.1

Let $\{Z_n, n \in N\}$ be a sequence of independent identically distributed random variables with zero mean, and let $X_n = \sum_{i=1}^n Z_i$ and $\mathcal{F}_n = \sigma\{Z_i, i \le n, n \in N\}$. Then X_n is a martingale with respect to the σ-field $\mathcal{F}_n$. For $m \le n$,

$$E^{\mathcal{F}_m} X_n = E^{\mathcal{F}_m}(X_n - X_m + X_m) = E^{\mathcal{F}_m}(X_n - X_m) + E^{\mathcal{F}_m} X_m$$

Since $X_n - X_m$ is independent of $\mathcal{F}_m$ and X_m is $\mathcal{F}_m$-measurable, we have

$$E^{\mathcal{F}_m} X_n = E(X_n - X_m) + X_m = X_m$$

Example 3.3.2

In Example 3.3.1, if $\Phi_{X_n}(u)$ is the characteristic function of X_n given by Ee^{juX_n}, then $e^{juX_n}/\Phi_{X_n}(u)$ is an $\mathcal{F}_n$-martingale. For $m \le n$,

$$E^{\mathcal{F}_m} \frac{e^{juX_n}}{\Phi_{X_n}(u)} = E^{\mathcal{F}_m} \frac{e^{ju(X_n - X_m)} e^{juX_m}}{\Phi_{X_n}(u)}$$

Since X_m is independent of $X_n - X_m$ and $\mathcal{F}_m$-measurable, we have

$$E^{\mathcal{F}_m}\frac{e^{juX_n}}{\Phi_{X_n}(u)} = \frac{Ee^{ju(X_n - X_m)}e^{juX_m}}{\Phi_{X_n}(u)}$$

$$= \frac{Ee^{ju(X_n - X_m)}e^{juX_m}}{\Phi_{X_n - X_m}(u)\Phi_{X_m}(u)}$$

$$= \frac{e^{juX_m}}{\Phi_{X_m}(u)}$$

Example 3.3.3

In Example 3.3.1 let the variance of $Z_n = \sigma^2$, $n = 1, 2, \ldots$ Let

$$X_n = \left(\sum_{i=1}^{n} Z_i\right)^2 - n\sigma^2$$

and $\mathcal{F}_n$ be the σ-field as defined in that example. Then X_n is an $\mathcal{F}_n$-martingale.

Clearly $E|X_n| \leq 2n\sigma^2 < \infty$, and for $m \leq n$,

$$E^{\mathcal{F}_m}X_n = E^{\mathcal{F}_m}\left[\left(\sum_{i=1}^{n} Z_i\right)^2 - \left(\sum_{i=1}^{m} Z_i\right)^2 - n\sigma^2 + m\sigma^2 + \left(\sum_{i=1}^{m} Z_i\right)^2 - m\sigma^2\right]$$

$$= E^{\mathcal{F}_m}\left[\left(\sum_{i=m}^{n-m} Z_i\right)^2 - (n-m)\sigma^2\right] + \left(\sum_{i=1}^{m} Z_i\right)^2 - m\sigma^2$$

Since the first term is independent of the σ-field $\mathcal{F}_m$, we obtain

$$E^{\mathcal{F}_m}X_n = \left(\sum_{i=1}^{m} Z_i\right)^2 - m\sigma^2 = X_m$$

Example 3.3.4

Let $\{X_n, n \in N\}$ be any integrable $\mathcal{F}_n$-martingale and let ϕ be a convex function. According to Jensen's inequality (eq. 1.9.6) for $m \leq n$,

$$E^{\mathcal{F}_m}\phi(X_n) \geq \phi(E^{\mathcal{F}_m}X_n) = \phi(X_m)$$

Thus if $E\phi(X_n) < \infty$ for all n, then $\phi(X_n)$ is a submartingale.

As particular cases of this example we have

1. $|X_n|$ is a submartingale.
2. X_n^2 is a submartingale if $EX_n^2 < \infty$.
3. $|X_n|^\alpha$, $\alpha \geq 1$, is a submartingale if $E|X_n|^\alpha < \infty$.

In the previous section we discussed stopping times. We now discuss the connection between stopping times and stopping with reference to submartingales and martingales.

We have briefly discussed that the martingale property is connected with the fairness of a game. We consider a fair game where a player wins or loses a unit of money with equal probability. Let $\{Z_n, n \in N\}$ be a sequence of independent identically distributed random variables as in Example 3.3.1 with $P\{Z_i = 1\} = P\{Z_i = -1\} = \frac{1}{2}$. Then $X_n = \sum_{i=1}^{n} Z_i$ is the player's net gain at the nth stage and is a martingale. We know that $EX_n = 0$, meaning that the average net gain if the game is played over a long time is zero. But the player need not play forever, even though the game may continue, nor need he predetermine a particular n when he is going to stop. The player may decide to stop when ahead. Let τ now represent the random time at which the player decides to end the play and his net gain is X_τ. The question is whether the game continues to be fair, even though the player has stopped. In other words, even though $EX_n = 0$ for all n, is it necessarily true that $EX_\tau = 0$? The answer to the question whether a martingale continues to be a martingale after stopping, or more generally whether a submartingale continues to be a submartingale, is yes under certain conditions. In order to study these conditions, we now define a process which is a transformation under optional stopping.

Definition 3.3.2 Transformation under Stopping (Doob, 14, p. 300)

Let $\{X_n, n \in N\}$ be a discrete stochastic process adapted to the discrete filtration σ-field $\{\mathcal{F}_n, n \in N\}$. Let $\tau(\omega)$ be a bounded stopping time adapted to the same family $\{\mathcal{F}_n, n \in N\}$. The stochastic process

$$X_{n \wedge \tau}(\omega) = \begin{cases} X_n(\omega) & n \le \tau(\omega) \\ X_\tau(\omega) & n > \tau(\omega) \end{cases} \tag{3.3.2}$$

is called a *transformation under a system of optional stopping.*

We have now the following very important theorem, which deals with transformations of submartingales under a system of optional stopping.

Theorem 3.3.1 Doob's Optional Sampling Theorem (14)

Let $\{X_n, n \in N\}$ be a discrete stochastic process defined on $(\Omega, \mathcal{F}, P)$ adapted to the discrete filtration σ-field $\{\mathcal{F}_n, n \in N\}$, and let $\sup_n E|X_n| < \infty$ for all $n \in N$. Then the following statements are equivalent:

1. $\{X_n, n \in N\}$ is an $\mathcal{F}_n$-submartingale.
2. If τ_1 and τ_2 are bounded stopping times such that $\tau_1 \le \tau_2$, then

$$EX_{\tau_2} \ge EX_{\tau_1} \tag{3.3.3a}$$

3. If τ_1 is a stopping time and τ_2 a bounded stopping time, then

$$E^{\mathcal{F}_{\tau_1}} X_{\tau_2} \geq X_{\tau_1 \wedge \tau_2} \tag{3.3.3b}$$

Proof. $1 \Rightarrow 2$

Let $\tau_1 \leq \tau_2 \leq n$. Then

$$\begin{aligned} X_{\tau_2} - X_{\tau_1} &= \sum_{k=1}^{n} \sum_{i=0}^{n} I_{\{\tau_2 = k\}} I_{\{\tau_1 = i\}} (X_k - X_i) \\ &= \sum_{k=1}^{n} I_{\{\tau_2 = k\}} I_{\{\tau_1 < k\}} X_k - \sum_{i=0}^{n} I_{\{\tau_1 = i\}} I_{\{\tau_2 > i\}} X_i \\ &= \sum_{k=1}^{n} I_{\{\tau_2 = k\}} I_{\{\tau_1 < k\}} X_k - \sum_{k=1}^{n} I_{\{\tau_1 = k-1\}} I_{\{\tau_2 \geq k\}} X_{k-1} \end{aligned}$$

By adding and subtracting the quantity

$$\sum_{k=1}^{n} I_{\{\tau_1 < k-1\}} I_{\{\tau_2 \geq k\}} X_k$$

to the above equation, we obtain

$$X_{\tau_2} - X_{\tau_1} = \sum_{k=1}^{n} I_{\{\tau_2 \geq k\}} I_{\{\tau_1 < k\}} X_k - \sum_{k=1}^{n} I_{\{\tau_2 \geq k\}} I_{\{\tau_1 < k\}} X_{k-1}$$

Taking expectations on both sides,

$$\begin{aligned} E(X_{\tau_2} - X_{\tau_1}) &= \sum_{k=1}^{n} E I_{\{\tau_2 \geq k\}} I_{\{\tau_1 < k\}} (X_k - X_{k-1}) \\ &= \sum_{k=1}^{n} E E^{\mathcal{F}_{k-1}} I_{\{\tau_2 \geq k\}} I_{\{\tau_1 < k\}} (X_k - X_{k-1}) \end{aligned}$$

Since

$$\{\tau_2 \geq k\} = \{\tau_2 < k-1\}^c \in \mathcal{F}_{k-1}$$

and

$$\{\tau_1 < k\} \subset \{\tau_1 \leq k-1\} \in \mathcal{F}_{k-1}$$

we have

$$\begin{aligned} E(X_{\tau_2} - X_{\tau_1}) &= \sum_{k=1}^{n} E I_{\{\tau_2 \geq k\}} I_{\{\tau_1 < k\}} E^{\mathcal{F}_{k-1}} (X_k - X_{k-1}) \\ &\geq 0 \end{aligned}$$

since X_n is a submartingale.

$2 \Rightarrow 3$

Let $\xi = \tau_1 \wedge \tau_2$, and let A be any set measurable with respect to $\mathcal{F}_\xi$. Let $R = \xi_A \wedge n$ and $S = \tau_{2A} \wedge n$ where n is the bound on τ_2. Clearly $R \leq S$, and since

$$EX_S \geq EX_R$$

by statement 2, we have

$$\int_A X_{\tau_2}\, dP + \int_{A^c} X_n\, dP \geq \int_A X_\xi\, dP + \int_{A^c} X_n\, dP \qquad \text{for all } A \in \mathcal{F}_\xi$$

or

$$\int_A X_{\tau_2}\, dP \geq \int_A X_\xi\, dP$$

which is equivalent to

$$E^{\mathcal{F}_\xi} X_{\tau_2} \geq E^{\mathcal{F}_\xi} X_\xi = X_\xi$$

or

$$E^{\mathcal{F}_{\tau_1}} X_{\tau_2} \geq X_{\tau_1 \wedge \tau_2}$$

since $\mathcal{F}_{\tau_1} \subset \mathcal{F}_\xi$.

$3 \rightarrow 1$

This is fairly simple because the equivalent form of statement 3 can be given by $E^{\mathcal{F}_{\tau_1}} X_{\tau_2} \geq X_{\tau_1}$ for $\tau_1 \leq \tau_2$, which is the submartingale property. □

Remarks

1. The condition that the X_n are uniformly integrable or $E|X_{n \wedge \tau}| < \infty$ where τ is a stopping time is equivalent to $\sup_{n \in N} E|X_n| < \infty$ (Doob, 14, p. 302).

2. If $\{X_n, n \in N\}$ is an $\mathcal{F}_n$-martingale, then the inequalities in Theorem 3.3.1 become equalities, that is,

a. For bounded stopping times τ_1 and τ_2 with $\tau_1 \leq \tau_2$,

$$EX_{\tau_2} = EX_{\tau_1} \tag{3.3.4a}$$

b. For a stopping time τ_1 and a bounded stopping time τ_2,

$$E^{\mathcal{F}_{\tau_1}} X_{\tau_2} = X_{\tau_1 \wedge \tau_2}$$

or, equivalently,

$$E^{\mathcal{F}_{\tau_1}} X_{\tau_2} = X_{\tau_1} \qquad \tau_1 \leq \tau_2 \tag{3.3.4b}$$

From the above discussion we might intuitively guess that a stopped martingale is a martingale. This is made precise by the following theorem.

Theorem 3.3.2 Stopped Martingale

Let $\{X_n, n \in N\}$, $n \geq 1$, be an $\mathcal{F}_n$-martingale (submartingale) defined on a probability space $(\Omega, \mathcal{F}, P)$. Let $\tau(\omega)$ be a stopping time with respect to the family $\{\mathcal{F}_n, n \in N\}$, $n \geq 1$. Then the stopped sequence $\{X_{n \wedge \tau}, \mathcal{F}_n\}$, $n \geq 1$, is also a martingale (submartingale).

Proof. We prove this theorem when X_n is a submartingale. We have

$$X_{n \wedge \tau} = \sum_{m<n} X_m I_{\{\tau=m\}} + X_n I_{\{\tau \geq n\}}$$

Since all terms in the right-hand side are $\mathcal{F}_n$-measurable and integrable, we come to the conclusion that $X_{n \wedge \tau}$ is $\mathcal{F}_n$-measurable and integrable for all n. Hence

$$X_{(n+1) \wedge \tau} - X_{n \wedge \tau} = I_{\{\tau > n\}}(X_{n+1} - X_n)$$

Taking conditional expectation on both sides

$$\begin{aligned} E^{\mathcal{F}_n}(X_{(n+1) \wedge \tau} - X_{n \wedge \tau}) &= E^{\mathcal{F}_n}(I_{\{\tau > n\}}(X_{n+1} - X_n)) \\ &= I_{\{\tau > n\}} E^{\mathcal{F}_n}(X_{n+1} - X_n) \geq 0 \end{aligned}$$

thus proving the theorem.

Alternatively from eq. 3.3.3b, by substituting $\tau_1 = m$ and $\tau_2 = n \wedge \tau$, we have for $n \geq m$,

$$X_{m \wedge (n \wedge \tau)} = X_{m \wedge \tau} \leq E^{\mathcal{F}_m} X_{n \wedge \tau} \quad \text{(a.s.)}$$

which again proves the theorem. □

We now define the concept of a martingale difference.

Definition 3.3.3 Martingale Difference

Let $(\Omega, \mathcal{F}, P)$ be a probability space, and let $\{\mathcal{F}_i, i \in N\}$ be a discrete filtration σ-field defined on it. The sequence $\{x_i, i \in N\}$ is a *martingale difference* if

1. $x_0 = 0$.
2. $\{x_i, i \in N\}$ is adapted to $\{\mathcal{F}_n, n \in N\}$.
3. $E|x_i| < \infty$.
4. $E^{\mathcal{F}_{i-1}} x_i = 0 \quad \text{(a.s.)} \qquad i \in N$

(3.3.5)

If $E^{\mathcal{F}_{i-1}} x_i \geq 0$, then we have a submartingale difference. Clearly if the sequence $\{x_i, i \in N\}$ is an $\mathcal{F}_i$-martingale difference, then $X_n = \sum_{i=1}^n x_i$ is an $\mathcal{F}_n$-martingale.

Example 3.3.5

In Example 3.3.1 Z_n is a sequence of independent random variables with zero mean and is adapted to $\mathcal{F}_n$ with $Z_0 = 0$ and $E|Z_n| < \infty$. Hence $E^{\mathcal{F}_{n-1}} Z_n = EZ_n = 0$, and Z_n is a martingale difference.

Next we introduce the concepts of increasing processes and predictable processes.

Definition 3.3.4 Discrete Increasing Process

Let $(\Omega, \mathcal{F}, P)$ be a probability space, and let $\{\mathcal{F}_n, n \in N\}$ be a filtration σ-field defined on it. The integrable random process $\{A_n, n \in N\}$ defined on the filtration σ-field is *increasing* if

1. $A_0 = 0$
2. $A_{n+1} \geq A_n \qquad n \in N$

or

3. $a_{n+1} = A_{n+1} - A_n \geq 0 \qquad n \in N$

(3.3.6)

Definition 3.3.5 Predictable Process

An integrable stochastic process $\{A_n, n \in N\}$ defined on $(\Omega, \mathcal{F}, P)$ is *predictable* or *previsible* with respect to the filtration σ-field $\{\mathcal{F}_n, n \in N\}$ if either A_{n+1} or $a_{n+1} = A_{n+1} - A_n$ is $\mathcal{F}_n$-measurable for all $n \in N$.

The predictable process is also called a *natural* process. Note that a predictable process neither implies nor is implied by an increasing process.

Let us now give intuitive meaning to predictability by means of the following example.

Example 3.3.6

A gambler plays a game at times $n = 0, 1, 2, \ldots$. We denote the outcome of each successive game by x_n and the amount of money the gambler bets at each game by a_n. Whereas the random variable x_n is known only at time n, the random variable a_n must be known before time n. If we now define a filtration σ-field $\{\mathcal{F}_n, n \in N\}$, then x_n is adapted to the family $\{\mathcal{F}_n, n \in N\}$, and a_n is predictable with respect to the same family, that is, a_n is $\mathcal{F}_{n-1}$-measurable.

Predictability leads us to the concept of martingale transforms, which we now define.

Definition 3.3.6 Martingale Transform

Let $\{\mathcal{F}_n, n \in N\}$ be a filtration σ-field defined on a probability space $(\Omega, \mathcal{F}, P)$, let $\{A_n, n \in N\}$ be an $\mathcal{F}_n$-predictable process, and let $\{X_n, n \in N\}$ be an $\mathcal{F}_n$-martingale. Then the process Y_n given by

$$Y_n = A_0 X_0 + \sum_{i=0}^{n-1} A_{i+1}(X_{i+1} - X_i)$$

$$= A_0 X_0 + \sum_{i=0}^{n-1} A_{i+1} x_{i+1} \tag{3.3.7}$$

is called the *martingale transform* of X by A and is denoted by $Y = A \cdot X$.

The extension of the martingale transform to the continuous case is called a stochastic integral, which is discussed later.

We now state the following proposition as to when any process $\{A_n, n \in N\}$ can be called predictable.

Proposition 3.3.1 Predictable Process

Let $(\Omega, \mathcal{F}, P)$ be a probability space, and let $\{\mathcal{F}_n, n \in N\}$ be a filtration σ-field on it. In order for a stochastic process $\{A_n, n \in N\}$ to be $\mathcal{F}_{n-1}$-measurable it is necessary and sufficient that for each bounded martingale Y_n

$$E \sum_{n=0}^{\infty} Y_n(A_{n+1} - A_n) = EY_\infty A_\infty \tag{3.3.8}$$

where

$$Y_\infty = \lim_{n \to \infty} Y_n \qquad \text{and} \qquad EA_\infty < \infty$$

Proof

Necessity. Let A_{n+1} be $\mathcal{F}_n$-measurable. Then

$$E[Y_{n+1}A_{n+1}] = E\left[E^{\mathcal{F}_n} Y_{n+1} A_{n+1}\right]$$

$$= E\left[A_{n+1} E^{\mathcal{F}_n} Y_{n+1}\right]$$

$$= E[Y_n A_{n+1}] \tag{3.3.9}$$

Hence

$$
\begin{aligned}
E\sum_{n=0}^{\infty} Y_n(A_{n+1}-A_n) &= \lim_{K\to\infty} E\sum_{n=0}^{K} Y_n(A_{n+1}-A_n)\\
&= \lim_{K\to\infty} \sum_{n=0}^{K} (EY_nA_{n+1}-EY_nA_n)\\
&= \lim_{K\to\infty} \sum_{n=0}^{K} (EY_{n+1}A_{n+1}-EY_nA_n) \qquad \text{from eq. 3.3.9}\\
&= \lim_{K\to\infty} EY_KA_K = EY_\infty A_\infty
\end{aligned}
$$

Sufficiency. Let eq. 3.3.8 be satisfied with Y_n being any bounded martingale. Then

$$
\begin{aligned}
&E[Y_0(A_1-A_0)+Y_1(A_2-A_1)+\cdots+Y_K(A_{K+1}-A_K)+\cdots]\\
&\quad -EY_\infty A_\infty = 0
\end{aligned}
$$

or

$$
E\sum_{n=0}^{\infty} A_{n+1}(Y_n - Y_{n+1}) = 0 \tag{3.3.10}
$$

By Theorem 3.3.2 a stopped martingale is also a martingale for any stopping time τ. Hence the stopped sequence $\{Y_{n\wedge\tau}, n\in N\}$ is also an $\mathfrak{F}_n$-martingale. Equation 3.3.10 can now be applied to the stopped martingale $Y_{n\wedge\tau}$ with $\tau = k$, and we obtain

$$
EA_{k+1}(Y_k - Y_{k+1}) = 0 \qquad k = 0,1,2,\ldots \tag{3.3.11}
$$

Equation 3.3.11 shows the existence of equalities given by eq. 3.3.9 for any bounded martingale Y_n under the assumption that eq. 3.3.8 is satisfied. Hence

$$
EE^{\mathfrak{F}_k}A_{k+1}(Y_{k+1} - Y_k) = 0 \qquad k = 0,1,2\ldots \tag{3.3.12}
$$

Since Y_k is an $\mathfrak{F}_k$-martingale, one can conclude from eq. 3.3.12 that A_{k+1} is $\mathfrak{F}_k$-measurable. □

By the definition of an increasing process we have $E^{\mathfrak{F}_n}A_{n+1} \geq A_n$, implying that $\{A_n, n\in N\}$ is a submartingale with respect to the filtration σ-field $\{\mathfrak{F}_n, n\in N\}$. In fact, all increasing processes are submartingales with respect to the σ-fields they are adapted to. Further, if X_n is an $\mathfrak{F}_n$-martingale, then obviously the sum $A_n + X_n$ is also an $\mathfrak{F}_n$-submartingale. The question now arises as to whether any discrete submartingale can be decomposed into a martingale and an increasing process, and if so whether this decomposition is unique. The answer to this question is the Doob decomposition theorem (14). The extension to the continuous parameter submartingales is not trivial.

Theorem 3.3.3 Doob Decomposition Theorem (14, p. 297)

Let $(\Omega, \mathcal{F}, P)$ be a probability space, and let $\{\mathcal{F}_n, n \in N\}$ be the filtration σ-field. Let $\{X_n, n \in N\}$ be $\mathcal{F}_n$-adapted submartingale with $\sup_n E|X_n| < \infty$. Then there exists a unique decomposition (to within stochastic equivalence) for X_n for all $n \in N$ such that

$$X_n = M_n + A_n \tag{3.3.13}$$

where M_n is an $\mathcal{F}_n$-martingale and A_n is an $\mathcal{F}_n$-increasing predictable process.

Proof. The proof will be by construction. We will first show the existence. Let A_n be an $\mathcal{F}_n$-increasing predictable process with $a_n = A_n - A_{n-1}$, and let x_n be an $\mathcal{F}_n$-submartingale difference. Then for all $n \in N$ we set for a_n

$$a_n = A_n - A_{n-1} = E^{\mathcal{F}_{n-1}}(X_n - X_{n-1}) = E^{\mathcal{F}_{n-1}}x_n \geq 0 \tag{3.3.14}$$

and

$$X_n - X_{n-1} - (A_n - A_{n-1}) = x_n - E^{\mathcal{F}_{n-1}}x_n = x_n - a_n = m_n \tag{3.3.15}$$

From eqs. 3.3.14 and 3.3.15 we have

1. A_n is an increasing process since $a_n \geq 0$.
2. For each $n \in N$, a_n is $\mathcal{F}_{n-1}$-measurable and hence $A_n = \sum_{k=0}^{n} a_k$ is $\mathcal{F}_{n-1}$-measurable. Therefore A_n is an increasing predictable process.
3. m_n is a martingale difference because

$$E^{\mathcal{F}_{n-1}}m_n = E^{\mathcal{F}_{n-1}}\left(x_n - E^{\mathcal{F}_{n-1}}x_n\right) = 0$$

   Hence

$$M_n = \sum_{k=0}^{n} m_k$$

   is an $\mathcal{F}_n$-martingale.
4. From $x_n = m_n + a_n$ we have

$$\sum_{k=0}^{n} x_k = \sum_{k=0}^{n} m_k + \sum_{k=0}^{n} a_k$$

   or

$$X_n = M_n + A_n$$

Hence the existence of the decomposition has been shown.

We now show the uniqueness. Let there be another decomposition with $X_n = M_n' + A_n'$ or, equivalently, $x_n = m_n' + a_n'$ for all $n \in N$. Hence $m_n' = x_n - a_n'$, and taking conditional expectation with respect to $\mathcal{F}_{n-1}$ we have

$$E^{\mathcal{F}_{n-1}} m_n' = 0 = E^{\mathcal{F}_{n-1}} x_n - E^{\mathcal{F}_{n-1}} a_n' = a_n - a_n'$$

(since $a_n' \in \mathcal{F}_{n-1}$). $a_n - a_n' = 0$ implies $m_n - m_n' = 0$, and hence the decomposition is unique. □

What the Doob decomposition theorem conveys is that, among all decompositions of a discrete submartingale X_n into a martingale and an increasing process, one and only one decomposition consists of a martingale and an increasing predictable process, which is given by

$$A_n = \sum_{k=1}^{n} E^{\mathcal{F}_{k-1}}(X_k - X_{k-1}) \tag{3.3.16}$$

As already stated before, the extension of the Doob decomposition theorem to the continuous case was an open problem for a long time until it was extended by Meyer (43).

3.4 CONTINUOUS PARAMETER MARTINGALES AND SUBMARTINGALES

In the last section we discussed discrete martingales. Even though some concepts can be extended to continuous parameter martingales, some other concepts require delicate arguments and may not be so readily extendable. The Brownian motion process discussed in Chapter 2 is an example of a continuous parameter martingale. We now define a continuous parameter martingale.

Definition 3.4.1 Continuous Martingale

Let $(\Omega, \mathcal{F}, P)$ be a probability space, and let $\{\mathcal{F}_t, t \in T\}$ be a filtration σ-field defined on it and $\{X_t, t \in T\}$ a real-valued stochastic process adapted to $\{\mathcal{F}_t, t \in T\}$. Then the process $\{X_t, t \in T\}$ is a martingale with respect to the family $\{\mathcal{F}_t, t \in T\}$ if

1. $E|X_t| < \infty$.
2. For all $s, t \in T$ and $s \leq t$,

$$E^{\mathcal{F}_s} X_t = X_s \quad \text{(a.s.)} \tag{3.4.1}$$

X_t is a submartingale if

$$E^{\mathcal{F}_s} X_t \geq X_s \quad \text{(a.s.)}$$

Remarks

1. Since $E^{\mathcal{F}_s} X_t = X_s$ for a martingale, we have for $s \le t$,

$$EE^{\mathcal{F}_s} X_t = EX_s \Rightarrow EX_t = EX_s$$

As a consequence if X_0 is the initial value and if X_t is a martingale, then $EX_t = EX_0$ for all $t \in T$.

2. For $s \le t$, $E^{\mathcal{F}_s} X_t$ is increasing for a submartingale and decreasing for a supermartingale.

The right continuity plays an important role in continuous martingales, and we define this concept next.

Definition 3.4.2 Right Continuous Martingales

The martingale (submartingale) $\{X_t, \mathcal{F}_t, t \in T\}$ is right continuous if

1. The sample paths of X_t are right continuous almost surely.
2. The filtration σ-field $\{\mathcal{F}_t, t \in T\}$ is right continuous, that is,

$$\mathcal{F}_t = \bigcap_{s > t} \mathcal{F}_s = \mathcal{F}_{t+} \quad t \in T$$

We now give some examples of martingales.

Example 3.4.1

Let Z be any integrable random process defined on $(\Omega, \mathcal{F}, P)$, and let $\{\mathcal{F}_t, t \in T\}$ be the filtration σ-field. Then the stochastic process

$$X_t = E^{\mathcal{F}_t} Z$$

is a martingale because for $s \le t$ we can write

$$E^{\mathcal{F}_s} X_t = E^{\mathcal{F}_s} E^{\mathcal{F}_t} Z = E^{\mathcal{F}_s} Z = X_s$$

Example 3.4.2

Let $\{X_t, t \in T\}$ be an integrable stochastic process, adapted to $\{\mathcal{F}_t, t \in T\}$, with independent increments, that is, for $s \le t$, $X_t - X_s$ is independent of the σ-field $\mathcal{F}_s$. Then the process $\{X_t - EX_t, t \in T\}$ is an $\mathcal{F}_t$-martingale, since

$$\begin{aligned} E^{\mathcal{F}_s}(X_t - EX_t) &= E^{\mathcal{F}_s}(X_t - EX_t - X_s + EX_s + X_s - EX_s) \\ &= E^{\mathcal{F}_s}(X_s - EX_s) + E^{\mathcal{F}_s}(X_t - X_s - EX_t + EX_s) \\ &= E^{\mathcal{F}_s}(X_s - EX_s) \end{aligned}$$

because of independent increments.

In particular, the Brownian motion process W_t is an independent increment process with $EW_t = 0$. Hence W_t by itself is a martingale with respect to the underlying σ-field, as we have already seen. The Poisson process N_t is also an independent increment process with $EN_t = \lambda t$. Hence $N_t - \lambda t$ is a martingale with respect to the underlying σ-field.

Example 3.4.3

We also have the continuous counterpart of Example 3.3.2. Let $\{X_t, t \in T\}$ be an independent increment process, not necessarily integrable. Let $\Phi_{X_t}(u)$ be the characteristic function of X_t. Then the process

$$\frac{e^{juX_t}}{\Phi_{X_t}(u)}$$

is a martingale with respect to the underlying σ-field.

Example 3.4.4. Likelihood Ratios

Let $(\Omega, \mathcal{F}, P)$ be a probability space, and let Q be another measure absolutely continuous with respect to P, $Q \ll P$. Let $\{\mathcal{F}_t, t \in T\}$ be a filtration σ-field. The restriction of the measures P and Q to $\mathcal{F}_t$ is denoted by P_t and Q_t. It can be verified that Q_t is also absolutely continuous with respect to the measure P_t. Hence the Radon–Nikodym derivative L_t given by

$$L_t = \frac{dQ_t}{dP_t} \tag{3.4.2}$$

exists and is called the *likelihood ratio* between Q_t and P_t on the σ-field $\mathcal{F}_t$. We now show that L_t is an $\mathcal{F}_t$-martingale with respect to the probability measure P.

We denote by E and E_Q the expectation operators with respect to P and Q, respectively. Then for all $A \in \mathcal{F}_t$, we have from eq. 3.4.2,

$$E_Q I_A = E(I_A L_t)$$

and for $s \leq t$ and A being $\mathcal{F}_s$-measurable, we have

$$E_Q I_A = E(I_A L_s) = E(I_A L_t) \tag{3.4.3}$$

But from the definition of conditional expectation, eq. 1.7.5,

$$E(I_A L_t) = E\left(I_A E^{\mathcal{F}_s} L_t\right)$$

implying

$$L_s = E^{\mathcal{F}_s} L_t \qquad \text{for all } t \in T \tag{3.4.4}$$

Example 3.4.5

We also have a continuous counterpart of Jensen's inequality corresponding to the discrete Example 3.3.4. If $\{X_t, t \in T\}$ is any $\mathcal{F}_t$-martingale and ϕ is any convex function with $\phi(x)$ integrable, then from Jensen's inequality for $s \leq t$,

$$E^{\mathcal{F}_s}\phi(X_t) \geq \phi\left(E^{\mathcal{F}_s}X_t\right) = \phi(X_s) \quad \text{(a.s.)} \tag{3.4.5}$$

Properties of Continuous Martingales. We now enumerate the properties of continuous martingales (Lipster and Shiryaev, 34, pp. 55–62).

1. If $\{X_t, t \in T\}$ is a submartingale, then it is a martingale if and only if EX_t is a constant independent of t.
2. Let the filtration σ-field $\{\mathcal{F}_t, t \in T\}$ be right continuous. Then an $\mathcal{F}_t$-submartingale $\{X_t, t \in T\}$ admits of a right continuous modification if and only if EX_t is right continuous for all $t \in T$. In particular any $\mathcal{F}_t$-martingale $\{X_t, t \in T\}$ always has a right continuous modification.
3. Let $\{X_t, t \in T\}$ be a right continuous $\mathcal{F}_t$-submartingale. Let $T = [a, b]$, and let λ be a positive constant. Then we have the following inequalities:

a. $$\lambda P\left\{\sup_{t \in T} X_t \geq \lambda\right\} \leq E\left(X_b I_{\{\sup_{t\in T} X_t \geq \lambda\}}\right) \leq EX_b^+ \leq E|X_b| \tag{3.4.6}$$

b. $$\lambda P\left\{\inf_{t \in T} X_t \leq -\lambda\right\} \leq -EX_a + E\left(X_b I_{\{\inf_{t\in T} X_t \geq -\lambda\}}\right)$$

4. Let $\{X_t, t \in T\}$ be a nonnegative right continuous $\mathcal{F}_t$-submartingale, and let $T = [a, b]$. Let p and q be numbers such that $1 < p < \infty$ and $1/p + 1/q = 1$. Further if $E|X_b|^p < \infty$, then

$$E\left(\sup_{t \in T} X_t\right)^p \leq q^p E(X_b)^p \tag{3.4.7}$$

In particular if M_t is a right continuous $\mathcal{F}_t$-martingale with $E|M_t|^p < \infty$, then we have Doob's inequality

$$E\left(\sup_{t \in T}|M_t|\right)^p \leq q^p E|M_b|^p \tag{3.4.8}$$

5. Let $\{X_t, t \in T\}$ be a right continuous $\mathcal{F}_t$-martingale with $T = R^+$. If there exists a random variable X_∞ with $E|X_\infty| < \infty$ such that $E^{\mathcal{F}_t}X_\infty = X_t$ for all $t \in T$, then X_t is uniformly integrable. A uniformly integrable martingale is sometimes referred to as a *regular martingale*.
6. Let $\{X_t, t \in T\}$ be a uniformly integrable right continuous $\mathcal{F}_t$-submartingale. Let $\tau_1 \geq \tau_2 \geq \cdots \geq \tau_n \geq \cdots$ be a decreasing sequence of stopping times. Then the family of random variables $\{X_{\tau_n}, n \in N\}$ is uniformly integrable.

Let us now state and prove the optional sampling theorem corresponding to Theorem 3.2.1 in the discrete case.

Theorem 3.4.1 Optional Sampling Theorem

Let $(\Omega, \mathcal{F}, P)$ be a probability space, and let $\{\mathcal{F}_t, t \in T\}$ be a filtration σ-field defined on it. Let $\{X_t, t \in T\}$ be a uniformly integrable submartingale with right continuous trajectories. If τ_1 and τ_2 are two stopping times, then

$$E^{\mathcal{F}_{\tau_1}} X_{\tau_2} \geq X_{\tau_1 \wedge \tau_2} \tag{3.4.9}$$

Proof. Let n be a positive integer belonging to N. Let D_n be a collection of numbers of the form $k/2^n$, $k = 1, 2, \ldots$. We now consider the discrete submartingale $\{X_t, t \in D_n\}$ with respect to the family of σ-fields $\{\mathcal{F}_t, t \in D_n\}$. We define stopping times τ_{1n} for each n as

$$\tau_{1n}(\omega) = \frac{k+1}{2^n} \quad \text{if} \quad \frac{k}{2^n} \leq \tau(\omega) < \frac{k+1}{2^n} \qquad k = 1, 2, \ldots$$

and similarly for τ_{2n}.

From the results of the discrete optional sampling theorem, Theorem 3.3.1, we have

$$E^{\mathcal{F}_{\tau_{1n}}} X_{\tau_{2n}} \geq X_{\tau_{1n} \wedge \tau_{2n}} \qquad n \in N$$

Let $A \in \mathcal{F}_{\tau_1}$. Since the sequence $\{\tau_{1n}, n \in N\}$ is a decreasing sequence $\mathcal{F}_{\tau_1} \subset \mathcal{F}_{\tau_{1n}}$, and hence $A \in \mathcal{F}_{\tau_{1n}}$. Therefore

$$\int_A X_{\tau_{2n}}\, dP \geq \int_A X_{\tau_{1n} \wedge \tau_{2n}}\, dP$$

By property 6 the random variables $\{X_{\tau_{1n}}, n \in N\}$ and $\{X_{\tau_{2n}}, n \in N\}$ are uniformly integrable, and $\tau_{1n}(\omega) \downarrow \tau_1(\omega)$, $\tau_{2n}(\omega) \downarrow \tau_2(\omega)$ for all ω. Hence passing to the limit as $n \to \infty$ and invoking right continuity,

$$X_{\tau_{2n}} \to X_{\tau_2} \qquad \text{and} \qquad X_{\tau_{1n} \wedge \tau_{2n}} \to X_{\tau_1 \wedge \tau_2}$$

Hence

$$\int_A X_{\tau_2}\, dP \geq \int_A X_{\tau_1 \wedge \tau_2}\, dP$$

and the theorem is proven. □

Remark. If we have a uniformly integrable right continuous $\mathcal{F}_t$-martingale X_t and if τ is a stopping time, the stopped process $\{X_{t \wedge \tau}, t \in T\}$ will also be an $\mathcal{F}_t$-martingale.

3.5 DOOB – MEYER DECOMPOSITION

We have seen that the Doob decomposition (Theorem 3.3.3) of a submartingale into a martingale and an increasing predictable process is unique. The question now arises as to whether the decomposition concept can be extended to a continuous submartingale. Before this question can be answered, concepts such as predictability have to be extended to continuous time and new concepts introduced. The predictable process in discrete time was given by eq. 3.3.16,

$$A_n = \sum_{k=1}^{n} E^{\mathfrak{F}_{k-1}}(X_k - X_{k-1}) \tag{3.5.1}$$

and before this can be expressed as an analogous integral, we introduce some definitions.

Definition 3.5.1 Class DL (Meyer, 41)

Let $(\Omega, \mathfrak{F}, P)$ be a probability space, and let $\{\mathfrak{F}_t, t \in T\}$ be a right continuous filtration σ-field on it. Let τ belong to a set of stopping times with respect to the family $\{\mathfrak{F}_t, t \in T\}$. A submartingale $\{X_t, t \in T\}$ with right continuous trajectories belongs to the class DL if for any constant c, $0 \leq c < \infty$, the family of random variables $\{X_\tau$ such that $\tau \leq c$ (a.s.)$\}$ is uniformly integrable.

According to Meyer (41) not every submartingale X_t is decomposable uniquely unless it belongs to the class DL. However, this condition is really a weak one, as shown by the following proposition given without proof (Lipster and Shiryaev, 34, p. 62).

Proposition 3.5.1

Let $\{\mathfrak{F}_t, t \in T\}$ be a right continuous filtration σ-field defined on a probability space $(\Omega, \mathfrak{F}, P)$. Then

1. Any $\mathfrak{F}_t$-martingale $\{X_t, t \in T\}$ with right continuous trajectories belongs to the class DL.
2. Any positive submartingale $\{X_t, t \in T\}$ with right continuous trajectories belongs to the class DL.

We now extend the definition of an increasing predictable process to continuous time.

Definition 3.5.2 Increasing Process

Let $(\Omega, \mathfrak{F}, P)$ be a probability space, and let $\{\mathfrak{F}_t, t \in T\}$ be a right continuous filtration σ-field defined on it. A real right continuous stochastic process

$\{A_t, t \in T\}$ is an increasing process with respect to the family $\{\mathcal{F}_t, t \in T\}$ if

$$\begin{aligned}&1.\ A_0 = 0\\ &2.\ A_t \text{ is } \mathcal{F}_t\text{-measurable}\\ &3.\ A_s \le A_t \qquad \text{for } s \le t \text{ (a.s.)}\\ &4.\ EA_t < \infty \qquad \text{for all } t \in T\end{aligned} \tag{3.5.2}$$

Remark. If $T = R^+$, then the increasing process is integrable if $EA_\infty < \infty$, and if $T = [a, b]$ then the definition implies that the process is integrable. We assume that the process $\{A_t, t \in T\}$ is integrable.

Definition 3.5.3 Predictable Process

An integrable increasing process is predictable (also called natural) if for all $t \in T$,

$$E\int_0^t Y_s\, dA_s = E\int_0^t Y_{s-}\, dA_s \tag{3.5.3}$$

for any nonnegative bounded right continuous $\mathcal{F}_t$-martingale $\{Y_t, t \in T\}$.

As a consequence of the definition we have the following proposition (Meyer, 41; Lipster and Shiryaev, 34, p. 63).

Proposition 3.5.2

Let $\{A_t, t \in T\}$ be an integrable increasing process. Then A_t is predictable if and only if

$$E\int_0^\infty Y_s\, dA_s = E\int_0^\infty Y_{s-}\, dA_s \tag{3.5.4}$$

for any nonnegative bounded right continuous $\mathcal{F}_t$-martingale Y_t.

Properties of Increasing Predictable Processes

1. Just as in a discrete $\mathcal{F}_n$-predictable process$\{A_n, n \in N\}$ the values A_{n+1} are $\mathcal{F}_n$-measurable, so also for a continuous $\mathcal{F}_t$-predictable process $\{A_t, t \in T\}$ the random variable A_t is $\mathcal{F}_s$-measurable, $s \le t$.

2. If X_t is any $\mathcal{F}_t$-submartingale, the $\mathcal{F}_t$-increasing predictable process $\{A_t, t \in T\}$ can be found as a weak limit (Meyer's weak limit) by

$$A_t = \lim_{h \downarrow 0} \int_0^t \frac{E^{\mathcal{F}_s}(X_{s+h} - X_s)}{h}\, ds$$

that is,

$$A_t = \int_0^t E^{\mathcal{F}_s} \dot{X}_s\, ds \tag{3.5.5a}$$

or

$$dA_t = E^{\mathfrak{F}_t} dX_t \tag{3.5.5b}$$

Equation 3.5.5a is the integral analog of the summation of eq. 3.5.1 for discrete time.

We are now in a position to answer the question posed in the beginning of the section as to whether Doob decomposition can be extended to continuous submartingales.

Theorem 3.5.1 Doob – Meyer Decomposition

Let $(\Omega, \mathfrak{F}, P)$ be a probability space, and let $\{\mathfrak{F}_t, t \in T\}$ be a right continuous filtration σ-field defined on it. Let $\{X_t, t \in T\}$ be a right continuous $\mathfrak{F}_t$-submartingale belonging to the class DL. Then there exists a right continuous $\mathfrak{F}_t$-martingale $\{M_t, t \in T\}$ and an $\mathfrak{F}_t$-increasing predictable process such that for all $t \in T$,

$$X_t = M_t + A_t \tag{3.5.6}$$

Further, the decomposition is unique to within stochastic equivalence.

For a proof see Lipster and Shiryaev (34, p. 65), and Kallianpur (29, p. 28). The increasing predictable process $\{A_t, t \in T\}$ is referred to as the process associated with the submartingale X_t on the σ-fields $\{\mathfrak{F}_t, t \in T\}$.

Remarks

1. All increasing processes may not be predictable.
2. All predictable processes may not be increasing. In fact, from eq. 3.5.5 we can conclude that all continuous $\mathfrak{F}_t$-adapted processes are predictable, not necessarily increasing. (A continuous $\mathfrak{F}_t$-adapted martingale X_t may not be given by eq. 3.5.5 since $E^{\mathfrak{F}_s}(X_{s+h} - X_s) = 0$, $h \geq 0$.)
3. Remark 2 implies that if the submartingale $\{X_t, \mathfrak{F}_t, t \in T\}$ has a decomposition with A_t continuous, then that A_t is the unique predictable increasing process associated with the submartingale $\{X_t, \mathfrak{F}_t, t \in T\}$.
4. We can also have an analogous theorem connecting submartingale differences: if x_t is an $\mathfrak{F}_t$-measurable submartingale difference, then there exists a unique process a_t which is a difference of two continuous increasing processes such that $x_t - a_t = m_t$ is a martingale difference.

Corollary 3.5.1

We have an interesting corollary to Theorem 3.5.1 that all continuous martingales have *unbounded* variation.

Proof. We prove this by rejection. Let us assume that the continuous martingale $\{X_t, \mathfrak{F}_t, t \in T\}$ has a bounded variation. However, any continuous function of bounded variation can be given as a difference of two continuous increasing functions A_t and B_t, or

$$A_t = X_t + B_t \tag{3.5.7}$$

is the Doob–Meyer decomposition of the submartingale A_t. But $A_t = 0 + A_t$ is another Doob–Meyer decomposition of A_t. Therefore by uniqueness $X_t = 0$. Hence X_t as a continuous nontrivial martingale other than zero cannot exist with bounded variation. □

Note. In eqs. 3.5.3 and 3.5.4 we have defined a bounded martingale. As a consequence of the above corollary this martingale cannot be continuous since continuous martingales have unbounded variation.

We shall now use the Doob–Meyer decomposition theorem for decomposing continuous submartingales with respect to different σ-fields. We like to reemphasize that all decompositions are with respect to the underlying σ-fields. If there are different σ-fields, there may be different decompositions. We shall state the following preliminaries.

Let $\{X_t, t \in T\}$ be any submartingale on a complete probability space $(\Omega, \mathfrak{F}, P)$ not necessarily adapted to $\{\mathfrak{F}_t, t \in T\}$. Let $\{A_t, t \in T\}$ be an integrable increasing predictable process with respect to the σ-field $\{\mathfrak{F}_t, t \in T\}$, and from Meyer's weak limit, eq. 3.5.5, we have

$$dA_t = E^{\mathfrak{F}_t}\, dX_t \tag{3.5.8}$$

Let us now define the conditional expectation of X_t on the σ-field $\mathfrak{F}_t$ as $\hat{X}_t$,

$$\hat{X}_t = E^{\mathfrak{F}_t} X_t \tag{3.5.9}$$

Obviously if X_t is $\mathfrak{F}_t$-measurable, then $\hat{X}_t = X_t$. We have to find in eq. 3.5.8 $E^{\mathfrak{F}_t}\, dX_t$. We now recall from the smoothing properties of conditional expectations that if $\mathfrak{F}_1$ and $\mathfrak{F}_2$ are two σ-fields of ω-sets defined on the probability space $\{\Omega, \mathfrak{F}, P\}$ with $\mathfrak{F}_1 \subset \mathfrak{F}_2$, and if X is any random variable defined on the space $\{\Omega, \mathfrak{F}, P\}$, then

$$E^{\mathfrak{F}_1} E^{\mathfrak{F}_2} X = E^{\mathfrak{F}_1} X \tag{3.5.10}$$

We now define $E^{\mathfrak{F}_t}\, d\hat{X}_t$ (note that we already have an expression for $E^{\mathfrak{F}_t}\, dX_t$ in eq. 3.5.8):

$$E^{\mathfrak{F}_t}\, d\hat{X}_t = E^{\mathfrak{F}_t}\left\{ E^{\mathfrak{F}_{t+dt}} X_{t+dt} - E^{\mathfrak{F}_t} X_t \right\} \tag{3.5.11}$$

Using eq. 3.5.10 in eq. 3.5.11 and since $\mathcal{F}_{t+dt} \supset \mathcal{F}_t$, we have

$$E^{\mathcal{F}_t} d\hat{X}_t = E^{\mathcal{F}_t} X_{t+dt} - E^{\mathcal{F}_t} X_t$$

$$= E^{\mathcal{F}_t}\{X_{t+dt} - X_t\}$$

$$= E^{\mathcal{F}_t} dX_t = dA_t$$

Thus we arrive at the very interesting equation

$$E^{\mathcal{F}_t} d\hat{X}_t = E^{\mathcal{F}_t} dX_t = dA_t \tag{3.5.12}$$

even though $\hat{X}_t = E^{\mathcal{F}_t} X_t$ from eq. 3.5.9.

In eq. 3.5.12 both $d\hat{X}_t$ and dA_t are $\mathcal{F}_t$-measurable. As a consequence we have

$$E^{\mathcal{F}_t} d(\hat{X}_t - A_t) = 0 \Rightarrow d\hat{X}_t - dA_t = dM_t \tag{3.5.13}$$

and hence $\hat{X}_t - A_t = M_t$ is an $\mathcal{F}_t$-martingale.

If we now assume that X_t is also an $\mathcal{F}_t$-measurable process, then $dX_t = d\hat{X}_t$, and hence $dM_t = dX_t - E^{\mathcal{F}_t} dX_t$ represents the new information in dX_t available after t.

The fact that dM_t is the new information can be shown as follows:

$$dM_t = dX_t - E^{\mathcal{F}_t} dX_t$$

$$= X_{t+dt} - X_t - E^{\mathcal{F}_t}(X_{t+dt} - X_t)$$

Since $X_t \in \mathcal{F}_t$, we have

$$dM_t = X_{t+dt} - E^{\mathcal{F}_t} X_{t+dt}$$

Thus dM_t represents the difference between X_{t+dt} and the projection of X_{t+dt} on the σ-field, $\mathcal{F}_t$. This dM_t is indeed the new information. Clearly $E^{\mathcal{F}_t} dM_t = 0$. The process M_t is known as the *innovations* process for X_t and is an $\mathcal{F}_t$-martingale.

We are now in a position to discuss Doob–Meyer decomposition with respect to different σ-fields. Let a stochastic process $\{X_t, t \in T\}$ be given by

$$X_t = \int_0^t Z_\tau \, d\tau + Y_t \qquad t \in T \tag{3.5.14}$$

where $Z_\tau \geq 0$ satisfies the condition $\int_0^t E|Z_\tau| \, d\tau < \infty$ for all t (implying integrability), and Y_t is a martingale defined on the σ-field $\mathcal{Y}_t = \sigma\{Y_\tau, \tau \leq t, t \in T\}$ and assumed independent of Z_t.

We now define the following σ-fields:

$$\mathcal{F}_t = \sigma\{X_\tau, \tau \le t, t \in T\}$$

$$\mathcal{Y}_t = \sigma\{Y_\tau, \tau \le t, t \in T\}$$

$$\mathcal{X}_t = \sigma\{X_\tau, Y_\tau, \tau \le t, t \in T\}$$

$$= \sigma\{Z_\tau, Y_\tau, \tau \le t, t \in T\}$$

We note that Y_t is both a $\mathcal{Y}_t$-martingale as well as an $\mathcal{X}_t$-martingale, but not an $\mathcal{F}_t$-martingale, and $\mathcal{F}_t \subset \mathcal{X}_t$, $\mathcal{Y}_t \subset \mathcal{X}_t$.

Decomposition with Respect to $\{\mathcal{X}_t\}$ Field. (Signals measurable with respect to $\mathcal{X}_t$.) Since X_t is measurable with respect to the σ-field $\{\mathcal{X}_t, t \in T\}$, $\hat{X}_t = E^{\mathcal{X}_t} X_t = X_t$, and hence from eq. 3.5.13 we have

$$E^{\mathcal{X}_t} d(X_t - A_t) = 0 \qquad dX_t - dA_t = dM_t \tag{3.5.15}$$

Let us now identify A_t and M_t, noting that X_t is the given process, eq. 3.5.14,

$$dA_t = E^{\mathcal{X}_t} dX_t$$

$$= E^{\mathcal{X}_t}\{Z_t\,dt + dY_t\}$$

where $Z_t \in \mathcal{X}_t$, and since dY_t is a martingale difference with respect to $\mathcal{X}_t$ also, $E^{\mathcal{X}_t} dY_t = 0$. As a consequence we have

$$dA_t = Z_t\,dt \Rightarrow A_t = \int_0^t Z_\tau\,d\tau \tag{3.5.16}$$

Hence by Doob–Meyer decomposition we have

$$X_t - \int_0^t Z_\tau\,d\tau = M_t \tag{3.5.17}$$

and from eq. 3.5.14 we see that M_t is nothing other than Y_t, which is also an $\mathcal{X}_t$-martingale. All quantities in eq. 3.5.17 are thus $\mathcal{X}_t$-measurable, and eq. 3.5.14 as it stands is a decomposition with respect to the σ-fields $\{\mathcal{X}_t, t \in T\}$.

Decomposition with Respect to $\{\mathcal{F}_t\}$ Field. (Signals measurable with respect to $\mathcal{F}_t$.) We note that $\mathcal{F}_t$ is contained in the σ-field $\mathcal{X}_t$, $\mathcal{F}_t \subset \mathcal{X}_t$. Also since $X_t \in \mathcal{F}_t$, $t \in T$ we have

$$\hat{X}_t = E^{\mathcal{F}_t} X_t = X_t$$

From eq. 3.5.12

$$
\begin{aligned}
dA_t &= E^{\mathcal{F}_t} dX_t \\
&= E^{\mathcal{F}_t}\{Z_t\,dt + dY_t\}
\end{aligned}
\qquad (3.5.18)
$$

Since $\mathcal{F}_t \subset \mathcal{X}_t$, we can use eq. 3.5.10 to obtain

$$E^{\mathcal{F}_t} dY_t = E^{\mathcal{F}_t} E^{\mathcal{X}_t} dY_t = 0$$

because $E^{\mathcal{X}_t} dY_t = 0$ since Y_t is an $\mathcal{X}_t$-martingale. Hence

$$dA_t = E^{\mathcal{F}_t} Z_t\,dt \qquad (3.5.19)$$

Since Z_t is not $\mathcal{F}_t$-measurable, we can define $\hat{Z}_t = E^{\mathcal{F}_t} Z_t$, and as a consequence, $A_t = \int_0^t \hat{Z}_\tau\,d\tau$. The Doob–Meyer decomposition with respect to the σ-field $\mathcal{F}_t$ is given by

$$X_t - \int_0^t \hat{Z}_\tau\,d\tau = M_t \qquad (3.5.20)$$

where M_t is an $\mathcal{F}_t$-martingale and is the innovations process as already indicated. It is denoted by ν_t. All quantities in eq. 3.5.20 are $\mathcal{F}_t$-measurable.

Remarks

1. The integral given by $\int_0^t \hat{Z}_\tau\,d\tau$ is equal to $\int_0^t E^{\mathcal{F}_\tau} Z_\tau\,d\tau$. It is not equal to $E^{\mathcal{F}_t}\int_0^t Z_\tau\,d\tau$ because the first one is an increasing process whereas the second one may not be increasing. In other words, if we define a process S_t by $\int_0^t Z_\tau\,d\tau$, then the projection $\hat{S}_t = E^{\mathcal{F}_t}\int_0^t Z_\tau\,d\tau$ is not a predictable increasing process. On the other hand, the projection $\bar{S}_t = \int_0^t E^{\mathcal{F}_\tau} Z_\tau\,d\tau$ is a predictable increasing process and is called the *dual predictable projection* in the terminology of Dellacherie and Meyer (11).
2. Note, however, that

$$E^{\mathcal{F}_s}\int_s^t Z_\tau\,d\tau = \int_s^t E^{\mathcal{F}_s} Z_\tau\,d\tau$$

Decomposition with Respect to $\{\mathcal{Y}_t\}$ Field. (Signals measurable with respect to $\mathcal{Y}_t$.) Since X_t is not $\mathcal{Y}_t$-measurable, we can define

$$\hat{X}_t = E^{\mathcal{Y}_t} X_t$$

and from eq. 3.5.12,

$$
\begin{aligned}
dA_t &= E^{\mathcal{Y}_t} dX_t = E^{\mathcal{Y}_t}\{Z_t\,dt + dY_t\} \\
&= E^{\mathcal{Y}_t} Z_t\,dt
\end{aligned}
$$

because Y_t is a $\mathcal{Y}_t$-martingale. But Z_t is independent of $\mathcal{Y}_t$, and hence we have

$$dA_t = EZ_t\,dt \qquad \text{or} \qquad A_t = \int_0^t EZ_\tau\,d\tau \tag{3.5.21}$$

The Doob–Meyer decomposition of the submartingale $\hat{X}_t$ is therefore given by

$$\hat{X}_t - \int_0^t EZ_\tau\,d\tau = M_t \tag{3.5.22}$$

We have to show that M_t is indeed a $\mathcal{Y}_t$-martingale. Equation 3.5.22 can be written as

$$E^{\mathcal{Y}_t}\left\{X_t - \int_0^t Z_\tau\,d\tau\right\} = E^{\mathcal{Y}_t}Y_t = Y_t$$

from eq. 3.5.14. Hence we have $M_t = Y_t$, which is indeed a $\mathcal{Y}_t$-martingale, or

$$\hat{X}_t - \int_0^t EZ_\tau\,d\tau = Y_t \tag{3.5.23}$$

Thus all quantities in eqs. 3.5.22 and 3.5.23 are $\mathcal{Y}_t$-measurable. We can summarize the above results.

The Doob–Meyer decomposition of the stochastic process $\{X_t, t \in T\}$ given by

$$X_t = \int_0^t Z_\tau\,d\tau + Y_t$$

with $\int_0^t E|Z_\tau|\,d\tau < \infty$ and Y_t a $\mathcal{Y}_t$-martingale, independent of Z_t, can be obtained with respect to the σ-fields

$$\begin{aligned}\mathcal{X}_t &= \sigma\{X_\tau, Y_\tau, \tau \le t, t \in T\}\\ &= \sigma\{Z_\tau, Y_\tau, \tau \le t, t \in T\}\\ \mathcal{F}_t &= \sigma\{X_\tau, \tau \le t, t \in T\}\\ \mathcal{Y}_t &= \sigma\{Y_\tau, \tau \le t, t \in T\}\end{aligned}$$

as follows:

1. $\{\mathcal{X}_t, t \in T\}$; $X_t - \int_0^t Z_\tau\,d\tau = Y_t \qquad X_t = \hat{X}_t$
2. $\{\mathcal{F}_t, t \in T\}$; $X_t - \int_0^t \hat{Z}_\tau\,d\tau = \nu_t \qquad X_t = \hat{X}_t$
   where ν_t is the innovations process
3. $\{\mathcal{Y}_t, t \in T\}$; $\hat{X}_t - \int_0^t EZ_\tau\,d\tau = Y_t \qquad X_t \neq \hat{X}_t = E^{\mathcal{Y}_t}X_t$,
   where obviously $\mathcal{F}_t \subset \mathcal{X}_t$ and $\mathcal{Y}_t \subset \mathcal{X}_t$.

Problems

1. $\{X_n, n \in N\}$ is a family of random variables defined on $(\Omega, \mathcal{F}, P)$. Show that
   a. If $\lim_{n\to\infty} EX_n \to EX$, then $\{X_n\}$ is uniformly integrable.
   b. If l.i.p.$_{n\to\infty} X_n \to X$, then $\lim_{n\to\infty} EX_n \to EX$ if and only if $\{X_n\}$ is uniformly integrable.

2. Show that $\mathcal{F}_\tau = \{A \in \mathcal{F}_\infty\colon\ A \cap \{\tau \le t\} \in \mathcal{F}_t,\ t \in T\}$ is a field where $\mathcal{F}_\infty = \sigma\{\cup_{t\in T} \mathcal{F}_t, T = R^+\}$.

3. $\{X_t, t \in T\}$ is a stochastic process on $(\Omega, \mathcal{F}, P)$ and $\{\mathcal{F}_t, t \in T\}$ is a filtration σ-field defined on it. Prove that if $\{X_t\}$ is a right (left) continuous process, then X_τ is $\mathcal{F}_\tau$-measurable.

4. If X_n is a process of independent increments, then show that $X_n - EX_n$ is a martingale.

5. Consider an urn containing one red and one green ball to start with. A ball is drawn at random, and it and one more of the same color are added to the urn. Let X_n be the fraction of red balls and let $Y_n = (n+2)X_n$ be the number of red balls. Let $\mathcal{F}_n$ be the σ-field generated by Y_n. Show that X_n is a martingale with respect to $\mathcal{F}_n$.

6. Let $\{X_n, n = 1, 2, \ldots, K\}$ be an $\mathcal{F}_n$-submartingale with τ_1 and τ_2 being bounded stopping times. Show that

$$EX_1 \le EX_{\tau_1} \le EX_{\tau_2} \le EX_K$$

7. Let $\{X_n, n = 1, 2, \ldots, k\}$ be an $\mathcal{F}_n$-submartingale with stopping time τ and $P\{\tau \le k\} = 1$. Show that

$$E|X_\tau| \le 3 \sup_{n \le k} E|X_n|$$

8. Let $\{X_1, X_2, \ldots, X_n\}$ be a sequence of submartingales and let $\lambda > 0$. Then show (Doob's inequality)
   a. $P\left\{\sup_{1\le k\le n} X_k \ge \lambda\right\} \le \dfrac{EX_1 + EX_n^-}{\lambda}$
   b. $P\left\{\inf_{1\le k\le n} X_k \le -\lambda\right\} \le \dfrac{E|X_n|}{\lambda}$

9. Let $\{X_n, n \in N\}$ be an $\mathcal{F}_n$-supermartingale which is either (a) positive or (b) uniformly integrable. If τ_1 and τ_2 are two $\mathcal{F}_n$-stopping times, then show that

$$E\left(X_{\tau_2} | \mathcal{F}_{\tau_1}\right) = X_{\tau_1 \wedge \tau_2}$$

10. *Strong law of large numbers*. Let $\{X_n, n \in N\}$ be a sequence of independent identically distributed random variables with $EX_n = \mu$ for all $n \in N$.

Let $S_n = \sum_{k=1}^{n} X_k$, $n \in N$. Then using martingale theory show that S_n/n converges almost surely to μ.

11. If Q is absolutely continuous with respect to the measure P defined on the measurable space $(\Omega, \mathfrak{F})$ and if P_t is the restriction of P to the filtration σ-field $\mathfrak{F}_t$, show that the restriction Q_t to $\mathfrak{F}_t$ is also absolutely continuous with respect to P_t. Hence show that if the Radon–Nikodym derivative $L = dQ/dP$, then

$$L_t = \frac{dQ_t}{dP_t} = E^{\mathfrak{F}_t}\frac{dQ}{dP}$$

12. Show that a sufficient condition for a right continuous modification of a submartingale $\{X_t, t \in T\}$ to exist is that the process $\{X_t, t \in T\}$ is right continuous in probability at every $t \in T$, that is, $\lim_{s \downarrow t} X_s = X_t$ in probability.

13. Show that the Brownian motion process has the strong Markov property in the sense that if $\{W_t, t \in T\}$ is an $\mathfrak{F}_t$-Brownian motion process and τ is an $\mathfrak{F}_t$-stopping time, then the process $\{W_{t+\tau} - W_t, t \in T\}$ is an $\mathfrak{F}_{t+\tau}$ Brownian motion process which is independent of $\mathfrak{F}_t$.

4 CLASSES OF MARTINGALES AND RELATED PROCESSES

In the previous chapter we discussed both discrete and continuous martingale processes. In this chapter we discuss different classes of martingales and the increasing processes associated with them. The basic theory of square integrable martingales is due to Kunita and Watanabe (33). The theory of local martingales is due to Meyer (39).

4.1 SQUARE INTEGRABLE MARTINGALES

Definition 4.1.1 Square Integrable Martingale

Let $(\Omega, \mathcal{F}, P)$ be a complete probability space, and let $\{\mathcal{F}_t, t \in T, T = R^+\}$ be a right continuous filtration σ-field defined on it. The family of martingales $\{M_t, t \in T\}$ defined on $\{\mathcal{F}_t, t \in T\}$ is called *square integrable* if

1. $\sup_{t \in T} EM_t^2 < \infty$.
2. $\{M_t, t \in T\}$ is a family of right continuous martingales.
3. $E^{\mathcal{F}_s} M_t = M_s$ (a.s.), for $s \leq t$. (4.1.1)

Square integrable martingales are also called L^2-martingales.

The random process $X_t = \{M_t^2, t \in T\}$ is adapted to $\mathcal{F}_t$ and is a nonnegative submartingale belonging to the class DL. We have more to say about these submartingales later on.

Remarks

1. Functions that are square integrable need not be absolutely integrable. For example, $\sin x/x$ is square integrable in the interval $(-\infty, \infty)$ but is not absolutely integrable in the same interval.

2. Martingales with continuous trajectories almost surely satisfy Definition 4.1.1, and hence all continuous martingales are square integrable. They are denoted by $\{M_t^c, t \in T\}$.

4.2 MARTINGALES WITH JUMPS

We now discuss the phenomenon of jumps in any right continuous stochastic process $\{X_t, t \in T\}$ with left-hand limits and determine what type of martingale can be associated with that process.

Let $\{\tau_n(\omega), n = 1, 2, \dots\}$ be a sequence of countable stopping times with the following properties:

1. $\tau_n(\omega) \neq \tau_m(\omega)$ for $n \neq m$ and for all ω
2. $X_t(\omega)$ jumps *only* at $t = \tau_n(\omega)$ for some n

For example, let ΔX_t be a positive jump in the process X_t, and let a sequence of stopping times $\{S_{i,j}, i = 0, 1, 2, \dots, j = 1, 2, \dots\}$ be constructed as follows:

$$S_{i,1} = \inf\left\{t\colon \quad \frac{1}{i+1} < \Delta X_t < \frac{1}{i}, i = 0, 1, 2, \dots\right\}$$

$= $ the first time the jump in the process X_t is in the range $\left(\frac{1}{i+1}, \frac{1}{i}\right)$, $i = 0, 1, 2, \dots$

$$S_{i,j} = \inf\left\{t > S_{i,j-1}\colon \quad \frac{1}{i+1} < \Delta X_t < \frac{1}{i}, i = 0, 1, 2 \dots\right\}$$

$= $ the jth time the jump in the process X_t is in the range $\left(\frac{1}{i+1}, \frac{1}{i}\right)$, $i = 0, 1, 2, \dots$

A similar sequence can be constructed for negative jumps, and the two sequences can be combined to form a single sequence of countable stopping times $\{\tau_n(\omega), n = 1, 2, \dots\}$.

It is clear that with the construction given above the sequence of countable stopping times $\{\tau_n(\omega), n = 1, 2, \dots\}$ exhausts *all* the jumps in the process X_t. What the example illustrates is that the construction of the sequence of stopping times which exhausts all the jumps in X_t must be done carefully.

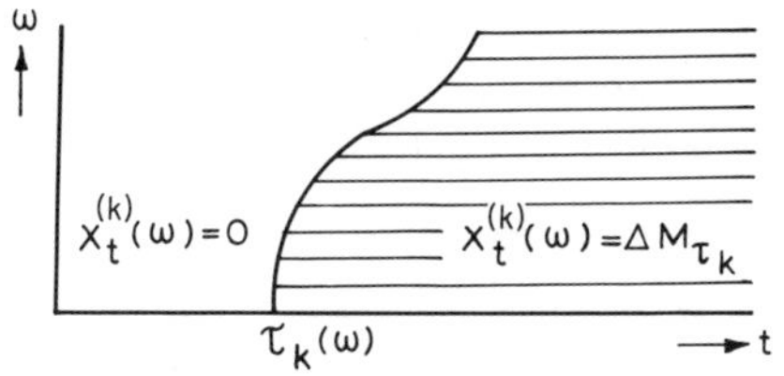

FIGURE 4.1.1

Let us now consider a martingale M_t with jumps adapted to $\{\mathcal{F}_t, t \in T\}$, and let $\{\tau_n(\omega)\}$ be a sequence of stopping times exhausting the jumps of M_t. We assume that at a stopping time $\tau_k(\omega)$ the corresponding jump of M_t is *positive*. We now define a process (Figure 4.1.1)

$$X_t^{(k)}(\omega) = \begin{cases} 0 & t < \tau_k(\omega) \\ \Delta M_{\tau_k} & t \geq \tau_k(\omega) \end{cases} \tag{4.2.1}$$

or equivalently

$$X_t^{(k)}(\omega) = \Delta M_{\tau_k} I_{\{t \geq \tau_k(\omega)\}}$$

By Doob's optional sampling theorem the process $X_t^{(k)}(\omega)$ is adapted to $\mathcal{F}_t$. Since it is also increasing, it is a submartingale. Therefore by Doob's decomposition theorem there exists a unique increasing predictable process $A_t^{(k)}$ such that $M_t^{(k)}$ given by

$$M_t^{(k)} = X_t^{(k)} - A_t^{(k)} \tag{4.2.2}$$

is an $\mathcal{F}_t$-martingale.

Similarly, if the jump in M_t is *negative*, the process $X_t^{(k)}$ will be a supermartingale, and we will obtain a decomposition similar to eq. 4.2.2. We sum all the decompositions at all the stopping times $\tau_n(\omega)$, $n = 1, 2, \ldots$ and write

$$M_t^d = \sum_{k=1}^{\infty} M_t^{(k)} \tag{4.2.3}$$

The process M_t^d, being the sum of martingales, is also a martingale. It can be given by

$$M_t^d = X_t - A_t = \sum_{k=1}^{\infty} X_t^{(k)} - \sum_{k=1}^{\infty} A_t^{(k)} \tag{4.2.4}$$

where the process X_t has piecewise constant paths and A_t is an increasing $\mathcal{F}_t$-predictable process. The martingale M_t^d is called a *discontinuous martingale*. Meyer (39, 41) calls it *compensated sum of jumps* martingale.

The process M_t^d exhausts all the jumps of the general martingale M_t. Hence the differenced martingale $M_t - M_t^d$ has trajectories which are almost surely continuous. Thus we have decomposed a general martingale M_t into a continuous martingale M_t^c and a discontinuous martingale M_t^d, or

$$M_t = M_t^c + M_t^d \tag{4.2.5}$$

Note. M_t^c, being a continuous martingale, has sample paths of unbounded variation, whereas the paths of M_t^d may or may not be of unbounded variation.

Example 4.2.1 Poisson Martingale

Let $\{N_t, t \in T\}$ be a Poisson process adapted to the filtration σ-field $\{\mathcal{F}_t, t \in T\}$. The process N_t consisting of only positive jumps with unit magnitude is an increasing process. Since it is also adapted to $\mathcal{F}_t$, it is a submartingale. In addition N_t is also a stationary independent increment process with $EN_t = \lambda t$. Hence using eq. 4.2.4, we have

$$M_t^d = N_t - \lambda t$$

where M_t^d is the Poisson martingale, and λt is the increasing $\mathcal{F}_t$-predictable process associated with the submartingale N_t. Thus the Poisson martingale is a discontinuous martingale. However, it is of bounded variation, unlike the continuous martingale, and is square integrable.

Square integrable martingales are extremely important, and the nonlinear filtering results of Fujisaki, Kallianpur, and Kunita (15) depend upon their concept. They are sometimes called *wide sense martingales*.

4.3 INCREASING PROCESSES OF SQUARE INTEGRABLE MARTINGALES

In the previous chapter we discussed increasing processes associated with submartingales. We now define increasing processes associated with L^2-martingales.

Definition 4.3.1 Quadratic Variance Process

Let $\{X_t, t \in T\}$ be a square integrable martingale belonging to the family of martingales $\{M_t, \mathcal{F}_t, t \in T\}$. The *quadratic variance* process of the L^2-martingale $\{X_t, t \in T\}$ is defined as

$$\langle X, X\rangle_t = \lim_{n\to\infty} \sum_{\nu=0}^{N(n)-1} E^{\mathcal{F}_{t_\nu}}\left(X_{t_{\nu+1}^{(n)}} - X_{t_\nu^{(n)}}\right)^2 \tag{4.3.1}$$

where the partitions $0 = t_0^{(n)} < t_1^{(n)} < \cdots < t_{N(n)}^{(n)} = t$ of the interval $[0, t)$, $t \in T$, become arbitrarily fine as $n \to \infty$.

By the very nature of the definition, $\langle X, X\rangle_t$ is measurable with respect to $\mathcal{F}_s$, where $s \leq t$, and hence they are predictable processes.

We now show that $\langle X, X\rangle_t$ is an increasing process as well. From eq. 4.3.1,

$$\langle X, X\rangle_t = \lim_{n\to\infty} \sum_{\nu=0}^{N(n)-1} \left[E^{\mathcal{F}_{t_\nu}} X^2_{t^{(n)}_{\nu+1}} - 2X_{t^{(n)}_{\nu+1}} X_{t^{(n)}_\nu} + X^2_{t^{(n)}_\nu}\right]$$

Since X_{t_ν} is a martingale, we have

$$\langle X, X\rangle_t = \lim_{n\to\infty} \sum_{\nu=0}^{N(n)-1} E^{\mathcal{F}_{t_\nu}}\left(X^2_{t^{(n)}_{\nu+1}} - X^2_{t^{(n)}_\nu}\right)$$

But by Jensen's inequality we have already seen that $X^2_{t^{(n)}_\nu}$ is a submartingale. Hence $X^2_{t^{(n)}_{\nu+1}} - X^2_{t^{(n)}_\nu}$ is a submartingale difference, and as a consequence $E^{\mathcal{F}_{t_\nu}}(X^2_{t^{(n)}_{\nu+1}} - X^2_{t^{(n)}_\nu}) \geq 0$. Since $\langle X, X\rangle_t$ is a running sum of a positive sequence, it is an increasing process.

Remark. The differential form of eq. 4.3.1 expressed by

$$d\langle X, X\rangle_t = E^{\mathcal{F}_t}\, dX_t^2$$

is exactly analogous to eq. 3.5.12 because by Jensen's inequality X_t^2 is a submartingale. Thus the quadratic variance process $\langle X, X\rangle_t$ is the $\mathcal{F}_t$-adapted increasing predictable process, associated with the submartingale X_t^2, where X_t is an L^2-martingale. This leads us to the Doob–Meyer decomposition theorem stated below.

Theorem 4.3.1 Doob – Meyer Decomposition Theorem for a Square Integrable Martingale

Let X_t be an L^2-martingale belonging to a class of square integrable martingales. Therefore X_t^2 is a submartingale on the filtration σ-field $\mathcal{F}_t$. Then there exists, according to Doob–Meyer decomposition, a unique $\mathcal{F}_t$-adapted predictable increasing process $\{A_t = \langle X, X\rangle_t, t \in T\}$ such that for all $t \in T$,

$$X_t^2 = M_t + \langle X, X\rangle_t \quad \text{(a.s.)} \tag{4.3.2}$$

and for $t \geq s$,

$$E^{\mathcal{F}_s}(X_t - X_s)^2 = E^{\mathcal{F}_s}(\langle X, X\rangle_t - \langle X, X\rangle_s) \tag{4.3.3}$$

Proof. Equation 4.3.2 is obvious by the Doob decomposition theorem, made clear from the preceding remark. We have to prove only eq. 4.3.3. Since both

X_t and M_t are martingales,

$$E^{\mathcal{F}_s}(X_t - X_s) = E^{\mathcal{F}_s}(M_t - M_s) = 0$$

$$\begin{aligned}
E^{\mathcal{F}_s}(X_t - X_s)^2 &= E^{\mathcal{F}_s}(X_t^2 - 2X_tX_s + X_s^2) \\
&= E^{\mathcal{F}_s}X_t^2 - 2X_sE^{\mathcal{F}_s}X_t + E^{\mathcal{F}_s}X_t^2 \\
&= E^{\mathcal{F}_s}X_t^2 - 2X_s^2 + X_s^2 \\
&= E^{\mathcal{F}_s}(X_t^2 - X_s^2) \\
&= E^{\mathcal{F}_s}(M_t + \langle X, X\rangle_t - M_s - \langle X, X\rangle_s) \\
&= E^{\mathcal{F}_s}(\langle X, X\rangle_t - \langle X, X\rangle_s) \qquad \square
\end{aligned}$$

The quadratic variance process $\langle X, X\rangle_t$ cannot be readily obtained from the fundamental definition, Definition 4.3.1. However, it can be obtained from other considerations, such as the uniqueness of Doob–Meyer decomposition.

We now give examples of quadratic variance processes associated with some familiar martingales.

Example 4.3.1 Brownian Motion

Let $\{W_t, t \in T\}$ be a Brownian motion process. Because of the stationary independent increment property, $W_t - W_s$ is independent of $\mathcal{F}_s$, and hence

$$E^{\mathcal{F}_s}(W_t - W_s)^2 = E(W_t^2 - W_s^2) = \sigma^2(t - s)$$

Hence from eq. 4.3.3,

$$\begin{aligned}
E^{\mathcal{F}_s}(\langle W, W\rangle_t - \langle W, W\rangle_s) &= \sigma^2(t - s) \\
&= \langle W, W\rangle_t - \langle W, W\rangle_s
\end{aligned}$$

The last equality follows from the $\mathcal{F}_s$-measurability of $\langle W, W\rangle_t$. Therefore

$$\sigma^2 t = \langle W, W\rangle_t$$

and the quantity $W_t^2 - \sigma^2 t$ is an $\mathcal{F}_t$-martingale.

Example 4.3.2 Poisson Process

If N_t is a Poisson process, then we have already seen that $X_t = N_t - \lambda t$ is an $\mathcal{F}_t$-martingale. Since N_t and hence X_t has independent increments,

$$E^{\mathcal{F}_s}(X_t - X_s)^2 = E(X_t - X_s)^2 = \text{var}(X_t - X_s) = \text{var}(N_t - N_s) = \lambda(t - s)$$

because the variance of the Poisson process is the same as the mean of the Poisson process. But

$$E^{\mathfrak{F}_s}(X_t - X_s)^2 = E^{\mathfrak{F}_s}(\langle X, X\rangle_t - \langle X, X\rangle_s)$$
$$= \langle X, X\rangle_t - \langle X, X\rangle_s = \lambda(t-s)$$

Hence $\langle X, X\rangle_t = \lambda t$. Therefore the process $X_t^2 - \lambda t$ is an $\mathfrak{F}_t$-martingale. Note that $N_t - \lambda t$ is also an $\mathfrak{F}_t$-martingale.

Remark. In the above examples if $\sigma^2 = \lambda$, we have the same quadratic variance process associated with two different martingales W_t and X_t. This shows that the quadratic variance process does not uniquely determine the underlying martingale, and the continuity of the quadratic variance process does not necessarily imply the continuity of the corresponding martingale. However, if the martingale is continuous, then the quadratic variance process is also continuous.

We can now define a quadratic covariance process between two L^2-martingales $\{X_t, \mathfrak{F}_t, t \in T\}$ and $\{Y_t, \mathfrak{F}_t, t \in T\}$ in a manner similar to that of the quadratic variance process.

Definition 4.3.2 Quadratic Covariance Process

Let $\{X_t, \mathfrak{F}_t, t \in T\}$ and $\{Y_t, \mathfrak{F}_t, t \in T\}$ be two martingales defined on a class of L^2-martingales. The quadratic covariance process of X_t and Y_t is defined by

$$\langle X, Y\rangle_t = \lim_{n\to\infty} \sum_{\nu=0}^{N(n)-1} E^{\mathfrak{F}_{t_\nu}}\left[\left(X_{t_{\nu+1}^{(n)}} - X_{t_\nu^{(n)}}\right)\left(Y_{t_{\nu+1}^{(n)}} - Y_{t_\nu^{(n)}}\right)\right] \qquad (4.3.4)$$

where $0 = t_0^{(n)} < t_1^{(n)} < t_2^{(n)} < \cdots < t_{N(n)}^{(n)} = t$ are the partitions of the interval $[0, t)$, $t \in T$, which become arbitrarily fine as $n \to \infty$.

We can also have a decomposition similar to Theorem 4.3.1 for the product X_tY_t of two L^2-martingales, as given by the following theorem.

Theorem 4.3.2 Doob – Meyer Theorem for a Product of Two L^2-Martingales

Let $\{X_t, \mathfrak{F}_t, t \in T\}$ and $\{Y_t, \mathfrak{F}_t, t \in T\}$ be two martingales defined on the family of L^2-martingales. Then there exists (to within stochastic equivalence) a unique process $\langle X, Y\rangle_t$, which is the difference between two unique $\mathfrak{F}_t$-adapted predictable increasing processes, and a martingale $\{M_t, \mathfrak{F}_t, t \in T\}$ such that for all $t \in T$,

$$X_tY_t = M_t + \langle X, Y\rangle_t \quad \text{(a.s.)} \qquad (4.3.5)$$

and if $s \le t$,

$$E^{\mathcal{F}_s}(X_t - X_s)(Y_t - Y_s) = E^{\mathcal{F}_s}[\langle X, Y\rangle_t - \langle X, Y\rangle_s] \tag{4.3.6}$$

Proof. From $XY = \frac{1}{4}[(X+Y)^2 - (X-Y)^2]$ and from eq. 4.3.1 we can also define the quadratic covariance process $\langle X, Y\rangle_t$ by

$$\langle X, Y\rangle_t = \tfrac{1}{4}(\langle X+Y, X+Y\rangle_t - \langle X-Y, X-Y\rangle_t)$$

From the above equation it is very clear that $\langle X, Y\rangle_t$ is the difference between two $\mathcal{F}_t$-adapted predictable increasing processes (since $\langle X+Y, X+Y\rangle_t$ and $\langle X-Y, X-Y\rangle_t$ are the quadratic variance processes associated with the martingales $X+Y$ and $X-Y$). We now show that M_t given by $X_tY_t - \langle X, Y\rangle_t$ is indeed an $\mathcal{F}_t$-martingale, as a consequence of which eq. 4.3.6 results. For $s \le t$,

$$\begin{aligned}
&E^{\mathcal{F}_s}(X_t - X_s)(Y_t - Y_s)\\
&\quad = E^{\mathcal{F}_s}(X_tY_t + X_sY_s - X_sY_t - X_tY_s)\\
&\quad = E^{\mathcal{F}_s}(X_tY_t + X_sY_s - 2X_sY_s) \qquad \text{(since } X_t, Y_t \text{ are martingales)}\\
&\quad = E^{\mathcal{F}_s}(X_tY_t - X_sY_s)\\
&\quad = \tfrac{1}{4}E^{\mathcal{F}_s}\{(X_t + Y_t)^2 - (X_t - Y_t)^2 - (X_s + Y_s)^2 + (X_s - Y_s)^2\}\\
&\quad = \tfrac{1}{4}E^{\mathcal{F}_s}\{(X_t + Y_t)^2 - (X_s + Y_s)^2 - [(X_t - Y_t)^2 - (X_s - Y_s)^2]\}
\end{aligned}$$

But from eq. 4.3.2,

$$(X_t + Y_t)^2 = M_{X_t+Y_t} + \langle X+Y, X+Y\rangle_t$$

$$(X_t - Y_t)^2 = M_{X_t-Y_t} + \langle X-Y, X-Y\rangle_t$$

Hence

$$\begin{aligned}
&E^{\mathcal{F}_s}(X_t - X_s)(Y_t - Y_s)\\
&\quad = \tfrac{1}{4}E^{\mathcal{F}_s}\big(M_{X_t+Y_t} + \langle X+Y, X+Y\rangle_t - M_{X_s+Y_s} - \langle X+Y, X+Y\rangle_s\\
&\qquad - M_{X_t+Y_t} - \langle X-Y, X-Y\rangle_t - M_{X_s-Y_s} + \langle X-Y, X-Y\rangle_s\big)
\end{aligned}$$

If $E^{\mathcal{F}_s}M_t = M_s$, that is, M_t is an $\mathcal{F}_t$-martingale we have

$$\begin{aligned}
E^{\mathcal{F}_s}(X_t - X_s)(Y_t - Y_s) &= \tfrac{1}{4}E^{\mathcal{F}_s}[\langle X+Y, X+Y\rangle_t - \langle X+Y, X+Y\rangle_s\\
&\qquad - (\langle X-Y, X-Y\rangle_t - \langle X-Y, X-Y\rangle_s)]\\
&= E^{\mathcal{F}_s}[\langle X, Y\rangle_t - \langle X, Y\rangle_s]
\end{aligned}$$

The uniqueness can be established in a manner similar to how the Doob–Meyer decomposition theorem was established. □

Properties of Covariance Processes. The quadratic variance process $\langle X, X\rangle_t$ and covariance process $\langle X, Y\rangle_t$ have very interesting properties which we enumerate below.

1. If $\{X_t, \mathcal{F}_t, t \in T\}$ and $\{Y_t, \mathcal{F}_t, t \in T\}$ are two L^2-martingales and for any constant $\alpha > 0$,

$$\langle \alpha X, X\rangle_t = \langle X, \alpha X\rangle_t = \alpha\langle X, X\rangle_t$$

$$\langle \alpha X, Y\rangle_t = \langle X, \alpha Y\rangle_t = \alpha\langle X, Y\rangle_t$$

2. $\langle X, Y_1 + Y_2\rangle_t = \langle X, Y_1\rangle_t + \langle X, Y_2\rangle_t$
3. If $\mathbf{X}_t$ is a k-vector and $\mathbf{Y}_t$ an r-vector, then $\langle \mathbf{X}, \mathbf{Y}^T\rangle_t$ is a $k \times r$ matrix with elements

$$\langle X_i, Y_j\rangle_t \qquad i = 1,\dots,k, \quad j = 1,\dots,r$$

4. $\langle X + Y, X + Y\rangle_t = \langle X, X\rangle_t + \langle Y, Y\rangle_t + 2\langle X, Y\rangle_t$
5. If $\langle X, Y\rangle_t = 0$, then martingales X and Y are *orthogonal.*

Remark. In general, $\langle X + Y, X + Y\rangle_t \neq \langle X, X\rangle_t + \langle Y, Y\rangle_t$. This is true only when the martingales X_t and Y_t are orthogonal, that is, $\langle X, Y\rangle_t = 0$, $t \in T$. The fact that the martingales X_t and Y_t are orthogonal clearly indicates from eq. 4.3.5 that the product $X_t Y_t$ of orthogonal martingales is also a martingale.

Example 4.3.3

If M_t^c is a continuous L^2-martingale and M_t^d is *any other* discontinuous L^2-martingale, then

$$\langle M_t^c, M_t^d\rangle = 0$$

or the martingales M_t^c and M_t^d are orthogonal, in which case the product $M_t^c \cdot M_t^d$ is also a martingale.

Note. It is not necessary that M_t^c and M_t^d be decompositions of a general martingale M_t.

4.4 LOCAL MARTINGALES

We now define concepts about local martingales, which are intimately tied to stopping times. First we discuss local L^2-martingales and later local martingales, not necessarily L^2.

Definition 4.4.1 Local Square Integrable Martingale

Let $(\Omega, \mathcal{F}, P)$ be a complete probability space, and let $\{\mathcal{F}_t, t \in T\}$ be a right continuous filtration σ-field defined on it. Let $\{\tau_n(\omega)\}$ be an increasing sequence of stopping times with $\tau_n \uparrow \infty$ almost surely. A real-valued process $\{X_t, t \in T, T = R^+\}$ adapted to $\{\mathcal{F}_t, t \in T\}$ is called *local* L^2-martingale if for each n, $X_{t \wedge \tau_n}$ is a square integrable martingale over the σ-field $\mathcal{F}_{t \wedge \tau_n}$.

What the definition really conveys is that if a square integrable martingale is stopped at $\tau_n(\omega)$, the resulting process is also a square integrable martingale.

Let X_t be an $\mathcal{F}_t$ martingale with *sample continuous* paths. Now consider

$$\tau_n(\omega) = \inf\{t: \quad |X_t| \geq n\} \tag{4.4.1}$$

the first value of time t when $|X_t|$ exceeds n (Figure 4.4.1). By Doob's optimal stopping theorem that every stopped martingale is a martingale, $X_{t \wedge \tau_n}$ is a martingale. This martingale is certainly bounded by n because of the continuity of paths.

Since $X_{t \wedge \tau_n}$ is bounded by n, it is certainly a square integrable martingale. Thus every martingale with continuous paths is also a local square integrable martingale. Hence the study of continuous martingales is also the study of local square integrable martingales.

We now show that a positive local martingale is a supermartingale. Let X_t be a local martingale, and let $\tau_n \uparrow \infty$ be a sequence of stopping times. Then by definition $X_{t \wedge \tau_n}$ is a local martingale. Or for $s \leq t$,

$$E^{\mathcal{F}_s} X_{t \wedge \tau_n} = X_{s \wedge \tau_n} \tag{4.4.2}$$

Since $X_{s \wedge \tau_n}$, being positive, is bounded from below, we have from Fatou's lemma (Proposition 1.6.2) for conditional expectations

$$\begin{aligned} \liminf_n E^{\mathcal{F}_s} X_{t \wedge \tau_n} &\geq E^{\mathcal{F}_s} \liminf_n X_{t \wedge \tau_n} \\ &= E^{\mathcal{F}_s} X_{t \wedge \tau_n} \end{aligned} \tag{4.4.3a}$$

But from eq. 4.4.2 we have

$$\liminf_n E^{\mathcal{F}_s} X_{t \wedge \tau_n} = \liminf_n X_{s \wedge \tau_n} = X_s \tag{4.4.3b}$$

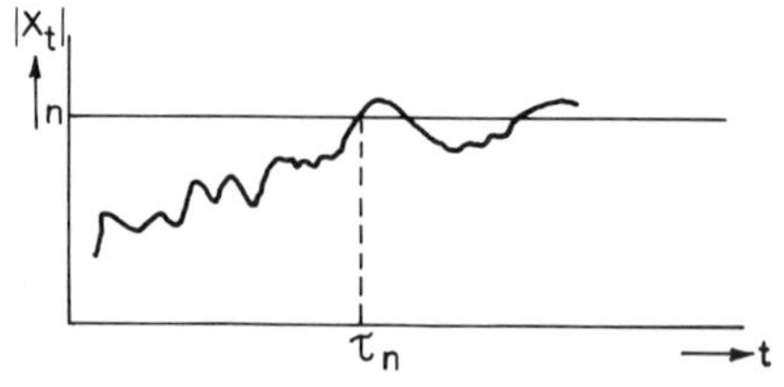

FIGURE 4.4.1

Hence from eqs. 4.4.3a and 4.4.3b we have

$$E^{\mathcal{F}_s} X_{t \wedge \tau_n} \le X_s \tag{4.4.4}$$

thus showing that $X_{t \wedge \tau_n}$ is a supermartingale.

Kunita and Watanabe (33) have proven a result similar to the decomposition of a square integrable martingale (eq. 4.3.2) for a local square integrable martingale. The theorem is stated without proof.

Theorem 4.4.1 Decomposition of Local L^2-Martingale

Let $X_{t \wedge \tau_n}(\omega)$ be a continuous local L^2-martingale on the filtration σ-field $\mathcal{F}_{t \wedge \tau_n}$ where $\tau_n(\omega) \uparrow \infty$ is a sequence of $\mathcal{F}_{\tau_n}$-measurable stopping times. Then $X^2_{t \wedge \tau_n}(\omega)$ is a submartingale, and there is a unique Doob–Meyer decomposition according to which there exists a unique continuous increasing predictable $\mathcal{F}_t$-adapted process $\langle X, X \rangle_{t \wedge \tau_n}$ such that

$$X^2_{t \wedge \tau_n}(\omega) - \langle X, X \rangle_{t \wedge \tau_n}(\omega) = M_{t \wedge \tau_n}(\omega) \tag{4.4.5}$$

where $\{M_{t \wedge \tau_n}, \mathcal{F}_{t \wedge \tau_n}\}$ is a local L^2-martingale.

For a proof see Kallianpur (20, p. 40) and Segall (50).

Just as continuous martingales have unbounded variation, so also continuous local L^2-martingales have unbounded variation.

Having defined a local L^2-martingale, we now define the concept of a local martingale. A discontinuous martingale whose jumps are bounded uniformly in t and ω is also a local L^2-martingale. In this case the stopped martingale $X_{t \wedge \tau_n}$ would be bounded by $n + K$ (Figure 4.4.2), where K is the bound on the jumps, namely, $\Delta X_{\tau_k} \le K$ for all stopping times τ_k. Hence in this case the discontinuous martingale will also be a local L^2-martingale. However, for a general discontinuous martingale X_t this argument is not possible. With $\tau_n = \inf(t\colon \ |X_t| > n)$, $|X_t| < n$ for all $t < \tau_n$, the value of X_{τ_n} itself may well exceed the bound $n + K$ (Figure 4.4.3). Hence Meyer (39) introduces a new definition to describe such martingales.

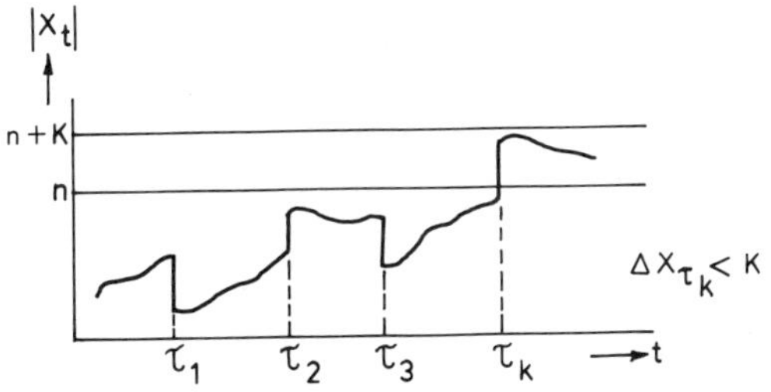

FIGURE 4.4.2

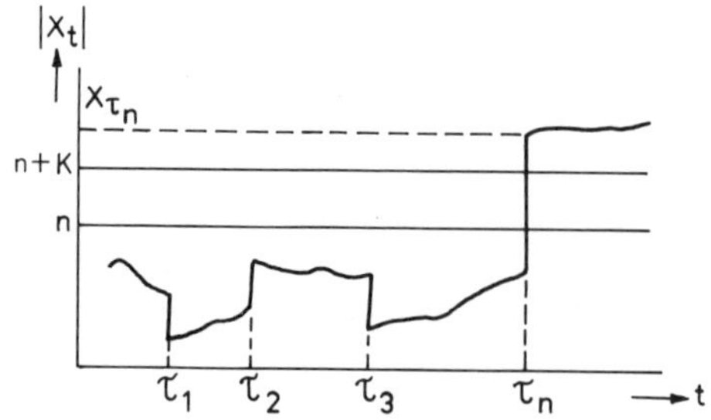

FIGURE 4.4.3

Definition 4.4.2 Local Martingale

The stochastic process $\{X_t, \mathfrak{F}_t, t \in T\}$ is a local martingale if there exists an increasing sequence of stopping times $\{\tau_n(\omega)\}$ with respect to the right continuous filtration σ-field $\{\mathfrak{F}_t, t \in T\}$ such that

1. $P\left\{\lim_{n \uparrow \infty} \tau_n = \infty\right\} = 1.$
2. For all n, the process $\{X_{t \wedge \tau_n}, \mathfrak{F}_{t \wedge \tau_n}, t \in T\}$ is a uniformly integrable martingale.

By its very definition we note that any martingale is a local martingale. The uniform integrability for the martingale X_t can be established as follows. For any $\{X_t, \mathfrak{F}_t\}$ martingale $\{X_{t \wedge \tau_n}, \mathfrak{F}_{t \wedge \tau_n}\}$ is also a martingale. Hence after $t = \tau_n$, $X_{t \wedge \tau_n} = X_{\tau_n}$ so that we can take $X_\infty = X_{\tau_n}$, thereby showing $E^{\mathfrak{F}_{\tau_n}} X_\infty = X_{\tau_n}$.

As with any L^2-martingale, we can also have decomposition of a local martingale X_t into a continuous martingale X_t^c and a discontinuous martingale X_t^d. However, the concept of predictable increasing processes $\langle X, X\rangle_t, \langle X, Y\rangle_t$, which are only defined for L^2-martingales (local or otherwise), may not exist in this case. However, Meyer (39) defines another increasing process (discontinuous in general) which is not predictable in general, called the quadratic variation process $[X, X]_t$, defined by a limit similar to eq. 4.3.1.

Definition 4.4.3 Quadratic Variation Process

Let $\{X_t, \mathfrak{F}_t, t \in T\}$ be any martingale (not necessarily L^2 nor continuous). The *quadratic variation* process of the martingale $\{X_t, \mathfrak{F}_t, t \in T\}$ is

$$[X, X]_t = \lim_{n \to \infty} \sum_{\nu=0}^{N(n)-1} \left(X_{t_{\nu+1}^{(n)}} - X_{t_\nu^{(n)}}\right)^2 \tag{4.4.6}$$

where the partitions $0 = t_0^{(n)} < t_1^{(n)} < \cdots < t_{N(n)}^{(n)} = t$ become arbitrarily fine as $n \to \infty$.

In a manner similar to Definition 4.3.2 we can define the quadratic covariation process.

Definition 4.4.4 Quadratic Covariation Process

Let $\{X_t, \mathcal{F}_t, t \in T\}$ and $\{Y_t, \mathcal{F}_t, t \in T\}$ be two martingales (not necessarily L^2 nor continuous). The *quadratic covariation* process $[X, Y]_t$ between X_t and Y_t is given by

$$[X, Y]_t = \lim_{n \to \infty} \sum_{\nu=0}^{N(n)-1} \left[\left(X_{t_{\nu+1}^{(n)}} - X_{t_\nu^{(n)}}\right)\left(Y_{t_{\nu+1}^{(n)}} - Y_{t_\nu^{(n)}}\right)\right] \tag{4.4.7}$$

where again the partitions $0 = t_0^{(n)} < t_1^{(n)} < \cdots < t_{N(n)}^{(n)} = t$ become arbitrarily fine as $n \to \infty$.

The difference between eqs. 4.3.1, 4.3.4 and eqs. 4.4.6, 4.4.7 is that whereas the former set is $\mathcal{F}_s$-measurable for $s \le t$, the latter is not. In other words, $[X, X]_t$ and $[X, Y]_t$ are *not* measurable with respect to $\mathcal{F}_s$, $s \le t$. However, by its very definition $[X, X]_t$ is an increasing process.

If $\{X_t, \mathcal{F}_t\}$ and $\{Y_t, \mathcal{F}_t\}$ are two general martingales given by the respective decompositions $X_t = X_t^c + X_t^d$ and $Y_t = Y_t^c + Y_t^d$, then the quadratic variation process $[X, X]_t$ is given by

$$[X, X]_t = \langle X^c, X^c \rangle_t + \sum_{s \le t} (\Delta X_s)^2 \tag{4.4.8}$$

and the quadratic covariation process is given by

$$[X, Y]_t = \langle X^c, Y^c \rangle_t + \sum_{s \le t} \Delta X_s \cdot \Delta Y_s \tag{4.4.9}$$

where X_t^c, Y_t^c are the continuous martingale parts (necessarily L^2) of the martingales X_t, Y_t, and ΔX_s, ΔY_s are the jumps of the martingales X_t and Y_t at time $t = s$ given by

$$\Delta X_s = X_s - X_{s-}$$

where

$$X_{s-} = \lim_{\tau \uparrow 0} X_{s-\tau}$$

Meyer (39) also shows that the decompositions $X_t^2 - [X, X]_t$ and $X_t Y_t - [X, Y]_t$ yield local martingales, as shown by the following theorem stated without proof.

Theorem 4.4.2 Meyer Decomposition

Let $\{X_t, \mathfrak{F}_t, t \in T\}$ and $\{Y_t, \mathfrak{F}_t, t \in T\}$ be two local martingales defined on the right continuous family of σ-fields $\{\mathfrak{F}_t, t \in T\}$. Let $[X, X]_t$ and $[X, Y]_t$ be the quadratic variation and covariation processes associated with X_t and (X_t, Y_t), respectively. Then the processes

$$
\begin{aligned}
M_{t_1} &= X_t^2 - [X, X]_t \\
M_{t_2} &= X_t Y_t - [X, Y]_t
\end{aligned}
\tag{4.4.10}
$$

are local $\mathfrak{F}_t$-martingales.

However, if both X_t and Y_t in eq. 4.4.10 are L^2-local martingales, then we have also the unique Doob–Meyer decomposition

$$
\begin{aligned}
M_{t_3} &= X_t^2 - \langle X, X\rangle_t \\
M_{t_4} &= X_t Y_t - \langle X, Y\rangle_t
\end{aligned}
\tag{4.4.11}
$$

where M_{t_3} and M_{t_4} are $\mathfrak{F}_t$ local L^2-martingales.

Remarks

1. If M_{t_1} and M_{t_2} are also $\mathfrak{F}_t$ local L^2-martingales, then $(M_{t_3} - M_{t_1})$ and $(M_{t_4} - M_{t_2})$ are $\mathfrak{F}_t$ local L^2-martingales. In other words,

$$M_{t_3} - M_{t_1} = X_t^2 - \langle X, X\rangle_t - X_t^2 + [X, X]_t = [X, X]_t - \langle X, X\rangle_t$$

$$M_{t_4} - M_{t_2} = X_t Y_t - \langle X, Y\rangle_t - X_t Y_t + [X, Y]_t = [X, Y]_t - \langle X, Y\rangle_t$$

are local L^2-martingales. This fact is used later on.

2. The $\mathfrak{F}_t$-martingales as defined by $[X, X]_t - \langle X, X\rangle_t$ and $[X, Y]_t - \langle X, Y\rangle_t$ are both locally square integrable. It may be possible that these may both be general $\mathfrak{F}_t$-martingales without X_t, Y_t being square integrable.

Note. In case X_t is an L^2-martingale, we have apparently two different decompositions,

$$X_t^2 - [X, X]_t \qquad \text{and} \qquad X_t^2 - \langle X, X\rangle_t$$

both yielding martingales. This seems to violate the Doob–Meyer uniqueness condition. Actually there is no violation involved because $\langle X, X\rangle_t$ is the only predictable process, whereas $[X, X]_t$, as emphasized before, is not predictable.

Example 4.4.1

If X_t and Y_t are two continuous martingales X_t^c and Y_t^c, then by eqs. 4.4.8 and 4.4.9, $\Delta X_s = \Delta Y_s = 0$, thus resulting in

$$[X^c, X^c]_t = \langle X^c, X^c \rangle_t$$

$$[X^c, Y^c]_t = \langle X^c, Y^c \rangle_t \tag{4.4.12}$$

In this case $[X^c, X^c]_t$ and $[X^c, Y^c]_t$ are also $\mathscr{F}_s$-measurable for $s \le t$.

Example 4.4.2

If $\{W_t, t \in T\}$ is a Brownian motion process, $\{W_t^2, \mathscr{F}_t\}$ is a submartingale,

$$W_t^2 - \langle W, W \rangle_t = M_t$$

is a martingale.

$$E^{\mathscr{F}_s}\left(W_t^2 - W_s^2 - \langle W, W \rangle_t + \langle W, W \rangle_s\right) = 0$$

$$\begin{aligned} E^{\mathscr{F}_s}\left(W_t^2 - W_s^2\right) &= E^{\mathscr{F}_s}(\langle W, W \rangle_t - \langle W, W \rangle_s) \\ &= E^{\mathscr{F}_s}(W_t - W_s)^2 && \text{from eq. 4.3.3} \\ &= E(W_t - W_s)^2 = \sigma^2(t - s) && \mathscr{F}_s \text{ independent of } W_t - W_s \end{aligned}$$

Hence $\langle W, W \rangle_t = \sigma^2 t = [W, W]_t$.

Since the Brownian motion is a continuous martingale, we see that $\langle W, W \rangle_t = [W, W]_t$.

Example 4.4.3

Let N_t be a Poisson process with rate λ. The Poisson martingale $X_t = N_t - \lambda t$ is a discontinuous martingale and $X_t^c = 0$. Hence from eq. 4.4.8, $[X, X]_t = \Sigma_{s \le t}(\Delta X_s)^2$, where ΔX_s is always a positive jump equal to 1 for a Poisson process. By definition of the Poisson process, the sum of all the jumps before t is given by N_t, the Poisson process itself, or

$$[X, X]_t = N_t$$

Since $[X, X]_t - \langle X, X \rangle_t$ and $N_t - \lambda t$ are martingales, we have

$$\langle X, X \rangle_t = \lambda t$$

thus looking at a Poisson martingale from a different point of view.

Example 4.4.4

If X_t^c is a continuous martingale and Y_t^d is a discontinuous martingale, then by eq. 4.4.9,

$$[X, Y]_t = \langle X^c, Y^c \rangle_t + \sum_{s \le t} \Delta X_s \Delta Y_s$$

we have $Y_t^c = 0$, $\Delta X_s = 0$, and hence $[X^c, Y^d]_t = 0$ and $\langle X^c, Y^d \rangle_t = 0$, and the martingales X_t^c and Y_t^d are orthogonal.

Example 4.4.5

If X_t^d and Y_t^d are two discontinuous martingales with no jumps in common, then also

$$[X^d, Y^d]_t = 0$$

Obviously $\langle X^c, Y^c \rangle = 0$ since there is no continuous component.

Example 4.4.6

Let $\{X_t, \mathcal{F}_t\}$ be an L^2-submartingale, and let A_t be an $\mathcal{F}_t$-adapted continuous predictable increasing process. Then by the Doob–Meyer decomposition we have

$$X_t = M_t + A_t$$

where M_t is an $\mathcal{F}_t$-martingale. Let us now calculate the quadratic variance process associated with X_t,

$$\langle X, X \rangle_t = \langle M, M \rangle_t + \langle A, A \rangle_t$$

since $\langle M, A \rangle_t = 0$. But

$$\langle A, A \rangle_t = \lim_{n \to \infty} \sum_{\nu=0}^{N(n)-1} E^{\mathcal{F}_{t_\nu^{(n)}}} \left(A_{t_{\nu+1}^{(n)}} - A_{t_\nu^{(n)}} \right)^2 = 0$$

since $A_{t_{\nu+1}^{(n)}}$ is $\mathcal{F}_{t_\nu^{(n)}}$-measurable and the partitions become finer and finer. Hence we have an important result that if $\{X_t, \mathcal{F}_t, t \in T\}$ is an L^2-submartingale, and $\{M_t, \mathcal{F}_t, t \in T\}$ is the martingale associated with X_t, then the quadratic variance processes of both of them are the same,

$$\langle X, X \rangle_t = \langle M, M \rangle_t$$

As a consequence of this result we now show that the innovations process is a Brownian motion. In Section 3.5 the Doob decompositions of the submartingale $\{X_t, \mathcal{F}_t, t \in T\}$, given by

$$X_t = \int_0^t Z_\tau \, d\tau + Y_t$$

with $\mathcal{X}_t = \sigma\{X_\tau, Y_\tau, \tau \leq t\}$, has been considered where $\{Y_t, t \in T\}$ is a Brownian motion process and an $\mathcal{X}_t$-martingale, with $\langle Y, Y \rangle_t = \sigma^2 t = \langle X, X \rangle_t$ (from Example 4.4.6.).

The decomposition of X_t with respect to the σ-field $\mathcal{F}_t = \sigma\{X_\tau, \tau \leq t\}$ is given by

$$X_t = \int_0^t \hat{Z}_\tau \, d\tau + M_t$$

Here $\langle X, X \rangle_t = \sigma^2 t = \langle M, M \rangle_t$. Hence the innovations process $\nu_t = M_t$ is a Brownian motion process and an $\mathcal{F}_t$-martingale.

Problems

1. Show that if T is a finite interval $[0, s]$, then the criterion for a square integrable martingale $\sup_{t \in T} EM_t^2 < \infty$ may be replaced by $EM_s^2 < \infty$.

2. Let $X_t(\omega)$ be a stochastic process equal to $f(t)$ for all ω with

$$f(t) = \begin{cases} 0 & t = 0 \\ \dfrac{1}{n} & \dfrac{1}{n+1} < t \leq \dfrac{1}{n}, \quad n = 1, 2, \ldots \\ 1 & t > 1 \end{cases}$$

Show that the sequence of stopping times cannot be chosen as

$$S_1 = \inf\{t | \Delta Z_t > 0\}$$

$$S_n = \inf\{t > S_{n-1} | \Delta Z_t > 0\}$$

3. If $\{X_t, \mathcal{F}_t, t \in T\}$ and $\{Y_t, \mathcal{F}_t, t \in T\}$ are two L^2-martingales, then prove the following results.
   a. For a constant $\alpha > 0$, $\langle \alpha X, Y \rangle_t = \langle X, \alpha Y \rangle_t = \alpha \langle X, Y \rangle_t$.
   b. $\langle X, Y_1 + Y_2 \rangle_t = \langle X, Y_1 \rangle_t + \langle X, Y_2 \rangle_t$
   c. $\langle X + Y, X + Y \rangle_t = \langle X, X \rangle_t + \langle Y, Y \rangle_t + 2\langle X, Y \rangle_t$

4. If $\{X_t, \mathcal{F}_t, t \in T\}$ is a continuous martingale, show that $\langle X, X \rangle_t$ is a continuous process.

5. If $\{X_t, t \in T\}$ is a local martingale and if $\{X_{t \wedge \tau}, t, \tau \in T\}$ is also a local martingale, show that τ is a stopping time.

6. If the sequence of stopping times $\tau_n \uparrow \infty$ satisfies the definition of a local martingale and if $\xi_n \uparrow \infty$ is any other sequence of stopping times, show that $\tau_n \wedge \xi_n$ also satisfies the condition of the definition of a local martingale.

7. Show that a bounded local martingale $\{X_{t \wedge \tau_n}, t \in T\}$ adapted to $\{\mathfrak{F}_t, t \in T\}$ is also a martingale.

8. Let $\{X_t, \mathfrak{F}_t, t \in T\}$ be a continuous L^2-martingale with the associated increasing process A_t. If τ is any stopping time, show that the increasing process associated with the martingale $\{X_{t \wedge \tau}, \mathfrak{F}_{t \wedge \tau}, t \in T\}$ is $A_{t \wedge \tau}$.

9. Prove the Doob–Meyer decomposition theorem (eq. 4.4.5) for a continuous local L^2-martingale.

5 WHITE NOISE AND WHITE NOISE INTEGRALS

5.1 INTRODUCTION

Before we define the concept of white noise we first give the classical definitions of Fourier transforms and Fourier integrals.

Definition 5.1.1 Fourier Transform

Let X_t belong to a space of square integrable functions L^2 satisfying

$$\int_{-\infty}^{\infty} X(t)^2 \, dt < \infty \tag{5.1.1}$$

Then the *Fourier transform* of X_t is given by

$$\underline{X}_\nu = \int_{-\infty}^{\infty} X_t e^{-j2\pi\nu t} \, dt \tag{5.1.2}$$

and the *inverse* Fourier transform is given by

$$X_t = \int_{-\infty}^{\infty} \underline{X}_\nu e^{j2\pi\nu t} \, d\nu \tag{5.1.3}$$

The Fourier transform $\underline{X}_\nu$ also belongs to the space L^2. What eq. 5.1.2 conveys is that there exists a function $\underline{X}_\nu \in L^2$ such that

$$\lim_{T_1, T_2 \to \infty} \int_{-\infty}^{\infty} \left| \underline{X}_\nu - \int_{-T_1}^{T_2} X_t e^{-j2\pi\nu t} \, dt \right|^2 d\nu \to 0$$

with a similar interpretation for eq. 5.1.3.

However, if X_t belongs to a class of infinitely differentiable functions satisfying

$$|t|^n \left| \frac{d^n X_t}{dt^n} \right| \xrightarrow[|t| \to \infty]{} 0$$

(the class consists of functions of rapid decay), then the integrals of both eqs. 5.1.2 and 5.1.3 are absolutely convergent for all ν, t in $(-\infty, \infty)$. We can also define Fourier transforms for X_t belonging to the class of generalized functions.

The convolution product of two functions g and h belonging to L^2 is defined by

$$(g * h)(t) = \int_{-\infty}^{\infty} g(t-\tau) h(\tau)\, d\tau = \int_{-\infty}^{\infty} g(\tau) h(t-\tau)\, d\tau \tag{5.1.4}$$

The Fourier transform of the convolution product has the interesting property

$$\underline{g * h} = \underline{g}\underline{h} \tag{5.1.5}$$

which is the product of individual Fourier transforms.

Now we define a power spectral density function.

Definition 5.1.2 Spectral Density

Let $\{X_t, -\infty < t < \infty\}$ be a quadratic mean continuous wide sense stationary process defined on the probability space $(\Omega, \mathfrak{F}, P)$ with autocorrelation function $R(\tau) = EX_{t+\tau}X_t$ belonging to the space L^2. The *power spectral density* function $S(\nu)$ is defined as the Fourier transform of the autocorrelation function $R(\tau)$ given by

$$S(\nu) = \int_{-\infty}^{\infty} R(\tau) e^{-j2\pi\nu\tau}\, d\tau \tag{5.1.6}$$

and the inversion integral of $S(\nu)$ gives us

$$R(\tau) = \int_{-\infty}^{\infty} S(\nu) e^{j2\pi\nu\tau}\, d\nu \tag{5.1.7}$$

Since $R(\tau)$ is nonnegative definite, $S(\nu)$ is also nonnegative definite, and since $R(\tau)$ is square integrable, $S(\nu)$ is also square integrable. The average energy contained in the process X_t is given by $R(0) = EX_t^2$, and hence from eq. 5.1.7,

$$EX_t^2 = \int_{-\infty}^{\infty} S(\nu)\, d\nu \tag{5.1.8}$$

5.2 WHITE NOISE

A *white noise* process is usually described by engineers as a wide sense stationary process whose power spectral density is a constant at all frequencies. If $S(\nu)$ is the power spectral density function, then

$$S(\nu) = \sigma^2 \qquad \text{for all } \nu \in R \tag{5.2.1}$$

For a white noise process given by eq. 5.2.1 the energy EX_t^2 as given by eq. 5.1.8 is

$$EX_t^2 = \int_{-\infty}^{\infty} S(\nu)\, d\nu = \int_{-\infty}^{\infty} \sigma^2\, d\nu = \infty \tag{5.2.2}$$

Since the average energy in a white noise process is infinite, it cannot represent any physical process, and it certainly is not a square integrable process, since $EX_t^2 = \infty$. Since the white noise process is not square integrable, no sequence of random processes $\{X_n(t), t \in T,\ T = (-\infty, \infty)\}$ which is convergent in the quadratic mean for each t can converge to a white noise process in the traditional (conventional) sense. Before we actually give a formal definition of white noise, we illustrate the concept of white noise by some examples. The key role played in the concept is the delta (δ) function, which even though it is not a function in the conventional sense, is defined by its effect under an integral on test functions of rapid decay. The delta function is defined as follows.

Definition 5.2.1 Delta Function

A *delta function* belongs to a class of generalized functions whose effect on a continuous function of rapid decay $\phi(\cdot)$ under an integral is given by

$$\int_{-\infty}^{\infty} \phi(t)\delta(t)\, dt = \phi(0)$$

The function $\phi(t)$ is said to belong to a class of test functions of rapid decay.

Delta functions are somewhat loosely defined by

$$\lim_{a \to 0} \frac{1}{a} f\left(\frac{t}{a}\right) = \lim_{b \to \infty} bf(bt) = \delta(t) \tag{5.2.3}$$

where $f(t)$ is a function satisfying the requirement $\int_{-\infty}^{\infty} f(t)\, dt = 1$. The definition is indeed a loose one without defining the limiting operation since $\lim_{a \to 0}(1/a)f(t/a)$ or $\lim_{b \to \infty} bf(bt)$ does not converge in any accepted sense to the delta function. We define the limit in eq. 5.2.3 to be the delta function in the sense

$$\begin{aligned} \lim_{a \to 0} \int_{-\infty}^{\infty} \phi(t) \frac{1}{a} f\left(\frac{t}{a}\right) dt &= \phi(0) \\ \lim_{b \to \infty} \int_{-\infty}^{\infty} \phi(t) bf(bt)\, dt &= \phi(0) \end{aligned} \tag{5.2.4}$$

where $\phi(t)$ belongs to the class of test functions of rapid decay. We are tacitly defining a delta function only inside an integral and not outside it.

Example 5.2.1 Formal Derivative of Brownian Motion (Gaussian White Noise)

We have showed earlier that the Brownian motion process, even though continuous everywhere, is differentiable nowhere in the conventional sense. However, let us proceed formally to differentiate a Brownian motion process. Let $\{W_t, t \in T\}$ be a Brownian motion process. Hence it is also a martingale. Its autocorrelation function, which because of the mean being zero is the same as the autocovariance function, is given by

$$R_W(t,s) = C_W(t,s) = EW_tW_s = \sigma^2(t \wedge s) \tag{5.2.5}$$

Let $\dot{W}_t$ be the formal derivative of W_t. It can be shown (Jazwinski, 22, p. 64; Papoulis, 45, p. 317) that the autocorrelation function of the derivative of any stochastic process X_t is given by

$$E\dot{X}_t\dot{X}_s = \frac{\partial^2 R_X(t,s)}{\partial t\,\partial s} \tag{5.2.6}$$

Applying this to the Brownian motion process, we obtain

$$E\dot{W}_t\dot{W}_s = \frac{\partial^2}{\partial t\,\partial s}\sigma^2(t \wedge s) = C_{\dot{W}}(t,s) = R_{\dot{W}}(t,s) = \sigma^2\delta(t-s) \tag{5.2.7}$$

which indicates that due to the presence of the delta function the derivative does not exist in the traditional sense, but only in the generalized sense. Since the autocorrelation of $\dot{W}$ is a function of the time differences $t - s = \tau$ with mean value zero, we have $\dot{W}$ as a wide sense stationary process with $R_{\dot{W}}(\tau) = \sigma^2\delta(\tau)$. The Fourier transform of the autocorrelation function yields σ^2, which by eq. 5.2.1 represents a process of constant power spectral density for all frequencies. Hence the formal derivative of the Brownian motion is a white noise. Since the increments are Gaussian distributed, this type of white noise is called Gaussian white noise.

Example 5.2.2 Formal Derivative of Poisson Process (Poisson White Noise)

Let N_t be a Poisson process with density parameter λ. The Poisson martingale M_t is given by $N_t - \lambda t$. Just as we formally differentiated the Brownian motion martingale and arrived at a white noise process, we also take the formal derivative of a Poisson martingale and show again that it is a white noise process.

Since $M_t = N_t - \lambda t$, we have formally

$$\dot{M}_t = \dot{N}_t - \lambda$$

and

$$\begin{aligned} E\dot{M}_t\dot{M}_s &= E\left[(\dot{N}_t - \lambda)(\dot{N}_s - \lambda)\right] \\ &= E(\dot{N}_t\dot{N}_s - \lambda\dot{N}_s - \lambda\dot{N}_t + \lambda^2) \end{aligned} \tag{5.2.8}$$

But $EN_t = \lambda t$, and hence

$$E\dot{N}_t = \lambda \quad \text{and} \quad E\dot{N}_s = \lambda \tag{5.2.9}$$

The autocorrelation function of a Poisson process is given by

$$EN_tN_s = R_N(t, s) = \lambda(t \wedge s) + \lambda^2 ts \tag{5.2.10}$$

From eq. 5.2.6,

$$E\dot{N}_t\dot{N}_s = \frac{\partial^2 R_N(t, s)}{\partial t\, \partial s} = \lambda^2 + \lambda\delta(t - s) \tag{5.2.11}$$

showing that the derivative does not exist in the conventional sense but only in the generalized sense.

Substituting eqs. 5.2.9 and 5.2.11 into eq. 5.2.8, we have

$$E\dot{M}_t\dot{M}_s = \lambda^2 + \lambda\delta(t - s) - \lambda^2 - \lambda^2 + \lambda^2 = \lambda\delta(t - s) \tag{5.2.12}$$

Equation 5.2.12 shows that the process $\dot{M}_t$ is wide sense stationary and corresponds to that of a white noise with parameter λ. This is known as the Poisson white noise.

From the above examples it may be hastily concluded that perhaps the formal derivative of any martingale may be considered as a white noise. The essential features of the above martingales are that both are martingales with stationary independent increments. Since the mean value of the increments is zero (recall that a sequence of independent random variables whose mean value is zero can be considered as a martingale difference), these martingales are also processes with orthogonal increments. These ideas are formalized in the following definition of a white noise process.

Definition 5.2.2 White Noise Process

Let $(\Omega, \mathcal{F}, P)$ be a complete probability space, and let $\{X_t^{(n)}, t \in T, T = (-\infty, \infty)\}$ be a sequence of stochastic processes defined on the probability space, continuous in the quadratic mean. The sequence $\{X_t^{(n)}\}$ "converges" to a white noise X_t if

1. For each square integrable function $g(\cdot)$ the sequence $\{X_n(g)\}$ is a quadratic mean convergent sequence, where $X_n(g)$ is defined by

$$X_n(g) \triangleq \int_{-\infty}^{\infty} g(t) X_t^{(n)}\, dt \tag{5.2.13}$$

2. There exist a positive constant σ^2 and square integrable functions $g(\cdot)$ and $h(\cdot)$ such that

$$\lim_{n\to\infty} EX_n(g) X_n^*(h) = \sigma^2 \int_{-\infty}^{\infty} g(t) h^*(t)\, dt \tag{5.2.14}$$

where * indicates complex conjugate.

Let us see the consequences of this definition. From eq. 5.2.13,

$$X_n(g) X_n^*(h) = \int_{-\infty}^{\infty} g(t) X_t^{(n)}\, dt \int_{-\infty}^{\infty} h^*(s) X_s^{(n)*}\, ds$$

Taking expectation on both sides,

$$EX_n(g) X_n^*(h) = \int_{-\infty}^{\infty} \int_{-\infty}^{\infty} g(t) h^*(s) E\left[X_t^{(n)} X_s^{(n)*}\right] dt\, ds$$

Taking the limit as $n \to \infty$,

$$\lim_{n\to\infty} EX_n(g) X_n^*(h) = \int_{-\infty}^{\infty} \int_{-\infty}^{\infty} g(t) h^*(s) \lim_{n\to\infty} E\left[X_t^{(n)} X_s^{(n)*}\right] dt\, ds$$

If the right-hand side of the above integral is to equal $\sigma^2 \int_{-\infty}^{\infty} g(t) h^*(t)\, dt$, as in eq. 5.2.14, then we must define

$$\lim_{n\to\infty} E\left[X_t^{(n)} X_s^{(n)*}\right] = \sigma^2 \delta(t-s) \tag{5.2.15}$$

which was exactly what happened in the examples, as shown by eqs. 5.2.7 and 5.2.12.

Note. The loose definition of eq. 5.2.15 can be made precise if the limiting operation is interpreted in the sense of eq. 5.2.4, namely,

$$\int_{-\infty}^{\infty} \int_{-\infty}^{\infty} g(t) h^*(s) \lim_{n\to\infty} E\left(X_t^{(n)} X_s^{(n)*}\right) dt\, ds = \sigma^2 \int_{-\infty}^{\infty} g(t) h^*(t)\, dt \tag{5.2.16}$$

Equation 5.2.13 is usually written in the limiting form as

$$X(g) = \int_{-\infty}^{\infty} g(t) X_t \, dt \tag{5.2.17}$$

and is called a white noise integral.

Equation 5.2.14 can be written in the limiting form as

$$EX(g) X^*(h) = \sigma^2 \int_{-\infty}^{\infty} g(t) h^*(t) \, dt$$

and if $g = h$,

$$EX(g) X^*(g) = \sigma^2 \int_{-\infty}^{\infty} |g(t)|^2 \, dt < \infty \tag{5.2.18}$$

The definition also implies that even though the white noise process $X(t)$ itself may not be amenable to square integrable representation, the function $X(g)$ does admit the representation as a square integrable function, as shown by eq. 5.2.18.

The function $X(g)$ given by eq. 5.2.17 also admits of a square integrable stochastic integral representation given by the following proposition.

Proposition 5.2.1 Stochastic Integral Representation of $X(g)$

Let $(\Omega, \mathfrak{F}, P)$ be a complete probability space. Let $\{X_t^{(n)}, t \in T, T = (-\infty, \infty)\}$ be a sequence of stochastic processes defined on the probability space, converging to a white noise process X_t in the sense of Definition 5.2.2. Let $g(\cdot)$ belong to a class of square integrable functions, and let

$$X(g) = \underset{n \to \infty}{\text{l.i.q.m.}} \int_{-\infty}^{\infty} g(t) X_t^{(n)} \, dt \qquad g \in L^2 \tag{5.2.19}$$

Then there exists a process $\{Z_t, t \in T, T = (-\infty, \infty)\}$ with orthogonal increments defined by

$$Z_t = \underset{n \to \infty}{\text{l.i.q.m.}} \int_{-\infty}^{t} X_s^{(n)} \, ds$$

or

$$dZ_t = X_t \, dt \tag{5.2.20}$$

such that

$$X(g) = \int_{-\infty}^{\infty} g(t) \, dZ_t \tag{5.2.21}$$

Proof. Let

$$Z_t = \underset{n\to\infty}{\text{l.i.q.m.}} \int_{-\infty}^{t} X_s^{(n)}\, ds$$

We first show that Z_t as defined above is an orthogonal increment process,

$$Z_b - Z_a = \underset{n\to\infty}{\text{l.i.q.m.}} \int_a^b X_s^{(n)}\, ds \tag{5.2.22}$$

Let $g(t)$ in eq. 5.2.13,

$$X_n(g) = \int_{-\infty}^{\infty} g(t)\, X_t^{(n)}\, dt$$

be the indicator function $I_{ab}(t)$ of $[a, b)$,

$$I_{ab}(t) = \begin{cases} 1 & a \le t < b \\ 0 & \text{otherwise} \end{cases}$$

Then

$$X_n(I_{ab}) = \int_{-\infty}^{\infty} I_{ab}(s)\, X_s^{(n)}\, ds = \int_a^b X_s^{(n)}\, ds$$

But by eq. 5.2.22,

$$Z_b - Z_a = \underset{n\to\infty}{\text{l.i.q.m.}}\, X_n(I_{ab}) \tag{5.2.23}$$

In a similar manner,

$$(Z_d - Z_c)^* = \underset{n\to\infty}{\text{l.i.q.m.}}\, X_n^*(I_{cd})$$

But from eq. 5.2.14,

$$\lim_{n\to\infty} EX_n(g)\, X_n^*(h) = \sigma^2 \int_{-\infty}^{\infty} g(t) h^*(t)\, dt$$

we have

$$\begin{aligned} E(Z_b - Z_a)(Z_d - Z_c)^* &= \underset{n\to\infty}{\text{l.i.q.m.}}\, X_n(I_{ab})\, X_n^*(I_{cd}) \\ &= \sigma^2 \int_{-\infty}^{\infty} I_{ab}(t) I_{cd}^*(t)\, dt \end{aligned} \tag{5.2.24}$$

However, the function $I_{ab}(t)I_{cd}^*(t) = 1$ if $[a, b) \cap [c, d) = [a, b)$ and 0 if $[a, b) \cap [c, d) = \varnothing$. Hence we have the following result:

$$E(Z_b - Z_a)(Z_d - Z_c)^* = \begin{cases} 0 & [a, b) \cap [c, d) = \varnothing \\ \sigma^2(b - a) & [a, b) \cap [c, d) = [a, b) \end{cases} \tag{5.2.25}$$

which shows that Z_t is a process of orthogonal increments. □

As a consequence of $\{Z_t, t \in T, T = (-\infty, \infty)\}$ being an orthogonal increment process we can write from eq. 5.2.25

$$E\, dZ_t\, dZ_s^* = \sigma^2\, dt\, \delta_{ts} \tag{5.2.26}$$

where δ_{ts} is the Kronecker delta.

Before we prove the stochastic integral part of the proposition, we have to introduce the concept of a *stochastic integral* by defining $\int_{-\infty}^{\infty} g(t)\, dZ_t$, where $\{Z_t, -\infty < t < \infty\}$ is a process with orthogonal increments.

Definition 5.2.3

Let $\{Z_t, -\infty < t < \infty\}$ be a quadratic mean right continuous process with orthogonal increments satisfying eq. 5.2.26. Let $g(t)$ be a function of t only (not dependent on ω). The stochastic integral $\int_{-\infty}^{\infty} g(t)\, dZ_t$ is defined for the following forms of $g(t)$:

1. $g(t) = I_{ab}$, the indicator function of the time interval $(a, b]$. Then we define

$$\int_{-\infty}^{\infty} g(t)\, dZ_t = \int_{-\infty}^{\infty} I_{ab}\, dZ_t = \int_a^b dZ_t = Z_b - Z_a$$

2. For $a = t_0 < t_1 < t_2 < \cdots < t_n = b$, $a \to -\infty$, $b \to \infty$, $g(t)$ is a step function of a special type given by

$$g(t) = \begin{cases} 0 & t \le t_0 \\ g_\nu & t_\nu < t \le t_{\nu+1} \quad \nu \le n - 1 \\ 0 & t > t_n \end{cases}$$

or,

$$g(t) = \sum_{\nu=0}^{n-1} g_\nu I_{(t_\nu, t_{\nu+1}]} \tag{5.2.27}$$

where the g_ν are constants. In this case we define

$$\int_{-\infty}^{\infty} g(t)\, dZ_t = \int_{-\infty}^{\infty} \sum_{\nu=0}^{n-1} g_\nu I_{(t_\nu, t_{\nu+1}]}\, dZ_t$$

$$= \sum_{\nu=0}^{n-1} g_\nu \int_{t_\nu}^{t_{\nu+1}} dZ_t$$

$$= \sum_{\nu=0}^{n-1} g_\nu \left(Z_{t_{\nu+1}} - Z_{t_\nu}\right)$$

It is not necessary to define Z_t as right continuous and $g(t)$ as left continuous. We could just as well define them the other way round, but we anticipate the formal definition of a general stochastic integral in Chapter 6.

3. $g(t)$ is approximated by a sequence of step functions $g_n(t)$ of the above special type converging to $g(t)$ in L^2-space with respect to a finite Borel measure F, namely

$$\int_{-\infty}^{\infty} |g_n(t) - g(t)|^2\, F(dt) \to 0 \qquad \text{as } n \to \infty \qquad (5.2.28)$$

In this case we define

$$\int_{-\infty}^{\infty} g(t)\, dZ_t = \underset{n\to\infty}{\text{l.i.q.m.}} \int_{-\infty}^{\infty} g_n(t)\, dZ_t$$

From the definition of the simple stochastic integral $\int_{-\infty}^{\infty} g(t)\, dZ_t$ given above we can conclude that the integral is well defined for all $g(t)$ which can be approximated by a sequence of special step functions $\{g_n(t)\}$ such that eq. 5.2.28 is satisfied. The class $\{g(t)\}$ is the class of functions satisfying

$$\int_{-\infty}^{\infty} |g(t)|^2\, F(dt) < \infty$$

If $g(t)$ is continuous in $L^2(F)$, the approximating sequence $\{g_n(t)\}$ can be constructed by sampling $g(t)$ at the continuity points of the measure F. For any arbitrary $g(t)$ in $L^2(F)$ the approximating sequence $\{g_n(t)\}$ can be constructed (Doob, 14, pp. 427–433).

Proof of the Second Part of Proposition 5.2.1. We see that if $g(t)$ is a step function, then it is clear from eq. 5.2.27 and from items 1 and 2 of Definition 5.2.3 that

$$X(g) = \int_{-\infty}^{\infty} g(t)\, dZ_t$$

If $g(t) \in L^2$ is not a step function, then there exists a sequence of step functions $\{g_n(t)\}$ satisfying eq. 5.2.28 such that

$$X(g) = \int_{-\infty}^{\infty} g_n(t)\, dZ_t + X(g(t) - g_n(t)) \xrightarrow[n\to\infty]{\text{l.i.q.m.}} \int_{-\infty}^{\infty} g(t)\, dZ_t \qquad \square$$

Summary

In summary, a white noise process $\{X_t, t \in T, T = (-\infty, \infty)\}$ is equivalent to a process $\{Z_t, t \in T, T = (-\infty, \infty)\}$ of orthogonal increments which satisfies the condition

$$E\, dZ_t\, dZ_s^* = \sigma^2 \delta_{ts}\, dt \qquad (5.2.26)$$

where δ_{ts} is the Kronecker delta. As a result of proposition 5.2.1, the white noise integral of the type $\int_{-\infty}^{\infty} g(t) X_t\, dt$, even though it does not exist in either the Riemann sense or the Lebesgue–Stieltjes sense, can still be formally manipulated as $\int_{-\infty}^{\infty} g(t)\, dZ_t$, yielding the function $X(g)$, which has bounded properties. This formal manipulation holds for g being a function of time only. In a later chapter we extend the concept of a stochastic integral to g being a function of ω also.

For a standard white noise process $\sigma^2 = 1$.

5.3 SPECTRAL REPRESENTATION

In Section 5.1 we introduced the concept of Fourier transform for square integrable functions. If $\{X_t, t \in T\}$ has a Fourier integral, eq. 5.1.2, then the inversion integral, eq. 5.1.3, will give a representation for X_t as a linear combination of sinusoids.

However, if $\{X_t, t \in T, T = (-\infty, \infty)\}$ is a stationary stochastic process continuous in the qua ratic mean, then the Fourier integral $\int_{-\infty}^{\infty} X_t e^{-j2\pi\nu t}\, dt$ may not necessarily exist as a quadratic mean integral or an integral of any other type.

Before we extend the concept of Fourier transform to stationary stochastic processes, we first introduce the concept of spectral distribution. Since engineers are more familiar with the spectral density function (eq. 5.1.6), we define spectral distribution starting from the spectral density function whose existence we shall tacitly assume.

Definition 5.3.1 Spectral Distribution

Let $\{X_t, t \in T, T = (-\infty, \infty)\}$ be a quadratic mean continuous wide sense stationary process defined on a complete probability space $(\Omega, \mathcal{F}, P)$. The *spectral distribution* $F(\nu)$ of X_t is defined as the integral of the power spectral density $S(\nu)$ in the interval $(-\infty, \nu)$ given by

$$F(\nu) = \int_{-\infty}^{\nu} S(\xi)\, d\xi \qquad F(\infty) < \infty \tag{5.3.1}$$

Remarks

1. The quadratic mean continuity condition on X_t implies that a standard modification of X_t that is separable and measurable exists.

2. Just as $P(d\omega)$ is called the probability measure on the σ-field of events, the quantity $F(d\nu)$ is called the *spectral measure* on the σ-field of Borel sets on the real line $(-\infty, \infty)$ and is a finite measure. Whereas the probability measure is normalized to unity over the sample space, the spectral measure is not normalized.

3. The spectral measure as defined above is an absolutely continuous measure with respect to the Lebesgue measure.

4. Since $R(0) = \int_{-\infty}^{\infty} S(\xi)\, d\xi$ we have $F(\infty) = R(0)$, and thus the spectral measure $F(d\nu)$ can be normalized to a probability measure $F(d\nu)/F(\infty)$ on the σ-field of Borel sets on the real line if $F(\infty) < \infty$.

5. $F(\nu)$ in eq. 5.3.1 represents the spectral measure in the interval $(-\infty, \nu)$ and can be written specifically in the form $F((-\infty, \nu))$. The spectral measure between any other points a and b is given by the integral of the spectral density function between a and b,

$$F([a, b)) = F(ab) = F(b) - F(a) = \int_a^b S(\xi)\, d\xi \tag{5.3.2}$$

6. The concept of $F(\nu)$ as a spectral distribution is very similar to the concept of $F(x)$ as the probability distribution. More generally, if the spectral distribution is differentiable, the spectral density $S(\nu)$ can be obtained by differentiating $F(\nu)$,

$$S(\nu) = \frac{d}{d\nu} F(\nu) \qquad \text{or} \qquad F(d\nu) = S(\nu)\, d\nu \tag{5.3.3}$$

7. Using this concept of measure, the autocorrelation function $R(\tau)$ of a quadratic mean wide sense stationary process $\{X_t, -\infty < t < \infty\}$ can be given by (Bochner's theorem)

$$R(\tau) = \int_{-\infty}^{\infty} e^{j2\pi\nu\tau} F(d\nu) \tag{5.3.4}$$

The autocorrelation function is the integral of $e^{j2\pi\nu\tau}$ with respect to the spectral measure F over the real line. In fact, using eq. 5.3.3 we can write eq.

5.3.4 as

$$R(\tau) = \int_{-\infty}^{\infty} e^{j2\pi\nu\tau}\, dF(\nu) = \int_{-\infty}^{\infty} e^{j2\pi\nu\tau} S(\nu)\, d\nu$$

which is the usual expression, eq. 5.1.7, for $R(\tau)$ using the power spectral density $S(\nu)$. Equation 5.3.4 is a generalization of eq. 5.1.7. The inversion formula of obtaining the spectral measure F from the autocorrelation $R(\tau)$ will be established after definition of the generalized Fourier transform.

8. Equation 5.3.4 is similar to writing the expected value of a random variable X as the integral of X with respect to the probability measure P over the sample space Ω, namely,

$$EX = \int_{\Omega} X(\omega)\, P(d\omega)$$

We are now in a position to define the generalized Fourier transform (an integrated Fourier transform) $\{\overline{X}_\lambda, -\infty < \lambda < \infty\}$ of a process $\{X_t, -\infty < t < \infty\}$.

Definition 5.3.2 Spectral Process

Let $\{X_t, -\infty < t < \infty\}$ be a quadratic mean continuous wide sense stationary process defined on the probability space $(\Omega, \mathcal{F}, P)$. Let λ be the *continuity point* of the spectral measure $F((-\infty, \nu))$. The generalized Fourier transform $\{\overline{X}_\lambda, -\infty < \lambda < \infty\}$ of the process $\{X_t, -\infty < t < \infty\}$ is defined by

$$\overline{X}_\lambda = \int_{-\infty}^{\lambda} \left(\int_{-\infty}^{\infty} e^{-j2\pi\nu t} X_t\, dt \right) d\nu \tag{5.3.5}$$

with

$$\underset{\lambda \to -\infty}{\text{l.i.q.m.}}\, \overline{X}_\lambda = 0$$

At the discontinuity points of the spectral measure F, $\overline{X}_\lambda$ is defined as quadratic mean continuous from the left.

The process $\{\overline{X}_\lambda, -\infty < \lambda < \infty\}$ will be called the *spectral process* of $\{X_t, -\infty < t < \infty\}$.

The definition given by eq. 5.3.5 can be given in a different form as follows:

$$\overline{X}_\lambda = \int_{-\infty}^{\infty} \left(\int_{-\infty}^{\lambda} e^{-j2\pi\nu t}\, d\nu \right) X_t\, dt \tag{5.3.6}$$

Using the concept of generalized limits, which yields $\lim_{\nu \to -\infty} e^{-j2\pi\nu t} = 0$ for any square integrable X_t, eq. 5.3.6 reduces to

$$\overline{X}_\lambda = \int_{-\infty}^{\infty} \frac{e^{-j2\pi\lambda t}}{-j2\pi t} X_t \, dt \tag{5.3.7}$$

for a square integrable X_t. However, in the case of a stochastic process X_t may not be square integrable. To avoid this difficulty, we do not define the generalized Fourier transform by eq. 5.3.7. However, at any two continuity points $[a, b)$ of the spectral measure F we can define the difference $\overline{X}_b - \overline{X}_a$ as the formal integration

$$\overline{X}_b - \overline{X}_a = \int_{-\infty}^{\infty} \left(\int_a^b e^{-j2\pi\nu t} \, d\nu \right) X_t \, dt \tag{5.3.8}$$

By performing the integration in brackets, eq. 5.3.8 can be expressed as

$$\overline{X}_b - \overline{X}_a = \int_{-\infty}^{\infty} \frac{e^{-j2\pi bt} - e^{-j2\pi at}}{-j2\pi t} X_t \, dt \tag{5.3.9}$$

which can be considered an alternate definition to eq. 5.3.5.

Remark

1. The integral within brackets in eq. 5.3.8 is the Fourier transform of the indicator function $I_{ab}(\nu)$, which can be expressed by

$$\begin{aligned} \underline{I}_{ab}(t) &= \int_{-\infty}^{\infty} I_{ab}(\nu) e^{-j2\pi\nu t} \, d\nu \\ &= \int_a^b e^{-j2\pi\nu t} \, d\nu \\ &= \frac{e^{-j2\pi bt} - e^{-j2\pi at}}{-j2\pi t} \end{aligned} \tag{5.3.10}$$

whose inverse Fourier transform is $I_{ab}(\nu)$ in the sense

$$I_{ab}(\nu) = \lim_{S \to \infty} \int_{-S}^{S} \underline{I}_{ab}(t) e^{j2\pi\nu t} \, dt \tag{5.3.11}$$

and the convergence is a bounded convergence. Substituting eq. 5.3.10 into eq. 5.3.8 or eq. 5.3.9 yields a different form for eq. 5.3.9:

$$\overline{X}_b - \overline{X}_a = \int_{-\infty}^{\infty} \underline{I}_{ab}(t) X_t \, dt \tag{5.3.12}$$

2. Using the above facts we can now obtain an inversion integral corresponding to eq. 5.3.4 as follows:

$$\int_{-\infty}^{\infty} \underline{I}_{ab}(\tau) R(\tau)\, d\tau = \int_{-\infty}^{\infty} \underline{I}_{ab}(\tau)\, d\tau \int_{-\infty}^{\infty} e^{j2\pi\nu\tau} F(d\nu)$$

$$= \int_{-\infty}^{\infty} F(d\nu) \int_{-\infty}^{\infty} \underline{I}_{ab}(\tau) e^{j2\pi\nu\tau}\, d\tau$$

$$= \int_{-\infty}^{\infty} I_{ab}(\nu)\, F(d\nu) \quad \text{(from eq. 5.3.11)}$$

$$= F(b) - F(a) = F([a, b)) \tag{5.3.13}$$

Equation 5.3.13 is the desired inversion integral which can be given in a different form by substituting for $\underline{I}_{ab}(\tau)$ from eq. 5.3.10,

$$F(b) - F(a) = F([a, b))$$

$$= \int_{-\infty}^{\infty} \frac{e^{-j2\pi b\tau} - e^{-j2\pi a\tau}}{-j2\pi\tau} R(\tau)\, d\tau$$

$$= \int_{a}^{b} S(\nu)\, d\nu \tag{5.3.14}$$

from eq. 5.3.2.

Properties of the Spectral Process $\{\overline{X}_\lambda, -\infty < \lambda < \infty\}$

1. $\{\overline{X}_\lambda, -\infty < \lambda < \infty\}$ is a process with orthogonal increments with the result that $E(\overline{X}_b - \overline{X}_a)(\overline{X}_d - \overline{X}_c)^* = 0$ for nonoverlapping intervals $[a, b), [c, d)$. If I_{ab} and I_{cd} are indicator functions, then from eq. 5.3.8,

$$E(\overline{X}_b - \overline{X}_a)(\overline{X}_d - \overline{X}_c)^* = \int_{-\infty}^{\infty}\int_{-\infty}^{\infty} EX_t X_s^*\, dt\, ds$$

$$\times \int_{-\infty}^{\infty}\int_{-\infty}^{\infty} I_{ab} I_{cd}^* e^{-j2\pi\nu t} e^{j2\pi\mu s}\, d\nu\, d\mu$$

Clearly

$$I_{ab} I_{cd}^* = \begin{cases} 1 & [a, b) \cap [c, d) = [a, b) \\ 0 & [a, b) \cap [c, d) = \varnothing \end{cases}$$

Hence

$$E(\overline{X}_b - \overline{X}_a)(\overline{X}_d - \overline{X}_c)^* = 0 \qquad [a, b) \cap [c, d) = \varnothing$$

and the process $\overline{X}_\lambda$ is indeed one of orthogonal increments.

2. Using property 1, the process $\bar{X}_\lambda$ can be expressed in differential form in terms of the spectral measure F with $d\bar{X}_\nu = \bar{X}_{\nu+d\nu} - \bar{X}_\nu$,

$$E\, d\bar{X}_\nu\, d\bar{X}_\mu^* = F(d\nu)\,\delta_{\nu\mu}$$

where

$$\delta_{\nu\mu} = \begin{cases} 1 & \nu = \mu \\ 0 & \nu \neq \mu \end{cases}$$

Hence

$$E|d\bar{X}_\nu|^2 = F(d\nu) = S_X(\nu)\, d\nu \tag{5.3.15}$$

Note. The power spectral density expression given by eq. 5.3.15 is very useful when we try to compute it using the fast Fourier transform algorithm.

We have defined the spectral process $\{\bar{X}_\lambda, -\infty < \lambda < \infty\}$ of a quadratic mean continuous wide sense stationary stochastic process $\{X_t, -\infty < t < \infty\}$. We now obtain the form for $\{X_t, -\infty < t < \infty\}$ from the spectral process $\{\bar{X}_\lambda, -\infty < \lambda < \infty\}$ by means of the following propositions.

Proposition 5.3.1

Let $\{\bar{X}_\lambda, -\infty < \lambda < \infty\}$ be the spectral process as defined by eq. 5.3.5 of a quadratic mean continuous wide sense stationary process $\{X_t, -\infty < t < \infty\}$. Let $f(\cdot)$ belong to a class of infinitely differentiable functions of rapid decay and let $\underline{f}(\cdot)$ be its Fourier transform in the sense of eq. 5.1.2. Then

$$\int_{-\infty}^{\infty} f(\lambda)\, d\bar{X}_\lambda = \int_{-\infty}^{\infty} \underline{f}(t)\, X_t\, dt \tag{5.3.16}$$

Proof. The definition of the spectral process $\bar{X}_\lambda$ as given by eq. 5.3.12 can be expressed as

$$\int_{-\infty}^{\infty} I_{ab}(\lambda)\, d\bar{X}_\lambda = \int_{-\infty}^{\infty} \underline{I}_{ab}(t)\, X_t\, dt \tag{5.3.17}$$

Now let $\{f_n\}$ be a sequence of step functions obtained by sampling f at continuity points of the spectral measure F. Since f belongs to the class of infinitely differentiable functions of rapid decay, the sequence $\{f_n\}$ converges to f uniformly in L^1-space as the sampling becomes finer. The same can be said of the corresponding sequence $\{\underline{f}_n\}$ of $\underline{f}$. Hence we can identify $f_n(\lambda)$ with $I_{ab}(\lambda)$ and $\underline{f}_n(t)$ with $\underline{I}_{ab}(t)$ in eq. 5.3.17 and obtain for each n

$$\int_{-\infty}^{\infty} f_n(\lambda)\, d\bar{X}_\lambda = \int_{-\infty}^{\infty} \underline{f}_n(t)\, X_t\, dt \tag{5.3.18}$$

We have to show that

$$E\left|\int_{-\infty}^{\infty} f(\lambda)\, d\overline{X}_\lambda - \int_{-\infty}^{\infty} \underline{f}(t) X_t\, dt\right|^2 = 0$$

or it is enough if we show that

$$\lim_{n\to\infty} E\left|\int_{-\infty}^{\infty} [f(\lambda) - f_n(\lambda)]\, d\overline{X}_\lambda - \int_{-\infty}^{\infty} [\underline{f}(t) - \underline{f}_n(t)]\, X_t\, dt\right|^2 = 0 \quad (5.3.19)$$

Using the inequality $(a - b)^2 \leq 2a^2 + 2b^2$, we can express the left-hand side of eq. 5.3.19 as an inequality,

$$E\left|\int_{-\infty}^{\infty} [f(\lambda) - f_n(\lambda)]\, d\overline{X}_\lambda - \int_{-\infty}^{\infty} [\underline{f}(t) - \underline{f}_n(t)]\, X_t\, dt\right|^2$$

$$\leq 2E\left|\int_{-\infty}^{\infty} [f(\lambda) - f_n(\lambda)]\, d\overline{X}_\lambda\right|^2 + 2E\left|\int_{-\infty}^{\infty} [\underline{f}(t) - \underline{f}_n(t)]\, X_t\, dt\right|^2$$

$$= 2\int_{-\infty}^{\infty}\int_{-\infty}^{\infty} [f(\lambda) - f_n(\lambda)][f(\mu) - f_n(\mu)]^* E\, d\overline{X}_\lambda\, d\overline{X}_\mu^*$$

$$+2\int_{-\infty}^{\infty}\int_{-\infty}^{\infty} [\underline{f}(t) - \underline{f}_n(t)][\underline{f}(s) - \underline{f}_n(s)]^* E X_t X_s^*\, dt\, ds$$

$$= 2\int_{-\infty}^{\infty} |f(\lambda) - f_n(\lambda)|^2 F(d\nu)$$

$$+2\int_{-\infty}^{\infty}\int_{-\infty}^{\infty} R(t-s)[\underline{f}(t) - \underline{f}_n(t)][\underline{f}(s) - \underline{f}_n(s)]^*\, dt\, ds \quad (5.3.20)$$

Since $f_n(\lambda)$ converges uniformly to $f(\lambda)$ by assumption, the first integral is zero as $n \to \infty$.

Using eq. 5.3.4 (Bochner's theorem) in the second integral, we obtain

$$\int_{-\infty}^{\infty}\int_{-\infty}^{\infty} R(t-s)[\underline{f}(t) - \underline{f}_n(t)][\underline{f}(s) - \underline{f}_n(s)]^*\, dt\, ds$$

$$= \int_{-\infty}^{\infty}\int_{-\infty}^{\infty}\int_{-\infty}^{\infty} e^{j2\pi\nu(t-s)}\, F(d\nu)[\underline{f}(t) - \underline{f}_n(t)][\underline{f}(s) - \underline{f}_n(s)]^*\, dt\, ds$$

$$= \int_{-\infty}^{\infty} F(d\nu) \int_{-\infty}^{\infty} [\underline{f}(t) - \underline{f}_n(t)]\, e^{j2\pi\nu t}\, dt \int_{-\infty}^{\infty} [\underline{f}(s) - \underline{f}_n(s)]^* e^{-j2\pi\nu s}\, ds$$

$$(5.3.21)$$

Since $f(t)$ is an infinitely differentiable function of rapid decay,

$$\int_{-\infty}^{\infty} [\underline{f}(t) - \underline{f}_n(t)] e^{j2\pi\nu t}\, dt = f(\nu) - f_n(\nu) \tag{5.3.22}$$

Using eq. 5.3.22 in eq. 5.3.21 results in the second integral being equal to $\int_{-\infty}^{\infty} |f(\nu) - f_n(\nu)|^2\, F(d\nu)$, which again tends to zero as $n \to \infty$. □

Now we can state the following proposition concerned with obtaining $\{X_t, -\infty < t < \infty\}$ from the spectral representation $\{\overline{X}_\lambda, -\infty < \lambda < \infty\}$.

Proposition 5.3.2

Let $\{\overline{X}_\lambda, -\infty < \lambda < \infty\}$ be a left continuous stochastic process with orthogonal increments such that $E|\overline{X}_\lambda|^2 < \infty$. A quadratic mean process $\{X_t, -\infty < t < \infty\}$ is wide sense stationary if and only if

$$X_t = \int_{-\infty}^{\infty} e^{j2\pi\lambda t}\, d\overline{X}_\lambda \tag{5.3.23}$$

Proof

Necessity. From eq. 5.3.15,

$$E\int_{-\infty}^{\infty} e^{j2\pi\lambda t}\, d\overline{X}_\lambda \int_{-\infty}^{\infty} e^{-j2\pi\nu s}\, d\overline{X}_\nu^* = \int_{-\infty}^{\infty} e^{j2\pi\lambda(t-s)}\, F(d\lambda)$$

From eq. 5.3.4 (Bochner's theorem),

$$\int_{-\infty}^{\infty} e^{j2\pi\lambda(t-s)}\, F(d\lambda)$$

represents the autocorrelation of a quadratic mean continuous wide sense stationary process. Hence the process defined by $\int_{-\infty}^{\infty} e^{j2\pi\lambda t}\, d\overline{X}_\lambda$ must be quadratic mean wide sense stationary.

Sufficiency. Let X_t be a quadratic mean continuous wide sense stationary process, and let $\overline{X}_\lambda$ be defined by eq. 5.3.5. Using the concept of generalized limits, the Fourier transform of $f(\lambda) = e^{j2\pi\lambda t_0}$ is given by

$$\int_{-\infty}^{\infty} e^{-j2\pi\lambda(t-t_0)}\, d\lambda = \delta(t - t_0) = \underline{f}(t)$$

where $\delta(t - t_0)$ is the impulse function as given in Definition 5.2.1.

Introducing these values† of $f(\lambda)$ and $\underline{f}(t)$ in eq. 5.3.16 of Proposition 5.3.1 yields

$$\int_{-\infty}^{\infty} e^{j2\pi\lambda t_0}\, d\overline{X}_\lambda = \int_{-\infty}^{\infty} \delta(t - t_0) X_t\, dt = X_{t_0} \qquad \square$$

† By introducing the values $e^{j2\pi\lambda t_0}$ and $\delta(t - t_0)$ for $f(\lambda)$ and $f(t)$ we have tacitly enlarged the class of functions to which $f(\lambda)$ belongs from square integrable to generalized functions.

The white noise process has an interesting property that its Fourier transform is also a white noise. The Fourier transform, however, has to be defined carefully as given in the following proposition.

Proposition 5.3.3

Let $\{X_t, -\infty < t < \infty\}$ represent a white noise process, and let $h(\nu)$ and its Fourier transform $\underline{h}(t)$ belong to a class of square integrable functions. Then there exists a second white noise process $\{\underline{X}_\nu, -\infty < \nu < \infty\}$, such that

$$\int_{-\infty}^{\infty} h(\nu)\underline{X}_\nu \, d\nu = \int_{-\infty}^{\infty} \underline{h}(t) X_t \, dt \tag{5.3.24}$$

Remark. From Proposition 5.2.1 an equivalent representation of eq. 5.3.24 can be given by

$$\int_{-\infty}^{\infty} h(\nu) \, d\bar{Z}_\nu = \int_{-\infty}^{\infty} \underline{h}(t) \, dZ_t$$

where $\bar{Z}_\nu$ and Z_t are processes of orthogonal increments corresponding to $\underline{X}_\nu$ and X_t.

Proof. Motivated by eq. 5.3.12, we *define* the process $\{\bar{Z}_\nu, -\infty < \nu < \infty\}$ by

$$\bar{Z}_b - \bar{Z}_a = \int_{-\infty}^{\infty} \underline{I}_{ab}(t) \, dZ_t$$

with $\bar{Z}_0 = 0$. Hence

$$E(\bar{Z}_b - \bar{Z}_a)(\bar{Z}_d - \bar{Z}_c)^* = \int_{-\infty}^{\infty}\int_{-\infty}^{\infty} \underline{I}_{ab}(t)\underline{I}_{cd}^*(s) E(dZ_t \, dZ_s^*) \tag{5.3.25}$$

Since Z_t is a process of orthogonal increments, we have from eq. 5.2.26,

$$E(dZ_t \, dZ_s^*) = \sigma^2 \delta_{ts} \, dt$$

Substituting this result in eq. 5.3.25,

$$E(\bar{Z}_b - \bar{Z}_a)(\bar{Z}_d - \bar{Z}_c)^* = \sigma^2 \int_{-\infty}^{\infty} \underline{I}_{ab}(t)\underline{I}_{cd}^*(t) \, dt$$

$$= \sigma^2 \int_{-\infty}^{\infty} I_{ab}(\nu) I_{cd}^*(\nu) \, d\nu$$

by Parseval's theorem. Hence $\bar{Z}_\nu$ is also a process of orthogonal increments with

$$E\left(d\bar{Z}_\nu\, d\bar{Z}_\mu^*\right) = \sigma^2 \delta_{\nu\mu}\, d\nu$$

which has exactly the same second-order properties as Z_t.

Equation 5.3.24 is proved in a manner analogous to proving eq. 5.3.16 by approximating $h(\nu)$ and $\underline{h}(t)$ by a sequence of step functions $h_n(\nu)$ and $\underline{h}_n(t)$ and showing that

$$\lim_{n\to\infty} E\left|\int_{-\infty}^{\infty} [h(\nu) - h_n(\nu)]\, d\bar{Z}_\nu - \int_{-\infty}^{\infty} [\underline{h}(t) - \underline{h}_n(t)]\, dZ_t\right|^2 \to 0 \qquad \square$$

5.4 WHITE NOISE DIFFERENTIAL EQUATION

We now investigate the problem of a differential equation driven by white noise. Suppose we are given the differential equation in the following form:

$$\frac{dY_t}{dt} = \alpha(t) Y_t + \beta(t) X_t \qquad t \in T, Y_a \tag{5.4.1}$$

where X_t is a white noise process. Presented in this form, eq. 5.4.1 cannot be interpreted as an ordinary differential equation without making assumptions on differentiability and separability of Y_t and X_t, even if X_t were not white but some other quadratic mean continuous random process. Instead of interpreting eq. 5.4.1 as a differential equation, we can interpret it as an integral equation without worrying about these assumptions. We interpret the stochastic process $\{Y_t, t \in [a, b)\}$ with $E|Y_t|^2 < \infty$ as the solution to the differential equation 5.4.1 if it satisfies the following integral equation:

$$Y_t = Y_a + \int_a^t \alpha(s) Y_s\, ds + \int_a^t \beta(s)\, dZ_s \qquad a \le t < b \tag{5.4.2}$$

where Z_t is the process of orthogonal increments associated with the white noise process X_t, Y_a is the initial condition satisfying $E|Y_a|^2 < \infty$, and $\alpha(t)$ and $\beta(t)$ belong to a class of square integrable functions.

The above integral equation an also be written as

$$dY_t = \alpha(t) Y_t\, dt + \beta(t)\, dZ_t \qquad a \le t < b, \quad Y_a, \quad E|Y_a|^2 < \infty \tag{5.4.3}$$

We have more to say about these differential equations when we discuss Ito stochastic differential equations.

Caution. We have tacitly assumed that eqs. 5.4.1, 5.4.2, and 5.4.3 are equivalent representations. These are equivalent representations if and only if

$\alpha(t)$ and $\beta(t)$ are functions of t only belonging to a class of square integrable functions. If α and β are stochastic processes (functions of ω and t), then the differential equation representation of eq. 5.4.1 *may not* be equivalent to the representations given by eqs. 5.4.2 and 5.4.3, even though eqs. 5.4.2 and 5.4.3 are equivalent by definition. We discuss in Chapter 7 the formulation of the stochastic differential equation corresponding to eq. 5.4.1 when α and β are random processes.

Let us take as an example the white noise differential equation

$$\dot{Y}_t = -Y_t + X_t \qquad a \le t < b, \quad Y_a, \quad E|Y_a|^2 < \infty \tag{5.4.4}$$

where X_t is a white noise process. We interpret eq. 5.4.4 as the integral equation

$$Y_t = Y_a - \int_a^t Y_s\, ds + \int_a^t dZ_s \tag{5.4.5}$$

For any arbitrary initial condition Y_a, the solution to eq. 5.4.5 is of the form

$$Y_t = Y_a e^{-(t-a)} + \int_a^t e^{-(t-s)}\, dZ_s \tag{5.4.6}$$

If $E|Y_a|^2 < \infty$ as $a \to -\infty$, we can rewrite eq. 5.4.6 as

$$Y_t = \int_{-\infty}^t e^{-(t-s)}\, dZ_s \tag{5.4.7}$$

However, in eq. 5.3.24

$$\int_{-\infty}^{\infty} h(\nu)\, d\bar{Z}_\nu = \int_{-\infty}^{\infty} \underline{h}(s)\, dZ_s \tag{5.3.24}$$

We can substitute† $\underline{h}(s) = e^{-(t-s)}$ and

$$h(\nu) = \int_{-\infty}^t \underline{h}(s) e^{j2\pi\nu s}\, ds = \frac{e^{j2\pi\nu t}}{j2\pi\nu + 1}$$

and obtain

$$\int_{-\infty}^{\infty} \frac{e^{j2\pi\nu t}}{j2\pi\nu + 1}\, d\bar{Z}_\nu = \int_{-\infty}^t e^{-(t-s)}\, dZ_s \tag{5.4.8}$$

Thus the solution to eq. 5.4.5 is given by

$$Y_t = \int_{-\infty}^{\infty} \frac{e^{j2\pi\nu t}}{j2\pi\nu + 1}\, d\bar{Z}_\nu \tag{5.4.9}$$

† Note that since $\underline{h}(s) = 0$ for $s > t$, $\underline{h}(s) \in L^2$.

If we formally Fourier transform eq. 5.4.4 (disregarding the fact that a conventional Fourier transform does not exist), we obtain the solution $\underline{Y}_\nu$ in the transform domain as

$$\underline{Y}_\nu = \frac{\underline{X}_\nu}{j2\pi\nu + 1} \tag{5.4.10}$$

the inverse Fourier transform of which results in

$$Y_t = \int_{-\infty}^{\infty} \frac{e^{j2\pi\nu t}\underline{X}_\nu \, d\nu}{j2\pi\nu + 1} = \int_{-\infty}^{\infty} \frac{e^{j2\pi\nu t}\, d\overline{Z}_\nu}{j2\pi\nu + 1} \tag{5.4.11}$$

Thus the heuristic solution of Y_t of eq. 5.4.11 agrees with the rigorous solution of eq. 5.4.9. Thus eq. 5.4.4 can be solved as such, using the concepts of an ordinary differential equation. This will not be possible for a more general stochastic differential equation.

Problems

1. Let $\{\mathbf{X}_t, -\infty < t < \infty\}$ be a vector quadratic mean continuous wide sense stationary process defined on the probability space $(\Omega, \mathcal{F}, P)$. Show that the correlation function $\mathbf{R}(\tau) = E\mathbf{X}_{t+\tau}\mathbf{X}^T$ is nonnegative definite.

2. Test whether the following functions can represent correlation functions:
   a. $g(t, s) - e^{|t-s|}$
   b. $g(t, s) = \begin{cases} 1 & |t-s| \le 1 \\ 0 & |t-s| > 1 \end{cases}$

3. Show that the autocorrelation function of a real process X_t satisfies the following inequality:

$$R(0) - R(\tau) \ge \frac{1}{4^n}[R(0) - R(2^n\tau)]$$

4. If $\{X_t, -\infty < t < \infty\}$ has a covariance function

$$R(\tau) = e^{-|2\tau|}(\cos 2\tau - \sin|2\tau|)$$

   find its power spectral density.

5. Show that the autocorrelation function of the derivative of any stochastic process $\{X_t, t \in T\}$ is

$$E\dot{X}_t\dot{X}_s = \frac{\partial^2 R_X(t, s)}{\partial t\, \partial s}$$

   and hence show that the autocorrelation function of the derivative of a

Poisson process is

$$E\dot{N}_t\dot{N}_s = \lambda^2 + \lambda\delta(t-s)$$

6. Let $\{X_t, t \in T, T = (-\infty, \infty)\}$ be a zero mean real process with orthogonal increments with $E|X_t - X_s|^2 = |t-s|$ and $X_0 = 0$.
   a. Show that the autocovariance function of X_t is given by

   $$C_X(t,s) = EX_tX_s = \tfrac{1}{2}(|t| + |s| - |t-s|)$$

   b. A sequence $\{Z_{nt}, t \in T, T = (-\infty, \infty)\}$ is defined by

   $$Z_{nt} = n(X_{t+1/n} - X_t) \qquad n = 1, 2, \ldots$$

   Find the autocovariance function for Z_{nt} and show that it converges to white noise in the sense of Definition 5.2.2.

7. Let $g(t)$ and $h(t)$ be two functions satisfying eq. 5.2.28. Prove the following results:
   a. $\int_{-\infty}^{\infty} [\alpha g(t) + \beta h(t)]\, dZ_t = \alpha \int_{-\infty}^{\infty} g(t)\, dZ_t + \beta \int_{-\infty}^{\infty} h(t)\, dZ_t$
   b. $\int_0^t g(\tau)\, dZ_\tau = \int_0^s g(\tau)\, dZ_\tau + \int_s^t g(\tau)\, dZ_\tau \qquad s \le t$

8. Show that the Brownian motion process $\{W_t, t \in T, T = [0, \infty)\}$ is a process with orthogonal increments. If the stochastic integral $\int_0^t g(t)\, dW_t$, $t \in T$, is a continuous function for all t, then show that
   a. $E\left[\int_0^t g(\tau)\, dW_\tau | \mathcal{F}_s\right] = \int_0^s g(\tau)\, dW_\tau$
   b. $E\left[\int_0^t g(\tau)\, dW_\tau\right]\left[\int_0^t h(\tau)\, dW_\tau\right] = E\int_0^t g(\tau)h(\tau)\, d\tau$

9. Using the fact that the power spectral density function is a nonnegative definite function, show that the spectral measure $F(d\nu)$ is an absolutely continuous measure with respect to the Lebesgue measure.

10. Show that the function $R(\tau)$ is the covariance function of a quadratic mean wide sense stationary process $\{X_t, t \in T, T = (-\infty, \infty)\}$ if and only if (Bochner's theorem)

$$R(\tau) = \int_{-\infty}^{\infty} e^{j2\pi\nu\tau} F(d\nu)$$

where F is a finite Borel measure on the real line.

11. Using the concept of generalized limits, show that for a square integrable X_t,

$$\int_{-\infty}^{\infty} \left(\int_{-\infty}^{\lambda} e^{-j2\pi\nu t}\, d\nu\right) X_t\, dt = \int_{-\infty}^{\infty} \frac{e^{-j2\pi\lambda t}}{-j2\pi t} X_t\, dt$$

12. Let $\{X_t, t \in T, T = (-\infty, \infty)\}$ be a quadratic mean wide sense stationary Markov process with autocorrelation function $R(\tau) = e^{-c\tau}R(0)$, $\tau \geq 0$, $c = \alpha + j\beta$. Find the spectral measure $F([a, b))$.

13. Let $\{X_t, t \in T, T = (-\infty, \infty)\}$ be a stochastic process defined by

$$X_t = \int_{-\infty}^{\infty} e^{j2\pi t\lambda}\, dY(\lambda)$$

where $Y(\lambda)$ is a stochastic process with orthogonal increments with $E|dY(\lambda)|^2 = dF(\lambda)$, $F(-\infty) = 0$. Show that the process X_t is a wide sense stationary process. Find its autocorrelation and the spectral measure.

14. Show that the spectral process $\{\overline{X}_\lambda, -\infty < \lambda < \infty\}$ satisfies

$$E(\overline{X}_b - \overline{X}_a)(\overline{X}_d - \overline{X}_c)^* = F([a, b) \cap [c, d))$$

where F is the spectral measure of the process $\{X_t, -\infty < t < \infty\}$, and hence show that

$$E\, d\overline{X}_\nu\, d\overline{X}_\mu = F(d\nu)\delta_{\nu\mu} \qquad \delta_{\nu\mu} = \begin{cases} 1 & \nu = \mu \\ 0 & \nu \neq \mu \end{cases}$$

15. Show that every process with a power spectral density $S(\nu)$ can be represented as a white noise passing through a linear filter whose transfer function $\underline{h}(\nu)$ satisfies the relationship $|\underline{h}(\nu)|^2 = S(\nu)$.

16. In the differential equation

$$\dot{Y}_t = -Y_t + X_t \qquad a \leq t < b, \quad Y_a, \quad E|Y_a|^2 < \infty$$

X_t is a zero mean process satisfying $EX_tX_s^* = e^{-|t-s|}$. Solve the differential equation.

6 STOCHASTIC INTEGRALS AND STOCHASTIC DIFFERENTIAL EQUATIONS

6.1 STOCHASTIC INTEGRALS

In Chapter 5 we defined on a probability space $(\Omega, \mathcal{F}, P)$ a simple stochastic integral of the form $\int_{-\infty}^{\infty} g(t)\, dZ_t$ where $g(t)$ was a function of t only and Z_t was a process of orthogonal increments corresponding to a white noise process X_t. A generalization of this simple stochastic integral is a quantity of the form

$$I_t(\varphi) = \int_0^t \varphi(\omega, s)\, dW_s \qquad t \in T \tag{6.1.1}$$

where T is the positive real line and W_t is a Brownian motion process defined on a complete probability space $(\Omega, \mathcal{F}, P)$ satisfying the following usual conditions with $s \geq 0$:

$$\begin{aligned} EW_t &= 0 \\ E^{\mathcal{F}_t} W_{t+s} &= W_t \\ E^{\mathcal{F}_t}(W_{t+s} - W_t)^2 &= \sigma^2 s \end{aligned} \tag{6.1.2}$$

In eq. 6.1.1 the integrand φ depends upon ω, and since W_t is neither differentiable nor of bounded variation, the integral $I_t(\varphi)$ has to be defined properly. The integral when φ is independent of ω has been defined in the last chapter where we have used only the orthogonal increment property of W_t but not the martingale property. For the stochastic integral $I_t(\varphi)$ to be properly defined, the integrand $\varphi(\omega, t)$ has to satisfy the following conditions:

1. If $\mathcal{L}$ is the σ-field of Borel sets on the positive real line, then φ is jointly measurable in the product σ-field $\mathcal{F} \otimes \mathcal{L}$,

$$\varphi \in \mathcal{F} \otimes \mathcal{L} \tag{6.1.3a}$$

2. If $\{\mathcal{F}_t, t \in T, T = R^+\}$ is a right continuous filtration σ-field of the probability space, then for each $t \in T$, $\varphi(\omega, t)$ is adapted to $\mathcal{F}_t$,

$$\varphi(\omega, t) \in \mathcal{F}_t \tag{6.1.3b}$$

As already seen, such functions are called nonanticipative with respect to the family $\{\mathcal{F}_t, t \in T\}$.

3. For each $t \in T$, $\varphi(\omega, t)$ satisfies

$$\int_0^t E|\varphi(\omega, s)|^2 \, ds < \infty \quad \text{(a.s.)} \tag{6.1.3c}$$

This condition can be weakened (Wong, 63, p. 163; Lipster and Shiryaev, 34, p. 103) to

$$\int_0^t |\varphi(\omega, s)|^2 \, ds < \infty \quad \text{(a.s.)}$$

4. $\varphi(\omega, t)$ belongs to a class of left continuous functions.

(6.1.3d)

The process $\varphi(\omega, t)$ under the four conditions given above is a predictable process with respect to the filtration σ-field $\{\mathcal{F}_t, t \in T, T = R^+\}$.

We now define a simple process the concept of which has already been used in the basic definition of a simple stochastic integral.

Definition 6.1.1 Simple Process

A function $g(\omega, t)$ is called *simple* if, for the partitions $0 \le t_0 < t_1 < \cdots < t_n = b$ of the interval $T = [0, b]$, it can be represented in the form

$$g(t, \omega) = \sum_{\nu=0}^{n-1} g_\nu(\omega) I_{(t_\nu, t_{\nu+1}]}(t) \tag{6.1.4}$$

where the g_ν are $\mathcal{F}_{t_\nu}$-measurable.

Defined as above, the simple function $g(\omega, t)$ is left continuous and adapted to the filtration σ-field $\{\mathcal{F}_t, t \in T, T = [0, b]\}$. Therefore it is a predictable process satisfying conditions 6.1.3. It is not essential that the function $g(\omega, t)$

be defined as left continuous. However, the left continuity and hence predictability plays a crucial role in the definition of the stochastic integral.

We state the following proposition, which is used in the more complete definition of a stochastic integral.

Proposition 6.1.1

Let $\{\varphi(\omega, t), t \in T\}$ be a random process satisfying conditions 6.1.3. Then there exists a sequence of simple processes $\{\varphi_n(\omega, t), n = 0, 1, 2, \ldots,\ t \in T\}$ satisfying conditions 6.1.3 such that

$$\lim_{n\to\infty} \int_T E|\varphi(\omega, t) - \varphi_n(\omega, t)|^2 \, dt \to 0 \tag{6.1.5}$$

For proof see Wong (63, p. 142), Lipster and Shiryaev (34, p. 92), and Kallianpur (29, p. 54).

Now we are in a position to define the stochastic integral of eq. 6.1.1.

Definition 6.1.2 Stochastic Integral

Let $(\Omega, \mathfrak{F}, P)$ be a complete probability space, and let $\{\mathfrak{F}_t, t \in T, T = [0, b]\}$ be a filtration σ-field. Let $\{W_t, t \in T\}$ be a Brownian motion martingale adapted to $\mathfrak{F}_t$.

1. If $\{\varphi(\omega, t), t \in T\}$ is a simple process of Definition 6.1.1 given by

$$\varphi(\omega, t) = \sum_{\nu=0}^{N(n)-1} \varphi_\nu(\omega) I_{(t_\nu^{(n)},\, t_{\nu+1}^{(n)}]}$$

for partitions $0 \le t_0^{(n)} < \cdots < t_{N(n)}^{(n)} = t$, then the stochastic integral is defined by

$$I_t(\varphi) = \int_0^t \varphi(\omega, s)\, dW_s = \sum_{\nu=0}^{N(n)-1} \varphi_\nu(\omega)\left[W_{t_{\nu+1}^{(n)}} - W_{t_\nu^{(n)}}\right] \tag{6.1.6}$$

2. If $\{\varphi(\omega, t), t \in T\}$ is a general process satisfying conditions 6.1.3, then from Proposition 6.1.1 there exists a sequence of simple functions $\{\varphi_n(\omega, t), n = 0, 1, \ldots, t \in T\}$ approximating $\varphi(\omega, t)$ in the quadratic mean. In this case the stochastic integral is defined as

$$I_t(\varphi) = \int_0^t \varphi(\omega, s)\, dW_s = \underset{n\to\infty}{\text{l.i.q.m.}} \int_0^t \varphi_n(\omega, s)\, dW_s$$

$$= \underset{n\to\infty}{\text{l.i.q.m.}}\, I_t(\varphi_n) \tag{6.1.7a}$$

Thus the sequence of random variables $I_t(\varphi_n) = \int_0^t \varphi_n(\omega, s)\, dW_s$ converges in the quadratic mean to the random variable $I_t(\varphi) = \int_0^t \varphi(\omega, s)\, dW_s$, which is called the stochastic integral of the function $\varphi(\omega, t)$ relative to the Brownian motion martingale $\{W_t, \mathfrak{F}_t, t \in T\}$. The limiting value (to within stochastic equivalence) of the integral $I_t(\varphi_n)$ is *independent* of the choice of the approximating sequence $\{\varphi_n\}$.

Condition 6.1.3c can also be weakened as indicated before (Wong, 63, p. 163; Lipster and Shiryaev, 34, p. 103) to

$$\int_0^t |\varphi(\omega, s)|^2\, ds < \infty \quad \text{(a.s.)} \qquad t \in T$$

3. Under the weakened condition we define the approximating sequence $\{\varphi_n(\omega, t), n = 0, 1, \ldots, t \in T\}$ as

$$\varphi_n(\omega, t) = \begin{cases} \varphi(\omega, t) & \int_0^t |\varphi(\omega, t)|^2\, dt < n \quad \text{(a.s.)} \\ 0 & \text{otherwise} \end{cases}$$

so that $\{\varphi_n(\omega, t)\}$ converges in probability to $\varphi(\omega, t)$ as $n \to \infty$.

In this case the stochastic integral is defined as

$$I_t(\varphi) = \int_0^t \varphi(\omega, s)\, dW_s = \underset{n \to \infty}{\text{l.i.p.}} \int_0^t \varphi_n(\omega, s)\, dW_s$$

$$= \underset{n \to \infty}{\text{l.i.p.}}\, I_t(\varphi_n) \tag{6.1.7b}$$

Properties of Stochastic Integrals. The stochastic integral $I_t(\varphi)$ as defined above satisfies the following basic properties:

1. $E\int_0^t \varphi(\omega, s)\, dW_s = 0 \qquad t \in T$ (6.1.8)
2. $I_t(a\varphi_1 + b\varphi_2) = aI_t(\varphi_1) + bI_t(\varphi_2)$ $\quad a, b$ are constants (6.1.9)
3. $\int_0^t \varphi(s, \omega)\, dW_s = \int_0^\tau \varphi(s, \omega)\, dW_s + \int_\tau^t \varphi(s, \omega)\, dW_s \qquad \tau \le t$ (6.1.10)
4. $I_t(\varphi)$ is progressively measurable for $t \in T$ and $\varphi(t, \omega)$ satisfying conditions 6.1.3. In particular, for each t, $I_t(\varphi)$ is $\mathfrak{F}_t$-measurable.

The concept of the stochastic integral can be further generalized. Let $\{M_t, t \in T, T = R^+\}$ be a right continuous square integrable or locally square integrable martingale with respect to a right continuous filtration σ-field $\{\mathfrak{F}_t, t \in T\}$. Then the stochastic integral given by

$$X_t = \int_0^t \varphi(s, \omega)\, dM_t \qquad t \in T \tag{6.1.11}$$

can be defined (Wong, 63, p. 165) in a manner analogous to Definition 6.1.2, provided

$$\int_0^t |\varphi(s, \omega)|^2 \, d\langle M, M\rangle_s < \infty$$

We now introduce the interesting property of the stochastic integrals being also martingales. For a class of functions $\varphi(\omega, t)$ satisfying conditions 6.1.3 the stochastic integral with respect to a square integrable or locally square integrable martingale $\{M_t, t \in T, \ T = R^+\}$ is also a square integrable or locally square integrable martingale with respect to the underlying filtration σ-field $\{\mathcal{F}_t, t \in T\}$. Or if M_t is a square integrable martingale, then

$$E^{\mathcal{F}_s} \int_0^t \varphi(\tau, \omega) \, dM_\tau = \int_0^s \varphi(\tau, \omega) \, dM_\tau \qquad s \le t$$

If the martingale M_t has paths of bounded variation (necessarily a discontinuous martingale), then the stochastic integral X_t is defined as a Stieltjes integral.

Before proving the martingale property of the stochastic integral, we give an example where the left continuity of $\varphi(\omega, t)$ is clearly brought out into focus in obtaining this property.

Example 6.1.1

Let N_t be a standard Poisson process, $\lambda = 1$. Then we have already seen that $M_t = N_t - t$ is a square integrable martingale defined on the right continuous filtration σ-field $\mathcal{F}_t$.

Now consider the Stieltjes integral (since M_t is a discontinuous martingale of bounded variation)

$$X_t = \int_0^t N_s \, dM_s = \int_0^t N_s \, dN_s - \int_0^t N_s \, dt \tag{6.1.12}$$

Since we have defined N_t as a right continuous process (in violation of condition 6.1.3), we investigate whether X_t is a martingale.

$$\begin{aligned} \int_0^t N_s \cdot dN_s &= \sum_{s \le t} N_s \cdot \Delta N_s \\ &= (1 + 2 + \cdots + N_t) \cdot 1 \quad \text{because } \Delta N_s = 1 \text{ for a Poisson process} \\ &= \frac{N_t(N_t + 1)}{2} \end{aligned} \tag{6.1.13}$$

The increment $N_t - N_s$ is independent of the σ-field $\mathcal{F}_s = \sigma\{N_\tau, \tau \le s\} = \sigma\{M_\tau, \tau \le s\}$, and hence

$$\begin{aligned} E^{\mathcal{F}_s}(N_t - N_s) &= E(N_t - N_s) = t - s \\ \operatorname{var}^{\mathcal{F}_s}(N_t - N_s) &= \operatorname{var}(N_t - N_s) = t - s \\ E(N_t - N_s)^2 &= (t - s) + (t - s)^2 \end{aligned} \tag{6.1.14}$$

From eq. 6.1.12 we have

$$X_t - X_s = \int_s^t N_\xi \, dN_\xi - \int_s^t N_\xi \, d\xi \tag{6.1.15}$$

and taking conditional expectation on both sides of eq. 6.1.15, we obtain

$$E^{\mathcal{F}_s}(X_t - X_s) = E^{\mathcal{F}_s}\int_s^t N_\xi \, dN_\xi - E^{\mathcal{F}_s}\int_s^t N_\xi \, d\xi \tag{6.1.16}$$

Using eq. 6.1.13, the first integral of eq. 6.1.16 is evaluated.

$$\begin{aligned}
E^{\mathcal{F}_s}\int_s^t N_\xi \, dN_\xi &= E^{\mathcal{F}_s}\tfrac{1}{2}[N_t(N_t+1) - N_s(N_s+1)] \\
&= E^{\mathcal{F}_s}\tfrac{1}{2}[N_t^2 - N_s^2 + N_t - N_s] \\
&= \tfrac{1}{2}E^{\mathcal{F}_s}\left[(N_t - N_s)^2 + 2N_s(N_t - N_s) + N_t - N_s\right] \\
&= \tfrac{1}{2}\left[E(N_t - N_s)^2 + 2N_s E(N_t - N_s) + E(N_t - N_s)\right] \\
&= \tfrac{1}{2}\left[t - s + (t-s)^2 + (2N_s + 1)(t - s)\right] \qquad \text{from eq. 6.1.14} \\
&= \frac{t-s}{2}(2N_s + t - s + 2) \qquad (6.1.17)
\end{aligned}$$

The second integral in eq. 6.1.16 is now evaluated:

$$\begin{aligned}
E^{\mathcal{F}_s}\int_s^t N_\xi \, d\xi &= E^{\mathcal{F}_s}\int_s^t (N_\xi - N_s + N_s) \, d\xi \\
&= \int_s^t E^{\mathcal{F}_s}(N_\xi - N_s) \, d\xi + N_s(t - s) \\
&= \int_s^t E(N_\xi - N_s) \, d\xi + N_s(t - s) \\
&= \int_s^t (\xi - s) \, d\xi + N_s(t - s) \qquad \text{from eq. 6.1.14} \\
&= \frac{t^2 - s^2}{2} - s(t - s) + N_s(t - s) \\
&= \frac{t-s}{2}(2N_s + t - s) \qquad (6.1.18)
\end{aligned}$$

If X_t is to be martingale, $E^{\mathcal{F}_s}(X_t - X_s) = 0$, so that eq. 6.1.17 must be equal to eq. 6.1.18. Subtracting eq. 6.1.18 from eq. 6.1.17, we obtain $E^{\mathcal{F}_s}(X_t - X_s) = t - s$, and hence X_t cannot be a martingale. This is due to the fact that we have defined N_t under the integral in eq. 6.1.12 as right continuous.

However, if we had defined the stochastic integral with N_t under the integral as a left continuous process,

$$X_t = \int_s^t N_{s-}\, dM_s \tag{6.1.19}$$

then

$$\int_0^t N_{s-} \cdot dN_s = \sum_{s \le t} N_{s-} \cdot \Delta N_s = (0 + 1 + \cdots + N_t - 1) \cdot 1$$

$$= \frac{N_t(N_t - 1)}{2}$$

In this case

$$E^{\mathfrak{F}_s} \int_s^t N_{\xi-} \cdot dN_\xi = \frac{(t-s)(2N_s + t - s)}{2}$$

with the result that X_t is now a martingale. Note that the martingale term M_t in the stochastic integral, eq. 6.1.12, has been defined as right continuous, while the integrand N_t has been defined as left continuous.

Having given an example where a stochastic integral can be represented as a martingale, we now prove the martingale property of a stochastic integral relative to the Brownian motion $\{W_t, t \in T\}$.

Proposition 6.1.2 Stochastic Integral as a Martingale

Let $(\Omega, \mathfrak{F}, P)$ be a complete probability space, and let $\{\mathfrak{F}_t, t \in T\}$ be a right continuous filtration σ-field. Let $\{W_t, \mathfrak{F}_t, t \in T,\ T = [a, b]\}$ be a Brownian motion process. Let φ be a function satisfying conditions 6.1.3, namely,

1. $\varphi(\omega, t) \in \mathfrak{F} \otimes \mathfrak{L}$
2. $\varphi(\omega, t) \in \mathfrak{F}_t$ for each t (6.1.3)
3. $\int_a^b E|\varphi(\omega, t)|^2\, dt < \infty$
4. $\varphi(\omega, t)$ belongs to a class of left continuous functions

then the stochastic integral

$$X_t(\varphi) = \int_a^t \varphi(\omega, s)\, dW_s(\omega) \qquad t \in T \tag{6.1.20}$$

is an $\mathfrak{F}_t$-martingale satisfying the martingale property

$$E^{\mathfrak{F}_s} X_t = X_s \qquad s \le t, \quad t \in T$$

Proof. Let us first assume that $\varphi(\omega, t)$ is a simple function as given by eq. 6.1.4,

$$\varphi(\omega, t) = \sum_{\nu=0}^{n-1} \varphi_\nu(\omega) I_{(t_\nu, t_{\nu+1}]}$$

for partitions $s = t_0 < t_1 < t_2 < \cdots < t_n < t$. Let $t_1, t_2, \ldots, t_n$ be the jump points of ω between s and t. Since

$$X_t(\omega) - X_s(\omega) = \int_s^t \varphi_\tau(\omega)\, dW_\tau(\omega) \quad s \leq t, \quad t \in T$$

using eq. 6.1.6, we have

$$\begin{aligned} X_t(\omega) - X_s(\omega) = {} & \varphi_0(\omega)\left[W_{t_1}(\omega) - W_s(\omega)\right] \\ & + \varphi_1(\omega)\left[W_{t_2}(\omega) - W_{t_1}(\omega)\right] \\ & + \varphi_2(\omega)\left[W_{t_3}(\omega) - W_{t_2}(\omega)\right] + \cdots \\ & + \varphi_n(\omega)\left[W_t(\omega) - W_{t_n}(\omega)\right] \end{aligned} \tag{6.1.21}$$

where $\varphi_0 \in \mathfrak{F}_s, \varphi_1 \in \mathfrak{F}_{t_1}, \ldots, \varphi_n \in \mathfrak{F}_{t_n}$ (note that the left continuity of φ_ν makes it also predictable), and $\mathfrak{F}_t$ is the usual filtration σ-field defined on the probability space $(\Omega, \mathfrak{F}, P)$.

We now take the expectation of eq. 6.1.21 with respect to $\mathfrak{F}_s$.

$$\begin{aligned} E^{\mathfrak{F}_s}\left[X_t(\omega) - X_s(\omega)\right] &= E^{\mathfrak{F}_s} E^{\mathfrak{F}_{t_1}} \cdots E^{\mathfrak{F}_{t_n}}\left[X_t(\omega) - X_s(\omega)\right] \\ &= E^{\mathfrak{F}_s} E^{\mathfrak{F}_{t_1}} \cdots E^{\mathfrak{F}_{t_n}}\left[\varphi_0(\omega)(W_{t_1} - W_s)\right. \\ & \quad \left. + \varphi_1(\omega)(W_{t_2} - W_{t_1}) + \cdots + \varphi_n(\omega)(W_t - W_{t_n})\right] \end{aligned} \tag{6.1.22}$$

Since the φ_ν are $\mathfrak{F}_{t_\nu}$-measurable by assumption we have

$$E^{\mathfrak{F}_{t_\nu}} \varphi_\nu(\omega)(W_{t_{\nu+1}} - W_{t_\nu}) = \varphi_\nu(\omega) E^{\mathfrak{F}_{t_\nu}}(W_{t_{\nu+1}} - W_{t_\nu}) = 0 \qquad \nu = 0, 1, 2, \ldots \tag{6.1.23}$$

and hence

$$E^{\mathfrak{F}_s}\left[X_t(\omega) - X_s(\omega)\right] = 0$$

and since X_s is $\mathfrak{F}_s$-measurable, we have $X_t(\omega)$ as an $\mathfrak{F}_t$-martingale.

If $\varphi(\omega, t)$ is not a sequence of step functions, let $\varphi_n(\omega, t)$ be an approximation to $\varphi(\omega, t)$ in the sense of eq. 6.1.5 and define

$$X_{nt}(\omega) = \int_a^t \varphi_n(\omega, \tau)\, dW_\tau(\omega) \tag{6.1.24}$$

From the previous result, $X_{nt}(\omega)$ is an $\mathcal{F}_t$-martingale for each n, and therefore

$$E^{\mathcal{F}_s}(X_t - X_s) = E^{\mathcal{F}_s}(X_t - X_{nt}) - E^{\mathcal{F}_s}(X_s - X_{ns})$$

Since $\lim_{n\to\infty} E|(X_t - X_{nt})|^2 \to 0$,

$$E^{\mathcal{F}_s}(X_t - X_s) = \underset{n\to\infty}{\text{l.i.q.m.}} \left[E^{\mathcal{F}_s}(X_t - X_{nt}) - E^{\mathcal{F}_s}(X_s - X_{ns})\right] \to 0$$

Hence the stochastic integral

$$X_t = \int_a^t \varphi(\omega, s)\, dW_s(\omega)$$

is an $\mathcal{F}_t$-martingale. In addition, it can be shown that the stochastic integral as defined by eq. 6.1.20 has sample continuous paths (Wong, 63, p. 145).

Note. However, if we have the weakened condition $\int_a^b |\varphi(\omega, t)|^2\, dt < \infty$ (a.s.), instead of $\int_a^b E|\varphi(\omega, t)|^2\, dt < \infty$, then the stochastic integral $X_t(\omega)$ will not be a martingale but will be a local martingale (Wong, 63, p. 165; Lipster and Shiryaev, 34, p. 111).

As a consequence of the stochastic integral being a martingale, the conventional properties of integration may not necessarily hold. We illustrate this by means of an example.

Example 6.1.2

Let an integral $I_t(W)$ be given by

$$I_t(W) = \int_0^t W_\tau(\omega)\, dW_\tau(\omega) \tag{6.1.25}$$

where $W_t(\omega)$ is a Brownian motion process. The integrand $W_t(\omega)$ can be defined to satisfy conditions 6.1.3, and $I_t(W)$ is a stochastic integral. Therefore $I_t(W)$ must be an $\mathcal{F}_t$-martingale by Proposition 6.1.2.

If $I_t(W)$ is treated as an ordinary integral, then

$$I_t(W) = \int_0^t W_\tau\, dW_\tau = \frac{W_t^2}{2} \tag{6.1.26}$$

Let us now check whether $W_t^2/2$ is a martingale.

$$E^{\mathfrak{F}_s}\frac{W_t^2}{2} = \frac{1}{2}E^{\mathfrak{F}_s}\left(W_s^2 + W_t^2 - W_s^2\right)$$

$$= \frac{1}{2}W_s^2 + \frac{1}{2}(t - s)$$

which is obviously not a martingale. Therefore the conventional rule for integration is not applicable here. We have to evolve a new set of integration rules which will make $I_t(W)$ a martingale. We continue the solution of this problem after enunciating the Ito rule or the Ito calculus.

6.2 ITO PROCESS (GENERALIZED STOCHASTIC INTEGRAL)

In the stochastic integral given by eq. 6.1.1 the integration was carried out with respect to the Brownian motion W_t. The stochastic integral with respect to W_t was carefully defined in eqs. 6.1.6 and 6.1.7. However, in many nonlinear filtering problems the integration may have to be carried out not with respect to the Brownian motion process but with respect to an Ito process. We now define the Ito process under the weakened condition $\int_0^t|\varphi(\omega, s)|^2\, ds < \infty$ (a.s.).

Definition 6.2.1 Ito Process

Let $(\Omega, \mathfrak{F}, P)$ be a complete probability space, with $\{\mathfrak{F}_t, t \in T\}$ being a right continuous filtration σ-field defined on it. Let $\{W_t, \mathfrak{F}_t, t \in T\}$ be a Brownian motion process. The continuous random process $\{X_t, \mathfrak{F}_t, t \in T\}$ is called an *Ito process* (relative to the Brownian motion process $\{W_t, \mathfrak{F}_t, t \in T\}$) if there exist two nonanticipative $\mathfrak{F}_t$-measurable random processes $a_t(\omega)$ and $b_t(\omega)$, satisfying for each $t \in T$

$$\int_0^t|a_s(\omega)|\, ds < \infty \quad \text{(a.s.)} \tag{6.2.1a}$$

$$\int_0^t|b_s(\omega)|^2\, ds < \infty \quad \text{(a.s.)} \tag{6.2.1b}$$

with $b_t(\omega)$ being left continuous, and if, with probability 1, $X_t(\omega)$ satisfies the equation

$$X_t(\omega) = X_0(\omega) + \int_0^t a_s(\omega)\, ds + \int_0^t b_s(\omega)\, dW_s \qquad t \in T \tag{6.2.2}$$

The Ito process is a basic stochastic differential equation which is discussed in its generality later. The existence of the stochastic integral $\int_0^t b_s(\omega)\, dW_s$ has been established under the weakened condition in Definition 6.1.2. The existence of the integral $\int a_s(\omega)\, ds$ is guaranteed by condition 6.2.1a. The left continuity condition for $a_t(\omega)$ is not necessary for the definition of this integral. Thus the integral equation 6.2.2 is well defined.

Equation 6.2.2 can also be given in a stochastic differential equation representation as

$$dX_t(\omega) = a_t(\omega)\, dt + b_t(\omega)\, dW_t \qquad t \in T, \quad X_0(\omega) \tag{6.2.3}$$

However, eq. 6.2.3, in general, is *not equivalent* to

$$\frac{dX_t}{dt} = a_t(\omega) + b_t(\omega)\frac{dW_t}{dt} \qquad t \in T \tag{6.2.4}$$

where dW_t/dt is a white noise process.

Equation 6.2.4 is the white noise differential equation and later we derive the stochastic differential equation representation for eq. 6.2.4. However, as shown in the previous chapter, eqs. 6.2.3 and 6.2.4 are equivalent only if a_t and b_t are not random processes.

Now we define a stochastic integral over an Ito process.

Definition 6.2.2

Let $\{X_t, \mathcal{F}_t, t \in T, T = [a, b]\}$ be an Ito process as given in Definition 6.2.1. Let $\varphi_t(\omega)$ be a nonanticipative process satisfying conditions 6.1.3. The stochastic integral over the Ito process X_t is given by

$$I_t(\varphi) = \int_a^t \varphi_\tau(\omega)\, dX_\tau(\omega) \qquad t \in T \tag{6.2.5}$$

or

$$I_t(\varphi) = \int_a^t \varphi_\tau(\omega) a_\tau(\omega)\, d\tau + \int_a^t \varphi_\tau(\omega) b_\tau(\omega)\, dW_\tau \tag{6.2.6}$$

and for both integrals to exist it is sufficient that

$$\int_T |\varphi_t(\omega) a_t(\omega)|\, dt < \infty \quad \text{(a.s.)}$$

$$\int_T |\varphi_t(\omega) b_t(\omega)|^2\, dt < \infty \quad \text{(a.s)}$$

The stochastic integral $I_t(\varphi)$ over the Ito process X_t can also be well defined analogous to Definition 6.1.2. By Proposition 6.1.1 an approximating sequence of simple functions $\{\varphi_{nt}(\omega), t \in T\}$ can be found such that

$$\underset{n\to\infty}{\text{l.i.p.}} \int_T \left[|a_t(\omega)|\ |\varphi_t(\omega) - \varphi_{nt}(\omega)| + |b_t(\omega)|^2 |\varphi_t(\omega) - \varphi_{nt}(\omega)|^2 \right] dt \to 0 \tag{6.2.7}$$

Then the stochastic integral of eq. 6.2.5 is the limit in probability of the integral sums $I_t(\varphi_n)$ given by

$$I_t(\varphi_n) = \sum_{\nu=0}^{N(n)-1} \varphi_{\nu, t_\nu^{(n)}}(\omega)\left(X_{t_{\nu+1}^{(n)}} - X_{t_\nu^{(n)}}\right) \qquad t \in T \tag{6.2.8}$$

for the partitions

$$a = t_0^{(n)} < t_1^{(n)} < t_2^{(n)} < \cdots < t_{N(n)}^{(n)} = t$$

or

$$I_t(\varphi) = \underset{n\to\infty}{\text{l.i.p.}}\, I_t(\varphi_n)$$

Remarks

1. The stochastic integral over a Wiener process is a martingale whereas the stochastic integral over the Ito process is not a martingale but a continuous semimartingale.
2. If the sufficiency condition $\int_0^t |\varphi_s(\omega) b_s(\omega)|^2\, ds < \infty$ is replaced by the strong condition

$$\int_0^t E|\varphi_s(\omega) b_s(\omega)|^2\, ds < \infty$$

then we have quadratic mean convergence of the integral sums $I_t(\varphi_n)$

$$I_t(\varphi) = \underset{n\to\infty}{\text{l.i.q.m.}}\, I_t(\varphi_n)$$

3. Under suitable assumptions the stochastic differential equation given by eq. 6.2.2 or eq. 6.2.3 can be generalized by replacing the Brownian motion process W_t by a general martingale M_t.

6.3 ITO FORMULA (LIPSTER AND SHIRYAEV, 34, P. 118; JAZWINSKI, 22, P. 112; VARADHAN, 54, P. 116)

Let us now discuss the Ito rule applied to stochastic integrals. First we discuss the rule for the scalar case and extend it to vector situations.

Let $\{X_t, \mathcal{F}_t, t \in T\}$ be an Ito process as defined by eq. 6.2.3. Let $\psi(t, \cdot)$ be a measurable function with continuous first and second partial derivatives. Then the function $\psi(t, X_t(\omega))$ also permits a stochastic differential equation representation, popularly known as the *Ito formula* or *Ito rule*.

Theorem 6.3.1 Ito Formula

Let the function $\psi(t, x)$ be continuous and have bounded continuous partial derivatives $\partial\psi/\partial t$, $\partial\psi/\partial x$, and $\partial^2\psi/\partial x^2$. Let $\{X_t, \mathcal{F}_t, t \in T\}$ be an Ito process having the stochastic differential equation representation

$$dX_t(\omega) = a_t(\omega)\,dt + b_t(\omega)\,dW_t \qquad t \in T, \quad X_0(\omega) \tag{6.2.3}$$

Then the process $Y_t(\omega) = \psi(t, X_t(\omega))$ also admits of a stochastic differential equation representation given by

$$dY_t(\omega) = \frac{\partial\psi(t, X_t)}{\partial t}\,dt + \frac{\partial\psi(t, X_t)}{\partial x}\,dX_t + \frac{1}{2}\sigma^2\frac{\partial^2\psi(t, X_t)}{\partial x^2}\,b_t^2\,dt \qquad t \in T, \quad Y_a \tag{6.3.1}$$

where σ^2 is the variance parameter associated with W_t.

By substituting eq. 6.2.3 into eq. 6.3.1, the Ito rule can be given in an alternate form as

$$dY_t(\omega) = \frac{\partial\psi(t, X_t)}{\partial t}\,dt + \frac{\partial\psi(t, X_t)}{\partial x}\,a_t(\omega)\,dt + \frac{\partial\psi(t, X_t)}{\partial x}\,b_t(\omega)\,dW_t + \frac{1}{2}\sigma^2\frac{\partial^2\psi(t, X_t)}{\partial x^2}\,b_t^2(\omega)\,dt \qquad t \in T, \quad Y_a \tag{6.3.2}$$

Proof. We shall not give a formal proof but a heuristic one for the above rule. Given $Y_t = \psi(t, X_t)$, we have

$$dY_t = Y_{t+dt} - Y_t = \psi(t + dt, X_{t+dt}) - \psi(t, X_t) \tag{6.3.3}$$

Since the first and second partials of ψ are assumed to exist, we can expand $\psi(t + dt, X_{t+dt})$ as a Taylor series in the neighborhood of $\psi(t, X_t)$,

$$\psi(t + dt, X_{t+dt}) = \psi(t, X_t) + \frac{\partial\psi}{\partial t}\,dt + \frac{\partial\psi}{\partial x}\,dX_t + \frac{1}{2}\frac{\partial^2\psi}{\partial x^2}\,dX_t^2 + \cdots \tag{6.3.4}$$

From $dX_t = a_t\,dt + b_t\,dW_t$ we have

$$dX_t^2 = a_t^2\,dt^2 + b_t^2\,dW_t^2 + 2a_t b_t\,dt\,dW_t$$

But $dW_t^2 = \sigma^2\, dt$ in the quadratic mean, as already shown, where σ^2 is the variance parameter associated with the Brownian motion process W_t. Since $dt\, dW_t \sim (dt)^{3/2}$, this term as well as the term containing dt^2 can be neglected in the equation for dX_t^2. Thus

$$dX_t^2 \cong \sigma^2 b_t^2\, dt \tag{6.3.5}$$

Substituting eqs. 6.3.4 and 6.3.5 in eq. 6.3.3, we have

$$dY_t = \frac{\partial\psi}{dt}dt + \frac{\partial\psi}{dx}dX_t + \frac{1}{2}\frac{\partial^2\psi}{\partial x^2}\sigma^2 b_t^2\, dt \qquad t \in T, \quad Y_a \tag{6.3.1}$$

which is eq. 6.3.1. Substitution of eq. 6.2.3 in eq. 6.3.1 yields eq. 6.3.2. □

Let us make some remarks about eq. 6.3.1 as to why it is different from ordinary differentials.

Remarks

1. If $Y_t = \psi(t, X_t)$ and X_t is a deterministic process, then the differential for dY_t will be

$$dY_t = \frac{\partial\psi}{\partial t}dt + \frac{\partial\psi}{\partial x}dX_t \tag{6.3.6}$$

since the higher order terms containing dt^2 and dX_t^2 and above are negligible.

2. Since W_t is a Brownian motion process, the quadratic term dW_t^2 is not negligible and it is of the order of dt.

3. The term $\frac{1}{2}\sigma^2(\partial^2\psi/\partial x^2)b_t^2\, dt$ in eq. 6.3.1 is the additional term because dW_t^2 cannot be neglected.

4. If W_t is a deterministic process, $\sigma^2 = 0$ and eq. 6.3.1 degenerates to eq. 6.3.6.

5. The presence of the extra term $\frac{1}{2}\sigma^2(\partial^2\psi/\partial x^2)b_t^2\, dt$ prevents us from using ordinary calculus, as given by eq. 6.3.6 for stochastic differentials.

Example 6.3.1

Let us now go back to Example 6.1.2 and use the Ito formula to show that the stochastic integral $I_t(W) = \int_0^t W_\tau(\omega)\, dW_\tau(\omega)$ is indeed a martingale. Let us now assume

$$Y_t = \psi(W_t) = \frac{W_t^2}{2} \tag{6.3.7}$$

and find the differential representation of Y_t using Ito's rule. The Ito process X_t associated with the Brownian motion process W_t is W_t itself,

$$X_t = W_t$$

or

$$dX_t = dW_t$$

so that $a_t = 0$ and $b_t = 1$ in eq. 6.2.3.

Applying Ito's rule to Y_t, we have from eq. 6.3.2,

$$dY_t = 0 \cdot dt + \frac{\partial \psi}{\partial w} \cdot 0 \cdot dt + \frac{\partial \psi}{dw} \cdot 1 \cdot dW_t + \frac{1}{2}\sigma^2 \frac{\partial^2 \psi}{\partial w^2} \cdot 1^2 \cdot dt$$

or

$$dY_t = W_t\, dW_t + \frac{1}{2}\sigma^2\, dt$$

Integrating,

$$Y_t = \int_0^t W_\tau\, dW_\tau + \frac{1}{2}\sigma^2 t$$

Hence

$$\int_0^t W_\tau\, dW_\tau = Y_t - \frac{1}{2}\sigma^2 t = \frac{1}{2}\left(W_t^2 - \sigma^2 t\right) \tag{6.3.8}$$

In eq. 6.1.26 the term $-\sigma^2 t/2$ is absent. It is very clear that $\frac{1}{2}(W_t^2 - \sigma^2 t)$ is indeed a martingale since $\sigma^2 t$ is the adapted continuous predictable increasing process $\langle W, W\rangle_t$ associated with the martingale W_t, as seen earlier. Hence $W_t^2 - \langle W, W\rangle_t$ is a martingale by the uniqueness of Doob's decomposition theorem. Note that if W_t is deterministic, $\sigma^2 = 0$ and eqs. 6.3.8 and 6.1.26 agree.

6.4 VECTOR FORMULATION OF ITO'S RULE

We can now enunciate the vector form of Ito's rule. We shall use **boldface** to represent both vectors and matrices. Let $\{\mathbf{X}_t, \mathcal{F}_t, t \in T\}$ be an n-vector Ito process, having the stochastic differential equation

$$d\mathbf{X}_t(\omega) = \mathbf{a}_t(\omega)\, dt + \mathbf{B}_t(\omega)\, d\mathbf{W}_t(\omega) \tag{6.4.1}$$

where $\mathbf{a}_t^T(\omega) = \{a_{1t}(\omega) \quad a_{2t}(\omega) \quad \cdots \quad a_{nt}(\omega)\}$ and $\mathbf{B}_t(\omega)$ is an $n \times m$ matrix of functions given by

$$\left\{\|b_{ijt}(\omega)\|, i = 1,2,\ldots,n,\ j = 1,2,\ldots,m\right\}$$

$\mathbf{W}_t(\omega)$ is an m-dimensional independent vector Brownian motion process with variance parameter $\boldsymbol{\sigma}^2$. The functions $a_{it}(\omega)$ and $b_{ijt}(\omega)$ satisfy conditions similar to Definition 6.2.1 with

$$\int_0^t |a_{is}(\omega)|\, ds < \infty \qquad i = 1,2,\ldots,n \quad \text{(a.s.)}$$

$$\int_0^t |b_{ijs}(\omega)|^2\, ds < \infty \qquad i = 1,2,\ldots,n, \quad j = 1,2,\ldots,m \quad \text{(a.s.)}$$

Let another scalar process $Y_t(\omega)$ be defined by $\psi(t, \mathbf{X}_t(\omega))$ where $\psi(t, \cdot)$ is a measurable function.

Theorem 6.4.1 Vector Form of Ito's Rule

Let the function $\psi(t, x_1, x_2,\ldots,x_n)$ be continuous and have bounded continuous partial derivatives

$$\frac{\partial\psi}{\partial t} \qquad \frac{\partial\psi}{\partial \mathbf{x}} \qquad \frac{\partial}{\partial \mathbf{x}}\left(\frac{\partial}{\partial \mathbf{x}}\right)^T \psi$$

Then the process $Y_t(\omega) = \psi(t, \mathbf{X}_t(\omega))$ has a stochastic differential representation given by

$$dY_t(\omega) = \frac{\partial\psi(t,\mathbf{X}_t)}{\partial t}dt + \left(\frac{\partial}{\partial \mathbf{x}}\right)^T \psi(t,\mathbf{X}_t)\, d\mathbf{X}_t$$

$$+ \frac{1}{2}\boldsymbol{\sigma}^T \mathbf{B}_t^T \frac{\partial}{\partial \mathbf{x}}\left(\frac{\partial}{\partial \mathbf{x}}\right)^T \psi(t,\mathbf{X}_t)\mathbf{B}_t\boldsymbol{\sigma}\, dt \quad t \in T, \quad Y_a(\omega) \tag{6.4.2}$$

or substituting for $d\mathbf{X}_t(\omega)$ from eq. 6.4.1, we obtain

$$dY_t(\omega) = \frac{\partial\psi(t,\mathbf{X}_t)}{\partial t}dt + \left(\frac{\partial}{\partial \mathbf{x}}\right)^T \psi(t,\mathbf{X}_t)\mathbf{a}_t(\omega)\, dt$$

$$+ \left(\frac{\partial}{\partial \mathbf{x}}\right)^T \psi(t,\mathbf{X}_t)\mathbf{B}_t(\omega)\, d\mathbf{W}_t(\omega)$$

$$+ \frac{1}{2}\boldsymbol{\sigma}^T \mathbf{B}_t^T \frac{\partial}{\partial \mathbf{x}}\left(\frac{\partial}{\partial \mathbf{x}}\right)^T \psi(\mathbf{X}_t, t)\mathbf{B}_t\boldsymbol{\sigma}\, dt \quad t \in T, \quad Y_a(\omega) \tag{6.4.3}$$

where $\boldsymbol{\sigma}^2$ is the m-vector variance parameter associated with the m-vector Brownian motion process $\mathbf{W}_t$.

Proof. The heuristic proof follows along lines similar to that in the scalar case,

$$dY_t = Y_{t+dt} - Y_t = \psi(t + dt, \mathbf{X}_{t+dt}) - \psi(t,\mathbf{X}_t)$$

$$= \frac{\partial\psi}{\partial t}dt + \left(\frac{\partial}{\partial \mathbf{x}}\right)^T \psi\, d\mathbf{X}_t + \frac{1}{2}d\mathbf{X}_t^T \frac{\partial}{\partial \mathbf{x}}\left(\frac{\partial}{\partial \mathbf{x}}\right)^T \psi\, d\mathbf{X}_t \tag{6.4.4}$$

From eq. 6.4.1,

$$d\mathbf{X}_t^T\,d\mathbf{X}_t = \left(\mathbf{a}_t^T\,dt + d\mathbf{W}_t^T\mathbf{B}_t^T\right)(\mathbf{a}_t\,dt + \mathbf{B}_t\,d\mathbf{W}_t)$$

If $\boldsymbol{\sigma}$ is the standard deviation parameter vector of the Brownian motion process $\mathbf{W}_t$, we have already seen that $d\mathbf{W}_t = \boldsymbol{\sigma}\sqrt{dt}$. Substituting this result and neglecting terms containing powers of dt greater than 1 (including 3/2), we obtain for the above equation

$$d\mathbf{X}_t^T\,d\mathbf{X}_t = \boldsymbol{\sigma}^T\mathbf{B}_t^T\mathbf{B}_t\boldsymbol{\sigma}\,dt$$

which when substituted in eq. 6.4.4, results in

$$dY_t = \frac{\partial\psi}{\partial t}dt + \left(\frac{\partial}{\partial\mathbf{x}}\right)^T\psi\,d\mathbf{X}_t + \frac{1}{2}\boldsymbol{\sigma}^T\mathbf{B}_t^T\frac{\partial}{\partial\mathbf{x}}\left(\frac{\partial}{\partial\mathbf{x}}\right)^T\psi\mathbf{B}_t\boldsymbol{\sigma}\,dt \qquad t\in T,\quad Y_a \tag{6.4.2}$$

which is exactly eq. 6.4.2.

Substitution of eq. 6.4.1 into eq. 6.4.2 results in eq. 6.4.3,

$$\begin{aligned} dY_t = {} & \frac{\partial\psi}{\partial t}dt + \left(\frac{\partial}{\partial\mathbf{x}}\right)^T\psi\mathbf{a}_t\,dt + \left(\frac{\partial}{\partial\mathbf{x}}\right)^T\psi\mathbf{B}_t\,d\mathbf{W}_t \\ & + \frac{1}{2}\boldsymbol{\sigma}^T\mathbf{B}_t^T\frac{\partial}{\partial\mathbf{x}}\left(\frac{\partial}{\partial\mathbf{x}}\right)^T\psi\mathbf{B}_t\boldsymbol{\sigma}\,dt \qquad t\in T,\quad Y_a \end{aligned} \tag{6.4.3}$$ □

Special Cases. Let us now consider some special cases where the Ito rule given by eq. 6.4.3 can be simplified.

1. The Brownian motion process $\mathbf{W}_t(\omega)$ is a scalar process $W_t(\omega)$. In this case the matrix of functions $\mathbf{B}_t(\omega)$ becomes an n-dimensional vector $\mathbf{b}_t(\omega)$, and the variance parameter $\boldsymbol{\sigma}^2$ becomes σ^2. Using these simplifications, eq. 6.4.3 becomes

$$\begin{aligned} dY_t(\omega) = {} & \frac{\partial\psi(t,\mathbf{X}_t)}{\partial t}dt + \left(\frac{\partial}{\partial\mathbf{x}}\right)^T\psi(t,\mathbf{X}_t)\mathbf{a}_t(\omega)\,dt \\ & + \left(\frac{\partial}{\partial\mathbf{x}}\right)^T\psi(t,\mathbf{X}_t)\mathbf{b}_t(\omega)\,dW_t(\omega) \\ & + \frac{1}{2}\sigma^2\mathbf{b}_t^T(\omega)\frac{\partial}{\partial\mathbf{x}}\left(\frac{\partial}{\partial\mathbf{x}}\right)^T\psi(t,\mathbf{X}_t)\mathbf{b}_t(\omega)\,dt \qquad t\in T,\quad Y_a(\omega) \end{aligned}$$

2. Let $Y_t = X_{1t}X_{2t}$, where X_{1t} and X_{2t} are Ito processes satisfying the stochastic differential equations

$$\begin{aligned} dX_{1t} &= a_{1t}\,dt + b_{1t}\,dW_t \\ dX_{2t} &= a_{2t}\,dt + b_{2t}\,dW_t \end{aligned} \tag{6.4.5}$$

Using Ito's rule,

$$dY_t = X_{2t}\,dX_{1t} + X_{1t}\,dX_{2t} + \tfrac{1}{2}\sigma^2 \cdot 2b_{1t}b_{2t}\,dt \tag{6.4.6}$$

Using eq. 6.4.5 in eq. 6.4.6, we obtain

$$dY_t = X_{2t}(a_{1t}\,dt + b_{1t}\,dW_t) + X_{1t}(a_{2t}\,dt + b_{2t}\,dW_t) + \sigma^2 \cdot b_{1t}b_{2t}\,dt \tag{6.4.7}$$

3. Let $Y_t = e^{X_t}$, and X_t is the Ito process satisfying the stochastic differential equation

$$dX_t = -\tfrac{1}{2}\sigma^2 g_t^2\,dt + g_t\,dW_t \tag{6.4.8}$$

Here

$$a_t = -\frac{\sigma^2 g_t^2}{2} \qquad b_t = g_t$$

Applying Ito's formula, eq. 6.3.2, to $Y_t = e^{X_t}$,

$$dY_t = 0 \cdot dt + \frac{\partial e^{X_t}}{\partial x} \cdot -\frac{\sigma^2 g_t^2}{2}\,dt + \frac{\partial e^{X_t}}{\partial x} g_t\,dW_t + \frac{1}{2}\sigma^2 \frac{\partial^2 e^{X_t}}{\partial x^2} g_t^2\,dt$$

Since

$$\frac{\partial e^{X_t}}{\partial x} = \frac{\partial^2 e^{X_t}}{\partial x^2} = Y_t$$

we have

$$dY_t = Y_t g_t\,dW_t \tag{6.4.9}$$

4. Let $\{W_t, \mathfrak{F}_t, t \in T\}$ be a Brownian motion process. Let $\varphi_t(\cdot)$ be a function satisfying conditions 6.1.3. Then according to Proposition 6.1.2, $X_t = \int_0^t \varphi_\tau(\omega)\,dW_\tau(\omega)$ is an $\mathfrak{F}_t$-martingale. Let $Y_t = X_t^2$. Clearly the Ito process X_t which is a martingale is given by the stochastic differential

$$dX_t = \varphi_t(\omega)\,dW_t$$

where $a_t = 0$ and $b_t = \varphi_t$. By Ito's formula, eq. 6.3.2,

$$\begin{aligned} dY_t &= 0 \cdot dt + 2X_t \cdot 0 \cdot dt + 2X_t \cdot \varphi_t \cdot dW_t + \tfrac{1}{2}\sigma^2 \cdot 2 \cdot \varphi_t^2\,dt \\ &= 2X_t\varphi_t\,dW_t + \sigma^2\varphi_t^2\,dt \end{aligned} \tag{6.4.10}$$

or in integral form,

$$Y_t = X_t^2 = Y_0 + 2\int_0^t \varphi_\tau(\omega) X_\tau \, dW_\tau + \sigma^2 \int_0^t \varphi_\tau^2(\omega) \, d\tau$$

Since the initial condition $Y_0 = 0$,

$$\tfrac{1}{2}\left[X_t^2 - \sigma^2 \int_0^t \varphi_\tau^2(\omega) \, d\tau\right] = \int_0^t \varphi_\tau(\omega) X_\tau(\omega) \, dW_\tau \tag{6.4.11}$$

is a martingale because the stochastic integral $\int_0^t \varphi_\tau(\omega) X_\tau(\omega) \, dW_\tau$ is a martingale assuming $\int_0^t E|\varphi_\tau X_\tau|^2 \, d\tau < \infty$. Hence invoking the uniqueness of the Doob–Meyer decomposition theorem, we have

$$\langle X, X \rangle_t = \sigma^2 \int_0^t \varphi_\tau^2(\omega) \, d\tau \tag{6.4.12}$$

as an $\mathcal{F}_t$-adapted increasing predictable process associated with the martingale X_t.

Example 6.4.1

Let us apply this situation to Example 6.3.1 considered earlier, namely, that of evaluating

$$\int_0^t W_\tau \, dW_\tau$$

In eq. 6.4.11 we substitute $\varphi_\tau(\omega) = 1$, $X_\tau(\omega) = W_\tau(\omega)$, and hence

$$\int_0^t W_\tau \, dW_\tau = \frac{W_t^2}{2} - \frac{\sigma^2}{2} \int_0^t 1 \cdot d\tau = \frac{1}{2}\left(W_t^2 - \sigma^2 t\right)$$

agreeing with the result of eq. 6.3.8.

5. Let $\{W_t, \mathcal{F}_t, t \in T\}$ be again a Brownian motion process, and let

$$dX_t = \alpha_t(\omega) \, dW_t \qquad dY_t = \beta_t(\omega) \, dW_t \qquad t \in T$$

where $\alpha_t(\omega)$ and $\beta_t(\omega)$ belong to the class of functions satisfying conditions 6.1.3. According to Proposition 6.1.2 the processes X_t and Y_t are martingales. Let Z_t be now equal to $X_t Y_t$. Then by Ito's formula,

$$\begin{aligned} dZ_t = d(X_t Y_t) &= 0 \cdot dt + (Y_t \cdot 0 \, dt + X_t \cdot 0 \cdot dt) \\ &\quad + \left[Y_t \alpha_t(\omega) \, dW_t + X_t \beta_t(\omega) \, dW_t\right] + \sigma^2 \alpha_t(\omega) \beta_t(\omega) \, dt \end{aligned}$$

or

$$dZ_t = (Y_t \alpha_t + X_t \beta_t) \, dW_t + \sigma^2 \alpha_t \beta_t \, dt \quad t \in T \tag{6.4.13}$$

In integral form eq. 6.4.13 can be expressed as

$$X_tY_t = X_0Y_0 + \int_0^t (Y_s\alpha_s + X_s\beta_s)\, dW_s + \sigma^2 \int_0^t \alpha_s\beta_s\, ds \qquad (6.4.14)$$

Since the stochastic integral

$$\int_0^t (Y_s\alpha_s + X_s\beta_s)\, dW_s$$

assuming

$$\int_0^t E(|Y_s\alpha_s|^2 + |X_s\beta_s|^2)\, ds < \infty \quad \text{(a.s.)}$$

is an $\mathcal{F}_t$-martingale by Proposition 6.1.2, we have with $X_0 = 0$ and $Y_0 = 0$ in eq. 6.4.14,

$$X_tY_t - \sigma^2 \int_0^t \alpha_s\beta_s\, ds = \int_0^t (Y_s\alpha_s + X_s\beta_s)\, dW_s \qquad (6.4.15)$$

as an $\mathcal{F}_t$-martingale. Then by the Doob–Meyer decomposition, the $\mathcal{F}_t$-adapted process $\langle X, Y\rangle_t$ given by

$$\langle X, Y\rangle_t = \sigma^2 \int_0^t \alpha_s(\omega)\beta_s(\omega)\, ds \qquad t \in T \qquad (6.4.16)$$

is the difference between two adapted increasing predictable processes.

Example 6.4.2

As an example, if $dX_t = \alpha_t(\omega)\, dW_t$ and $dY_t = dW_t$, then $\beta_t(\omega) = 1$ and we have from eq. 6.4.16

$$\langle X, W\rangle_t = \sigma^2 \int_0^t \alpha_s(\omega)\, ds \qquad t \in T \qquad (6.4.17)$$

If $\alpha_t(\omega)$ is also equal to 1, we obtain with $dX_t = dW_t$

$$\langle W, W\rangle_t = \sigma^2 \int_0^t ds = \sigma^2 t \qquad t \in T$$

a result already obtained earlier using other considerations.

6.5 STOCHASTIC INTEGRALS ON SQUARE INTEGRABLE MARTINGALES

In the previous sections we considered stochastic integrals driven by a Brownian motion process W_t. Since these are square integrable martingales, we obtained for such stochastic integrals quadratic variance (eq. 6.4.12) and quadratic covariance processes (eq. 6.4.16). As seen in Example 6.4.2, if X_t is the stochastic integral driven by W_t, namely,

$$X_t = \int_0^t \alpha_s(\omega)\, dW_s \qquad t \in T \tag{6.5.1}$$

with $\alpha_t(\omega)$ satisfying conditions 6.1.3 then the quadratic covariance $\langle X, W\rangle_t$ between the martingale $\{X_t, \mathfrak{F}_t, t \in T\}$ and the Brownian motion process $\{W_t, \mathfrak{F}_t, t \in T\}$ is given by

$$\langle X, W\rangle_t = \sigma^2 \int_0^t \alpha_s(\omega)\, ds \quad \text{(a.s.)} \qquad t \in T \tag{6.5.2}$$

The representation given by eq. 6.5.2 is not only true for stochastic integral martingales generated by W_t, but also for any square integrable martingale adapted to a family of right continuous σ-fields. This important result in square integrable martingale theory is stated in the following theorem.

Theorem 6.5.1

Let $(\Omega, \mathfrak{F}, P)$ be a complete probability space, and let $\{\mathfrak{F}_t, t \in T\}$ be a right continuous filtration σ-field defined on it. Let $\{X_t, \mathfrak{F}_t, t \in T\}$ be *any* square integrable martingale, and let $\{W_t, \mathfrak{F}_t, t \in T\}$ be a Brownian motion process. Then there exists a left continuous random process $\{\varphi_t, \mathfrak{F}_t, t \in T\}$ with $E\int_0^t |\varphi_s(\omega)|^2\, ds < \infty$ such that for all $t \in T$,

$$\langle X, W\rangle_t = \sigma^2 \int_0^t \varphi_s(\omega)\, ds \quad \text{(a.s.)} \tag{6.5.3}$$

The proof of this theorem follows Lipster and Shiryaev (34, p. 155), and we need the following lemma.

Lemma 6.5.1 Quadratic Variance Process as a Lebesgue–Stieltjes Integral

Let the filtration σ-field $\{\mathfrak{F}_t, t \in T\}$ defined on the probability space $(\Omega, \mathfrak{F}, P)$ be right continuous, and let $\{W_t, \mathfrak{F}_t, t \in T\}$ be a Brownian motion process. Let $\{X_t, \mathfrak{F}_t, t \in T\}$ be any L^2-martingale. Let the random process $\{g_t(\omega), \mathfrak{F}_t, t \in T\}$ satisfy, in addition to conditions 6.1.3,

$$\int_0^t E|g_s(\omega)|^2\, d\langle X, W\rangle_s < \infty \qquad t \in T$$

If Y_t is the stochastic integral given by

$$Y_t = \int_0^t g_s(\omega)\, dW_s \tag{6.5.4}$$

(Y_t has to be necessarily an L^2-martingale), then the quadratic covariance between X_t and Y_t is given by

$$\langle X, Y\rangle_t = \int_0^t g_s(\omega)\, d\langle X, W\rangle_s \quad \text{(a.s.)} \qquad t \in T \tag{6.5.5}$$

where the integral is a Lebesgue-Stieltjes integral.

Proof. For a partition $0 = t_0^{(n)} < t_1^{(n)} < \cdots < t_{N(n)}^{(n)} = t$ let $\{g_{nt}(\omega),\ n = 1, 2, \ldots\}$ be a sequence of simple functions, eq. 6.1.4,

$$g_{nt}(\omega) = \sum_{\nu=0}^{N(n)-1} g_{t_\nu^{(n)}}(\omega) I_{(t_\nu^{(n)}, t_{\nu+1}^{(n)}]}(t) \tag{6.5.6}$$

satisfying

$$\lim_{n\to\infty} E\int_0^t |g_s(\omega) - g_{ns}(\omega)|^2\, d\langle X, W\rangle_s \to 0$$

$$\lim_{n\to\infty} E\int_0^t |g_s(\omega) - g_{ns}(\omega)|^2\, ds \to 0$$

Then by eq. 4.3.6,

$$\begin{aligned}
E^{\mathcal{F}_s}(\langle X, Y\rangle_t - \langle X, Y\rangle_s) &= E^{\mathcal{F}_s}(X_t - X_s)(Y_t - Y_s) \\
&= E^{\mathcal{F}_s}X_t(Y_t - Y_s) - E^{\mathcal{F}_s}X_s(Y_t - Y_s) \\
&= E^{\mathcal{F}_s}X_t(Y_t - Y_s) - X_s E^{\mathcal{F}_s}(Y_t - Y_s) \\
&= E^{\mathcal{F}_s}X_t(Y_t - Y_s) \qquad \text{because } E^{\mathcal{F}_s}(Y_t - Y_s) = 0 \\
&= E^{\mathcal{F}_s}X_t\int_s^t g_\tau(\omega)\, dW_\tau \qquad \text{from eq. 6.5.4} \\
&= \underset{n\to\infty}{\text{l.i.q.m.}}\, E^{\mathcal{F}_s}X_t\int_s^t g_{n\tau}(\omega)\, dW_\tau
\end{aligned} \tag{6.5.7}$$

But from eq. 6.5.6,

$$\int_s^t g_{n\tau}(\omega)\, dW_\tau = \sum_{\nu=0}^{N(n)-1} g_{t_\nu^{(n)}}(\omega)\left(W_{t_{\nu+1}^{(n)}} - W_{t_\nu^{(n)}}\right) \tag{6.5.8}$$

where we have now taken the partitions of $[s, t]$ as

$$s = t_0^{(n)} < t_1^{(n)} < t_2^{(n)} < \cdots < t_{N(n)}^{(n)} = t \tag{6.5.9}$$

We can now write

$$E^{\mathcal{F}_s}(\langle X, Y\rangle_t - \langle X, Y\rangle_s) = E^{\mathcal{F}_s} E^{\mathcal{F}_{t_1^{(n)}}} E^{\mathcal{F}_{t_2^{(n)}}} \cdots E^{\mathcal{F}_{t_{N(n)}^{(n)}}}(\langle X, Y\rangle_t - \langle X, Y\rangle_s) \tag{6.5.10}$$

Using eqs. 6.5.8 and 6.5.10, eq. 6.5.7 can be written as

$$\begin{aligned} E^{\mathcal{F}_s}&(\langle X, Y\rangle_t - \langle X, Y\rangle_s) \\ &= \underset{n\to\infty}{\text{l.i.q.m.}}\, E^{\mathcal{F}_s} E^{\mathcal{F}_{t_1^{(n)}}} \cdots E^{\mathcal{F}_{t_{N(n)}^{(n)}}} \left\{ \sum_{\nu=0}^{N(n)-1} X_t g_{t_\nu^{(n)}} \left(W_{t_{\nu+1}^{(n)}} - W_{t_\nu^{(n)}} \right) \right\} \end{aligned} \tag{6.5.11}$$

Equation 6.5.11 can now be rewritten as

$$\begin{aligned} E^{\mathcal{F}_s}(\langle X, Y\rangle_t - \langle X, Y\rangle_s) &= \underset{n\to\infty}{\text{l.i.q.m.}}\, E^{\mathcal{F}_s} \sum_{\nu=0}^{N(n)-1} E^{\mathcal{F}_{t_{\nu+1}^{(n)}}} X_t g_{t_\nu^{(n)}} \left(W_{t_{\nu+1}^{(n)}} - W_{t_\nu^{(n)}} \right) \\ &= \underset{n\to\infty}{\text{l.i.q.m.}}\, E^{\mathcal{F}_s} \sum_{\nu=0}^{N(n)-1} g_{t_\nu^{(n)}} \left(W_{t_{\nu+1}^{(n)}} - W_{t_\nu^{(n)}} \right) E^{\mathcal{F}_{t_{\nu+1}^{(n)}}} X_t \end{aligned}$$

since the factor $g_{t_\nu^{(n)}}(W_{t_{\nu+1}^{(n)}} - W_{t_\nu^{(n)}})$ is $\mathcal{F}_{t_{\nu+1}^{(n)}}$-measurable. Using the martingale property of X_t and $\mathcal{F}_s \subset \mathcal{F}_{t_{\nu+1}^{(n)}} \subset \mathcal{F}_t$, we have

$$E^{\mathcal{F}_{t_{\nu+1}^{(n)}}} X_t = X_{t_{\nu+1}^{(n)}}$$

and

$$\begin{aligned} E^{\mathcal{F}_s}&(\langle X, Y\rangle_t - \langle X, Y\rangle_s) \\ &= \underset{n\to\infty}{\text{l.i.q.m.}}\, E^{\mathcal{F}_s} \sum_{\nu=0}^{N(n)-1} X_{t_{\nu+1}^{(n)}} g_{t_\nu^{(n)}} \left(W_{t_{\nu+1}^{(n)}} - W_{t_\nu^{(n)}} \right) \\ &= \underset{n\to\infty}{\text{l.i.q.m.}}\, E^{\mathcal{F}_s} \sum_{\nu=0}^{N(n)-1} E^{\mathcal{F}_{t_\nu^{(n)}}} g_{t_\nu^{(n)}} \left(W_{t_{\nu+1}^{(n)}} - W_{t_\nu^{(n)}} \right)\left(X_{t_{\nu+1}^{(n)}} - X_{t_\nu^{(n)}} + X_{t_\nu^{(n)}} \right) \end{aligned} \tag{6.5.12}$$

$$\begin{aligned} &= \underset{n\to\infty}{\text{l.i.q.m.}}\, E^{\mathcal{F}_s} \sum_{\nu=0}^{N(n)-1} g_{t_\nu^{(n)}} \Big\{ E^{\mathcal{F}_{t_\nu^{(n)}}} \left(W_{t_{\nu+1}^{(n)}} - W_{t_\nu^{(n)}} \right)\left(X_{t_{\nu+1}^{(n)}} - X_{t_\nu^{(n)}} \right) \\ &\qquad + E^{\mathcal{F}_{t_\nu^{(n)}}} X_{t_\nu^{(n)}} \left(W_{t_{\nu+1}^{(n)}} - W_{t_\nu^{(n)}} \right) \Big\} \end{aligned} \tag{6.5.13}$$

since $g_{t_\nu^{(n)}}$ is $\mathcal{F}_{t_\nu^{(n)}}$-measurable.

Since $X_{t_\nu^{(n)}}$ is also $\mathfrak{F}_{t_\nu^{(n)}}$-measurable, the term

$$E^{\mathfrak{F}_{t_\nu^{(n)}}} X_{t_\nu^{(n)}}\left(W_{t_{\nu+1}^{(n)}} - W_{t_\nu^{(n)}}\right) = X_{t_\nu^{(n)}} E^{\mathfrak{F}_{t_\nu^{(n)}}}\left(W_{t_{\nu+1}^{(n)}} - W_{t_\nu^{(n)}}\right)$$

vanishes. Therefore eq. 6.5.13 can be rewritten as

$$E^{\mathfrak{F}_s}(\langle X, Y\rangle_t - \langle X, Y\rangle_s)$$

$$= \underset{n\to\infty}{\text{l.i.q.m.}}\, E^{\mathfrak{F}_s} \sum_{\nu=0}^{N(n)-1} g_{t_\nu^{(n)}} E^{\mathfrak{F}_{t_\nu^{(n)}}}\left(W_{t_{\nu+1}^{(n)}} - W_{t_\nu^{(n)}}\right)\left(X_{t_{\nu+1}^{(n)}} - X_{t_\nu^{(n)}}\right)$$

$$= \underset{n\to\infty}{\text{l.i.q.m.}}\, E^{\mathfrak{F}_s} \sum_{\nu=0}^{N(n)-1} g_{t_\nu^{(n)}} E^{\mathfrak{F}_{t_\nu^{(n)}}}\left(\langle X, W\rangle_{t_{\nu+1}^{(n)}} - \langle X, W\rangle_{t_\nu^{(n)}}\right)$$

from eq. 4.1.6

$$= \underset{n\to\infty}{\text{l.i.q.m.}}\, E^{\mathfrak{F}_s} \sum_{\nu=0}^{N(n)-1} g_{t_\nu^{(n)}}\left(\langle X, W\rangle_{t_{\nu+1}^{(n)}} - \langle X, W\rangle_{t_\nu^{(n)}}\right) \tag{6.5.14}$$

Therefore

$$E^{\mathfrak{F}_s}(\langle X, Y\rangle_t - \langle X, Y\rangle_s) = \underset{n\to\infty}{\text{l.i.q.m.}}\, E^{\mathfrak{F}_s} X_t \int_s^t g_{n\tau}(\omega)\, dW_\tau$$

$$= \underset{n\to\infty}{\text{l.i.q.m.}}\, E^{\mathfrak{F}_s} \sum_{\nu=0}^{N(n)-1} g_{t_\nu^{(n)}}\left(\langle X, W\rangle_{t_{\nu+1}^{(n)}} - \langle X, W\rangle_{t_\nu^{(n)}}\right)$$

$$= \underset{n\to\infty}{\text{l.i.q.m.}}\, E^{\mathfrak{F}_s} \int_s^t g_{n\tau}(\omega)\, d\langle X, W\rangle_\tau$$

Since $\text{l.i.q.m.}_{n\to\infty} g_{nt}(\omega) = g_t(\omega)$ by assumption we have finally

$$E^{\mathfrak{F}_s}(\langle X, Y\rangle_t - \langle X, Y\rangle_s) = E^{\mathfrak{F}_s} \int_s^t g_\tau(\omega)\, d\langle X, W\rangle_\tau \tag{6.5.15}$$

Since $\langle X, Y\rangle_t$, $\langle X, W\rangle_t$ are $\mathfrak{F}_s$-measurable, we can write

$$\langle X, Y\rangle_t = \int_0^t g_\tau(\omega)\, d\langle X, W\rangle_\tau \tag{6.5.16}$$

thus proving the lemma. □

Proof of Theorem 6.5.1. We introduce a function $\{g_t(\omega), \mathfrak{F}_t, t \in T\}$, satisfying the conditions of Lemma 6.5.1, and

$$\int_0^t g_\tau(\omega)\, d\tau = 0 \qquad \text{and} \qquad g_t^2(\omega) = g_t(\omega) \qquad t \in T \tag{6.5.17}$$

Let Y_t be the L^2-martingale, as given by eq. 6.5.4. Then by Lemma 6.5.1,

$$\langle X, Y\rangle_t = \int_0^t g_\tau(\omega)\, d\langle X, W\rangle_\tau \qquad t \in T$$

However,

$$EY_t^2 = \int_0^t g_\tau^2(\omega)\, d\tau = 0$$

from eq. 6.5.17. Hence $Y_t = 0$ (a.s.). As a consequence,

$$\langle X, Y\rangle_t = 0 = \int_0^t g_\tau(\omega)\, d\langle X, W\rangle_\tau \qquad t \in T \quad \text{(a.s.)} \qquad (6.5.18)$$

We now define on the measure space $\{T \times \Omega, \mathfrak{L}_T \otimes \mathfrak{F}_T\}$, where $\mathfrak{L}_T$ is the σ-field of Borel subsets on the interval T, the measure Q,

$$Q(B \times A) = \int_A \left(\int_B d\langle X, W\rangle_\tau \right) dP(\omega)$$

on the sets $B \times A$ with $B \in \mathfrak{L}_T$ and $A \in \mathfrak{F}_T$. If another measure S is defined as $S(B \times A) = \lambda(B)P(A)$, where λ is the Lebesgue measure on T with $\lambda(dt) = \sigma^2\, dt$, then by eq. 6.5.18 the measure Q is absolutely continuous with respect to the measure S. Hence according to the Radon–Nikodym theorem there exists a $\mathfrak{L}_T \otimes \mathfrak{F}_T$ measurable function $\varphi_t(\omega)$ with

$$\int_\Omega \sigma^2 \int_T |\varphi_\tau(\omega)|\, d\tau\, dP(\omega) < \infty \qquad t \in T$$

such that

$$Q(B \times A) = \int_A \sigma^2 \int_B \varphi_\tau(\omega)\, d\tau\, dP(\omega)$$

As a consequence we have the result

$$\int_A \langle X, W\rangle_\tau\, dP(\omega) = \int_A \sigma^2 \left[\int_B \varphi_\tau(\omega)\, d\tau \right] dP(\omega)$$

Since the set A is arbitrary, we have

$$\langle X, W\rangle_t = \sigma^2 \int_0^t \varphi_\tau(\omega)\, d\tau \qquad t \in T$$

What we have shown is that $\varphi_t(\omega) \in \mathfrak{F}_T$, and we have to show that $\varphi_t(\omega) \in \mathfrak{F}_t$. It can be shown (Lipster and Shiryaev, 34, p. 158) that given a function $\varphi_t(\omega) \in \mathfrak{F}_T$, we can construct a modification $\tilde{\varphi}_t(\omega) \in \mathfrak{F}_t$, $t \in T$ with $E\int_T \tilde{\varphi}_t^2(\omega)\, dt < \infty$. □

Kunita and Watanabe (33) have shown that eq. 6.5.5 holds not only for a Brownian motion process W_t but also for any square integrable martingale M_t, as given by the following proposition, which is stated without proof.

Proposition 6.5.1 (Kunita and Watanabe, 33)

Let a family of increasing σ-fields $\{\mathfrak{F}_t, t \in T\}$ be right continuous, and let $\{M_t, \mathfrak{F}_t, t \in T\}$ be a family of square integrable martingales. Let $\{X_t, \mathfrak{F}_t, t \in T\}$ be any other square integrable martingale. Let the random process $\varphi_t(\omega)$ belong to a class of $\mathfrak{F}_t$-adapted left continuous nonanticipative processes satisfying in addition to conditions 6.1.3 the condition

$$E\int_0^t |\varphi_s(\omega)|^2\, d\langle X, M\rangle_s < \infty$$

If the stochastic integral Y_t is given by

$$Y_t = \int_0^t \varphi_s(\omega)\, dM_s \tag{6.5.19}$$

then the quadratic covariance process between X_t and Y_t is given by

$$\langle X, Y\rangle_t = \int_0^t \varphi_s(\omega)\, d\langle X, M\rangle_s \qquad t \in T \tag{6.5.20}$$

Remark. From Proposition 6.5.1 we can give an alternate definition of the stochastic integral $Y_t = \int_0^t \varphi_s(\omega)\, dM_s$ as the unique square integrable martingale such that

$$\langle X, \int \varphi_s\, dM_s\rangle_t = \int_0^t \varphi_s\, d\langle X, M\rangle_s$$

We had listed some properties of stochastic integrals in Section 6.1. We list below additional properties of stochastic integrals.

Additional Properties of Stochastic Integrals. Let $\varphi_t(\omega)$ and $\psi_t(\omega)$ be $\mathfrak{F}_t$-adapted left continuous nonanticipative real processes satisfying conditions 6.1.3.

1. If $\{M_t, \mathfrak{F}_t, t \in T\}$ and $\{N_t, \mathfrak{F}_t, t \in T\}$ are square integrable martingales, then

$$\langle \int \varphi_s\, dM_s, \int \psi_s\, dN_s\rangle_t = \int_0^t \varphi_s \psi_s\, d\langle M, N\rangle_s \tag{6.5.21}$$

2. If $\{W_t, \mathcal{F}_t, t \in T\}$ is a standard Brownian motion process,

$$E\int_0^t \varphi_s(\omega)\, dW_s \int_0^t \psi_s(\omega)\, dW_s = E\int_0^t \varphi_s(\omega)\psi_s(\omega)\, ds \qquad (6.5.22)$$

3. Equation 6.5.22 can be generalized further as

$$E^{\mathcal{F}_\tau}\int_\tau^t \varphi_s(\omega)\, dW_s \int_\tau^t \psi_s(\omega)\, dW_s = E^{\mathcal{F}_\tau}\int_\tau^t \varphi_s(\omega)\psi_s(\omega)\, ds \qquad (6.5.23)$$

4. If $\{M_t, \mathcal{F}_t, t \in T\}$ is a sample continuous martingale, then the stochastic integral $Y_t = \int_0^t \varphi_s(\omega)\, dM_s$ is also a sample continuous martingale.

5. If $\{M_t, \mathcal{F}_t, t \in T\}$ is a martingale with bounded variation, then the stochastic integral $Y_t = \int_0^t \varphi_s(\omega)\, dM_s$ is a Stieltjes integral and φ_t has to be left continuous at points where the martingale M_t jumps.

6. For any local martingales M_t and N_t we can also define the quadratic variation process

$$[N, \int \varphi_s\, dM_s]_t = \int_0^t \varphi_s\, d[N, M]_s \qquad (6.5.24)$$

6.6 REPRESENTATION OF SQUARE INTEGRABLE MARTINGALES

In the previous section we have seen that if $\{X_t, \mathcal{F}_t, t \in T\}$ is a local L^2-, or L^2-martingale and $\{\varphi_t, \mathcal{F}_t, t \in T\}$ belongs to a class of $\mathcal{F}_t$-adapted left continuous functions satisfying conditions 6.1.3, then the stochastic integral $Y_t = \int_0^t \varphi_s\, dX_s$ is also a local L^2-, or L^2-martingale. The question now is whether *any* $\mathcal{F}_t$-martingale can be represented as a stochastic integral with respect to *another* $\mathcal{F}_t$-martingale. This is not true in general, but there are special cases connected with processes of independent increments where this is true. The following results are due to Kunita and Watanabe (32).

1. If $\{X_t, \mathcal{F}_t, t \in T\}$ is a Brownian motion process, then every local L^2- or L^2-martingale on $\{\mathcal{F}_t, t \in T\}$ can be expressed as a stochastic integral with respect to X_t.

2. If $\{N_t, \mathcal{F}_t, t \in T\}$ is a Poisson process and X_t is a Poisson martingale, then every local L^2- or L^2-martingale on $\{\mathcal{F}_t, t \in T\}$ can be expressed as the stochastic integral of a predictable process with respect to X_t.

Let us now state an important result whereby square integrable martingales can be represented as the sum of two orthogonal martingales one of which is a stochastic integral with respect to a Brownian motion process. This result is a consequence of Theorem 6.5.1.

Theorem 6.6.1

Let $\{\mathfrak{F}_t, t \in T\}$ be a family of right continuous increasing σ-fields of a complete probability space $(\Omega, \mathfrak{F}, P)$. Let $\{X_t, \mathfrak{F}_t, t \in T\}$ be any square integrable martingale with $X_0 = 0$, and let $\{W_t, \mathfrak{F}_t, t \in T\}$ be a Brownian motion process. Then the representation for X_t is

$$X_t = \int_0^t \varphi_s(\omega)\, dW_s + Z_t \qquad t \in T \tag{6.6.1}$$

where the process $\{\varphi_t, \mathfrak{F}_t, t \in T\}$ is such that

$$\langle X, W\rangle_t = \sigma^2 \int_0^t \varphi_s(\omega)\, ds \qquad t \in T$$

with $\varphi_t(\omega)$ satisfying conditions 6.1.3 and $\{Z_t, \mathfrak{F}_t, t \in T\}$ is a martingale orthogonal to $Y_t = \int_0^t \varphi_s(\omega)\, dW_s$, that is,

$$\langle Z, Y\rangle_t = 0 \qquad t \in T \tag{6.6.2}$$

Proof. Clearly the existence of the process $\varphi_t(\omega)$ is guaranteed by Theorem 6.5.1. Since $Y_t = \int_0^t \varphi_s(\omega)\, dW_s$, eq. 6.6.1 can be written as

$$Z_t = X_t - Y_t$$

Since X_t and Y_t are $\mathfrak{F}_t$-martingales, Z_t is also an $\mathfrak{F}_t$-martingale.

By eq. 6.5.5, we have

$$\langle X, Y\rangle_t = \int_0^t \varphi_s(\omega)\, d\langle X, W\rangle_s \tag{6.6.3}$$

By eq. 6.5.3,

$$\langle X, W\rangle_t = \sigma^2 \int_0^t \varphi_s(\omega)\, ds$$

and hence

$$d\langle X, W\rangle_t = \sigma^2 \varphi_s(\omega)\, dt \tag{6.6.4}$$

Inserting eq. 6.6.4 into eq. 6.6.3, we obtain

$$\langle X, Y\rangle_t = \sigma^2 \int_0^t \varphi_s^2(\omega)\, ds \tag{6.6.5}$$

Now

$$\langle Z, Y\rangle_t = \langle X - Y, Y\rangle_t = \langle X, Y\rangle_t - \langle Y, Y\rangle_t \tag{6.6.6}$$

From eq. 6.5.21,

$$\langle Y, Y \rangle_t = \left\langle \int \varphi_s \, dW_s, \int \varphi_s \, dW_s \right\rangle = \int_0^t \varphi_s^2 \, d\langle W, W \rangle_s \tag{6.6.7}$$

Since the quadratic variance $\langle W, W \rangle_t$ of a Brownian motion process W_t is $\sigma^2 t$, eq. 6.6.7 reduces to

$$\langle Y, Y \rangle_t = \sigma^2 \int_0^t \varphi_s^2(\omega) \, ds \tag{6.6.8}$$

Comparing eqs. 6.6.5 and 6.6.8, we find that $\langle X, Y \rangle_t = \langle Y, Y \rangle_t$, and substituting this result in eq. 6.6.6, we obtain

$$\langle Z, Y \rangle_t = 0$$

showing that Z_t and Y_t are orthogonal martingales. □

Remark

1. If $EX_t^2 = \sigma^2 E \int_0^t \varphi_s^2(\omega) \, ds$, then $Z_t = 0$ for all $t \in T$. This result can be shown by noting

$$EX_t^2 = E(Y_t + Z_t)^2 = EY_t^2 + EZ_t^2$$

and since

$$EX_t^2 = EY_t^2 = \sigma^2 E \int_0^t \varphi_s^2(\omega) \, ds$$

we have $EZ_t^2 = 0$, implying $Z_t = 0$ almost surely.

In the case given above Theorem 6.6.1 can be written as

$$X_t = \int_0^t \varphi_s(\omega) \, dW_s$$

We stated in the beginning of this section that the stochastic integral is a martingale and that the converse, that any martingale can be given as a stochastic integral with respect to another martingale, is not generally true (see Problems).

We now state some theorems for which the converse is true.

Theorem 6.6.2 (Kallianpur, 29, pp. 157, 296)

Let $\{\mathcal{F}_t, t \in T\}$ be the natural filtration σ-field generated by a Brownian motion process, and let $\{W_t, \mathcal{F}_t, t \in T\}$ be that Brownian motion process. Let $\{X_t, \mathcal{F}_t, t \in T\}$ belong to a class of square integrable martingales with right continuous trajectories. Then there exists a process $\{\varphi_t(\omega), \mathcal{F}_t, t \in T\}$ with $\int_0^t E|\varphi_s(\omega)|^2 \, ds < \infty$ such that for all $t \in T$,

$$X_t = X_0 + \int_0^t \varphi_s(\omega) \, dW_s \quad \text{(a.s.)} \tag{6.6.9}$$

Proof. We give only an indication of the proof. Since the quantity $\tilde{X}_t = X_t - X_0$ is also an $\mathcal{F}_t$-martingale, we have from Theorem 6.5.1

$$\langle \tilde{X}, W \rangle_t = \sigma^2 \int_0^t \varphi_s(\omega) \, ds \qquad t \in T \tag{6.6.10}$$

and by Theorem 6.6.1,

$$\tilde{X}_t = \int_0^t \varphi_s(\omega) \, dW_s + Z_t \qquad t \in T \tag{6.6.11}$$

We have to show that $Z_t = 0$ for all $t \in T$. This is accomplished by partitioning the interval $[0, t]$ by a sequence $\{0, t_1, t_2, \ldots, t_n, t\}$ such that

$$0 < t_1 < t_2 < \cdots < t_n < t$$

and showing

$$EZ_t \prod_{j=1}^{n} \psi_j\left(W_{t_j}\right) = 0 \tag{6.6.12}$$

for any n, $n = 1, 2, \ldots$, and for any bounded Borel measurable function $\psi_j(\cdot)$. For details see Lipster and Shiryaev (34, p. 162) and Kallianpur (29, pp. 157, 296). □

We can also state a result corresponding to eq. 6.6.9 for martingales arising out of conditional expectations.

Let $\{W_t, \mathcal{F}_t, t \in T\}$ be a Brownian motion process, and let $\{X_t, \mathcal{B}_t, t \in T\}$ be a square integrable martingale with right continuous trajectories where $\mathcal{B}_t = \sigma\{X_s, W_s, s \le t, t \in T\}$ and $\mathcal{F}_t \subset \mathcal{B}_t \subset \mathcal{F}$. From Example 3.4.1 the conditional expectation $Y_t = E^{\mathcal{F}_t} X_t$ is also a square integrable martingale. We have the following theorem for the representation of Y_t.

Theorem 6.6.3 (Lipster and Shiryaev, 34, p. 183)

Let $\{X_t, \mathcal{B}_t, t \in T\}$ be a square integrable martingale on the complete probability space $(\Omega, \mathcal{F}, P)$, and let $\{\mathcal{F}_t, t \in T\}$ be the natural filtration σ-field generated by a Brownian motion process $\{W_t, \mathcal{B}_t, t \in T\}$. Then the martingale $Y_t = E^{\mathcal{F}_t} X_t$ admits the representation

$$Y_t = EX_0 + \int_0^t E^{\mathcal{F}_s} \varphi_s(\omega) \, dW_s \qquad t \in T \tag{6.6.13}$$

where the process $\varphi_t(\omega)$ is $\mathcal{B}_t$-measurable such that

$$\langle X, W\rangle = \sigma^2 \int_0^t \varphi_s(\omega)\, ds$$

with $\int_0^t E|\varphi_s|^2\, ds < \infty$.

Proof. Since Y_t is a square integrable martingale, we have from eq. 6.6.9

$$Y_t = Y_0 + \int_0^t \psi_s(\omega)\, dW_s \qquad t \in T \tag{6.6.14}$$

where $\psi_t(\omega)$ is $\mathcal{F}_t$-measurable. However, $Y_0 = E^{\mathcal{F}_0} X_0 = EX_0$ since $\mathcal{F}_0$ is the trivial σ-field $\{\Omega, \varnothing\}$.

By Theorem 6.5.1, we have

$$\langle X, W\rangle_t = \sigma^2 \int_0^t \varphi_s(\omega)\, ds \tag{6.6.15}$$

where $\varphi_s(\omega)$ is $\mathcal{B}_s$-measurable with $\int_0^t E|\varphi_s|^2\, ds < \infty$. We have to show that

$$\psi_s(\omega) = E^{\mathcal{F}_s} \varphi_s(\omega) \qquad s \in T \tag{6.6.16}$$

Let $\{g_t(\omega), \mathcal{F}_t, t \in T\}$ be a random process satisfying the conditions of Lemma 6.5.1. If Z_t is the square integrable $\mathcal{F}_t$-martingale given by the stochastic integral $\int_0^t g_s(\omega)\, dW_s$, then

$$EY_tZ_t = E\left[\left(E^{\mathcal{F}_t}X_t\right)Z_t\right] = EE^{\mathcal{F}_t}(X_tZ_t) = EX_tZ_t \tag{6.6.17}$$

We have also from Theorem 4.3.2 $Y_tZ_t - \langle Y, Z\rangle_t = W_t$, and hence

$$\begin{aligned} EY_tZ_t &= E\langle Y, Z\rangle_t \\ &= \sigma^2 \int_0^t E[\psi_s(\omega) g_s(\omega)]\, ds \end{aligned} \tag{6.6.18}$$

Since both X_t and Z_t are $\mathcal{B}_t$-martingales, we have from eq. 4.3.5 of Theorem 4.3.2,

$$EX_tZ_t = E\langle X, Z\rangle_t + EW_t = E\langle X, Z\rangle_t \tag{6.6.19}$$

By Lemma 6.5.1, eq. 6.5.5,

$$\begin{aligned} E\langle X, Z\rangle_t &= E\int_0^t g_s(\omega)\, d\langle X, W\rangle_s \\ &= E\sigma^2 \int_0^t g_s(\omega)\varphi_s(\omega)\, ds \qquad \text{from eq. 6.6.15} \\ &= \sigma^2 \int_0^t E\{[E^{\mathcal{F}_s}\varphi_s(\omega)]\, g_s(\omega)\}\, ds \end{aligned} \tag{6.6.20}$$

Substituting eqs. 6.6.20 and 6.6.18 into eq. 6.6.17, we have

$$\int_0^t E\{[\psi_s(\omega) - E^{\mathcal{F}_s}\varphi_s(\omega)]\sigma^2 g_s(\omega)\}\, ds = 0 \qquad (6.6.21)$$

Since $g_s(\omega)$ is an arbitrary function, we infer that

$$\psi_s(\omega) = E^{\mathcal{F}_s}\varphi_s(\omega) \qquad \square$$

6.7 EXTENSION OF ITO'S RULE

Ito's rule, eq. 6.4.2, can be given in an alternate form using quadratic variation processes. Let $\mathbf{X}_t(\omega)$ be an n-vector Ito process given by

$$d\mathbf{X}_t(\omega) = \mathbf{a}_t(\omega)\, dt + \mathbf{b}_t(\omega)\, dW_t(\omega), \quad t \in T, \quad \mathbf{X}_0(\omega) \qquad (6.7.1)$$

or in integral form,

$$\mathbf{X}_t(\omega) = \mathbf{X}_0(\omega) + \int_0^t \mathbf{a}_\tau(\omega)\, d\tau + \int_0^t \mathbf{b}_\tau(\omega)\, dW_\tau(\omega) \qquad t \in T \qquad (6.7.2)$$

where $\{a_{it}(\omega),\ i = 1, 2, \ldots, n\}$ satisfies the regularity condition 6.2.1a and $\{b_{it}(\omega),\ i = 1, 2, \ldots, n\}$ satisfies the conditions 6.1.3. Under these regularity conditions the stochastic integral $\int_0^t \mathbf{b}_\tau(\omega)\, dW_\tau(\omega)$ is an n-vector $\mathcal{F}_t$-martingale $\mathbf{M}_t$. Note that $\mathbf{M}_t$ is a continuous martingale. Equation 6.7.2 can be rewritten as

$$\mathbf{X}_t(\omega) = \mathbf{X}_0(\omega) + \int_0^t \mathbf{a}_\tau(\omega)\, d\tau + \mathbf{M}_t \qquad \text{or} \qquad d\mathbf{X}_t = \mathbf{a}_t\, dt + d\mathbf{M}_t$$

$$t \in T, \quad \mathbf{X}_0 \qquad (6.7.3)$$

Ito's rule for a scalar function $Y_t = \psi(t, \mathbf{X}_t)$ is given by eq. 6.4.4,

$$dY_t = \frac{\partial \psi}{\partial t} dt + \left(\frac{\partial}{\partial \mathbf{x}}\right)^T \psi\, d\mathbf{X}_t + \frac{1}{2} d\mathbf{X}_t^T \frac{\partial}{\partial \mathbf{x}} \left(\frac{\partial}{\partial \mathbf{x}}\right)^T \psi\, d\mathbf{X}_t \qquad (6.7.4)$$

From eq. 6.7.3,

$$d\mathbf{X}_t^T\, d\mathbf{X}_t = \mathbf{a}_t^T \mathbf{a}_t\, dt^2 + d\mathbf{M}_t^T\, d\mathbf{M}_t \qquad (6.7.5)$$

Substituting eq. 6.7.5 into eq. 6.7.4 and neglecting powers of dt greater than 1, we obtain

$$dY_t = \frac{\partial \psi}{\partial t} dt + \left(\frac{\partial}{\partial \mathbf{x}}\right)^T \psi\, d\mathbf{X}_t + \frac{1}{2} d\mathbf{M}_t^T \frac{\partial}{\partial \mathbf{x}} \left(\frac{\partial}{\partial \mathbf{x}}\right)^T \psi\, d\mathbf{M}_t \qquad (6.7.6)$$

If eq. 6.7.6 is expanded, there results

$$dY_t = \frac{\partial \psi}{\partial t} dt + \sum_{i=1}^{n} \frac{\partial \psi}{\partial x_i} dX_{it} + \frac{1}{2} \sum_{i}^{n} \sum_{j}^{n} \frac{\partial^2 \psi}{\partial x_i \, \partial x_j} dM_{it} \, dM_{jt} \tag{6.7.7}$$

We now show that

$$dM_{it} \, dM_{jt} = d\langle M_i, M_j \rangle_t$$

By definition, the quadratic covariation process $[M_i, M_j]_t$ is given by

$$\begin{aligned} \left[M_i, M_j\right]_t &= \lim_{n \to \infty} \sum_{\nu=0}^{N(n)-1} \left(M_{it_{\nu+1}^{(n)}} - M_{it_\nu^{(n)}}\right)\left(M_{jt_{\nu+1}^{(n)}} - M_{jt_\nu^{(n)}}\right) \\ &= \lim_{n \to \infty} \sum_{\nu=0}^{N(n)-1} \Delta M_{it_\nu^{(n)}} \Delta M_{jt_\nu^{(n)}} \end{aligned}$$

for partitions

$$0 = t_0^{(n)} < t_1^{(n)} < \cdots < t_{N(n)}^{(n)} = t$$

From the above equation it can be inferred

$$d\left[M_i, M_j\right]_t = \lim_{n \to \infty} \Delta M_{it_\nu^{(n)}} \Delta M_{jt_\nu^{(n)}} = dM_{it} \, dM_{jt} \tag{6.7.8}$$

By definition the martingale $\mathbf{M}_t$ is a stochastic integral with respect to a Brownian motion process, and hence it is a continuous martingale and as a consequence

$$d\left[M_i, M_j\right]_t = d\langle M_i, M_j \rangle_t$$

and hence

$$dM_{it} \, dM_{jt} = d\langle M_i, M_j \rangle_t \tag{6.7.9}$$

Note. If X_{it} and X_{jt} are submartingales, then it can be shown that

$$dX_{it} \, dX_{jt} = d\langle X_i, X_j \rangle_t = d\langle M_i, M_j \rangle_t \tag{6.7.10}$$

where M_{it} and M_{jt} are the continuous martingales associated with the submartingales X_{it} and X_{jt}.

Substituting eq. 6.7.9 in eq. 6.7.7, Ito's rule can be given in an alternate form as

$$dY_t = \frac{\partial \psi}{\partial t} dt + \sum_{i=1}^{n} \frac{\partial \psi}{\partial x_i} dX_{it} + \frac{1}{2} \sum_{i}^{n} \sum_{j}^{n} \frac{\partial^2 \psi}{\partial x_i \, \partial x_j} d\langle M_i, M_j \rangle_t \tag{6.7.11}$$

where M_{it} and M_{jt} are continuous martingales.

The corresponding integral representation of eq. 6.7.11 is

$$Y_t = \psi(t, \mathbf{X}_t) = \psi(0, \mathbf{X}_0) + \int_0^t \frac{\partial \psi}{\partial t} dt$$

$$+ \int_0^t \left(\sum_{i=1}^n \frac{\partial \psi}{\partial x_i} dX_{it} + \frac{1}{2} \sum_i^n \sum_j^n \frac{\partial^2 \psi}{\partial x_i \, \partial x_j} d\langle M_i, M_j \rangle_t \right) \qquad (6.7.12)$$

The Ito rule given by eq. 6.7.12 is for the scalar function Y_t of the vector Ito process $\mathbf{X}_t$, where $\mathbf{X}_t$ is driven by a scalar Brownian motion process W_t. Clearly $\mathbf{X}_t$ is a continuous semimartingale, being the sum of a continuous martingale and a process of bounded variation. The stochastic integral in the Ito process can also be driven by any general martingale (not necessarily continuous) in which case $\mathbf{X}_t$ will be a general semimartingale, not necessarily continuous. This leads us to the Doleans-Dade–Meyer (13) extension of Ito's rule as given by the following theorem.

Theorem 6.7.1 Doleans-Dade – Meyer Extension of Ito's Rule (13)

Let $\{\mathbf{X}_t, \mathcal{F}_t, t \in T\}$ be a general n-vector semimartingale, that is, a sum of a martingale, not necessarily continuous, and a process of bounded variation. Let $\psi(t, x)$ be a continuous function having continuous partial derivatives $\partial\psi/\partial t$, $\partial\psi/\partial x$, and $\partial^2\psi/\partial x^2$. The scalar process $Y_t(\omega) = \psi(t, \mathbf{X}_t(\omega))$ admits a stochastic differential equation given by

$$dY_t = \psi(t, \mathbf{X}_t) - \psi(t, \mathbf{X}_{t-}) + \frac{\partial \psi}{\partial t} dt + \sum_{i=1}^n \frac{\partial \psi}{\partial x_i}(t, \mathbf{X}_{t-}) \, dX_{it}$$

$$- \sum_{i=1}^n \frac{\partial \psi}{\partial x_i}(t, \mathbf{X}_{t-}) \, \Delta X_{it} + \frac{1}{2} \sum_i^n \sum_j^n \frac{\partial \psi(t, \mathbf{X}_{t-})}{\partial x_i \, \partial x_j} d\langle M_i^c, M_j^c \rangle_t$$

(6.7.13)

where M_{it}^c is the continuous $\mathcal{F}_t$-martingale associated with the semimartingale X_{it}, $\Delta \mathbf{X}_t$ is the amount of jump of $\mathbf{X}_t$ at t, and $\mathbf{X}_{t-}$ is the left-hand limit at t of the semimartingale $\mathbf{X}_t$.

Proof. We only give a heuristic proof to this theorem. Since $\mathbf{X}_t$ is a semimartingale, it can be given by

$$\mathbf{X}_t = \mathbf{B}_t + \mathbf{M}_t \qquad (6.7.14)$$

where $\mathbf{B}_t$ is a process of bounded variation, and $\mathbf{M}_t$ is the general martingale associated with $\mathbf{X}_t$. $\mathbf{M}_t$ can again be decomposed as

$$\mathbf{M}_t = \mathbf{M}_t^c + \mathbf{M}_t^d \qquad (6.7.15)$$

The discontinuous martingale $\mathbf{M}_t^d$ can be given as

$$\mathbf{M}_t^d = \mathbf{Z}_t^d - \mathbf{A}_t \tag{6.7.16}$$

where $\mathbf{Z}_t^d$ is a purely discontinuous process and $\mathbf{A}_t$ is again a process of bounded variation.

Substituting eqs. 6.7.15 and 6.7.16 into eq. 6.7.14, we obtain

$$\mathbf{X}_t = \mathbf{B}_t + \mathbf{M}_t^c - \mathbf{A}_t + \mathbf{Z}_t^d = \mathbf{Z}_t^c + \mathbf{Z}_t^d \tag{6.7.17}$$

where $\mathbf{Z}_t^c$ is the continuous part of the semimartingale $\mathbf{X}_t$.

The Ito role as enunciated in Theorems 6.3.1 and 6.4.1 is applicable only to a continuous semimartingale, namely, $\mathbf{X}_t = \mathbf{B}_t + \mathbf{M}_t^c$. We have to generalize this rule to the case $\mathbf{X}_t = \mathbf{M}_t^c + \mathbf{B}_t - \mathbf{A}_t + \mathbf{Z}_t^d$ where we have discontinuities also. The differential dY_t is now defined as

$$dY_t = \psi(t + dt, \mathbf{X}_{t+dt}) - \psi(t, \mathbf{X}_{t-})$$

The Taylor series expansion for $\psi(t + dt, \mathbf{X}_{t+dt})$ is given by

$$\psi(t + dt, \mathbf{X}_{t+dt}) = \psi(t, \mathbf{X}_t) + \frac{\partial \psi(t, \mathbf{X}_t)}{\partial t} dt + \sum_{i=1}^{n} \frac{\partial \psi}{\partial x_i}(t, \mathbf{X}_{t-})\, dZ_{it}^c$$
$$+ \frac{1}{2} \sum_i^n \sum_j^n \frac{\partial^2 \psi(t, \mathbf{X}_{t-})}{\partial x_i\, \partial x_j} dZ_{it}^c\, dZ_{jt}^c \tag{6.7.18}$$

or

$$dY_t = \psi(t, \mathbf{X}_t) - \psi(t, \mathbf{X}_{t-}) + \frac{\partial \psi}{\partial t}(t, \mathbf{X}_t)\, dt + \sum_{i=1}^{n} \frac{\partial \psi(t, \mathbf{X}_{t-})}{\partial x_i} dZ_{it}^c$$
$$+ \frac{1}{2} \sum_i^n \sum_j^n \frac{\partial^2 \psi(t, \mathbf{X}_{t-})}{\partial x_i\, \partial x_j} dZ_{it}^c\, dZ_{jt}^c \tag{6.7.19}$$

Since Z_{it}^c is a continuous semimartingale, we have from eq. 6.7.10,

$$dZ_{it}^c\, dZ_{jt}^c = d\left[Z_i^c, Z_j^c\right]_t = d\langle Z_i^c, Z_j^c\rangle_t = d\langle M_i^c, M_j^c\rangle_t \tag{6.7.20}$$

From eq. 6.7.17, $dZ_{it}^c = dX_{it} - \Delta Z_{it}^d$, where ΔZ_{it}^d is the jump in the process Z_{it} at t. But the jump ΔZ_{it}^d in Z_{it}^d is the same as the jump ΔX_{it} in X_{it}, and hence

$$dZ_{it}^c = dX_{it} - \Delta X_{it} \tag{6.7.21}$$

Substituting eqs. 6.7.20 and 6.7.21 into eq. 6.7.19, we arrive at

$$dY_t = \psi(t,\mathbf{X}_t) - \psi(t,\mathbf{X}_{t-}) + \frac{\partial\psi(t,\mathbf{X}_t)}{\partial t}dt + \sum_{i=1}^{n}\frac{\partial\psi(t,\mathbf{X}_{t-})}{\partial x_i}dX_{it}$$
$$+\frac{1}{2}\sum_{i}^{n}\sum_{j}^{n}\frac{\partial^2\psi(t,\mathbf{X}_{t-})}{\partial x_i\,\partial x_j}d\langle M_i^c, M_j^c\rangle_t - \sum_{i=1}^{n}\frac{\partial\psi(t,\mathbf{X}_{t-})}{\partial x_i}\Delta X_{it} \tag{6.7.22}$$

thus heuristically proving the Ito–Doleans-Dade–Meyer rule for a general semimartingale. □

The usefulness of this rule will be demonstrated when we find the variance process in the nonlinear filtering problem.

Special Cases

1. If Y is not explicitly dependent on t, that is, $Y_t = \psi(\mathbf{X}_t)$, then the term $\partial\psi/\partial t$ is not present, and eq. 6.7.22 reduces to

$$dY_t = \psi(\mathbf{X}_t) - \psi(\mathbf{X}_{t-}) + \sum_{i=1}^{n}\frac{\partial\psi(\mathbf{X}_{t-})}{\partial x_i}dX_{it}$$
$$+\frac{1}{2}\sum_{i}^{n}\sum_{j}^{n}\frac{\partial^2\psi(\mathbf{X}_{t-})}{\partial x_i\,\partial x_j}d\langle M_i^c, M_j^c\rangle_t - \sum_{i=1}^{n}\frac{\partial\psi(\mathbf{X}_{t-})}{\partial x_i}\Delta X_{it} \tag{6.7.23}$$

2. If $\mathbf{X}_t$ is not a vector but a scalar process X_t, then eq. 6.7.23 reduces to

$$dY_t = \psi(X_t) - \psi(X_{t-}) + \frac{\partial\psi(X_{t-})}{\partial x}dX_t$$
$$+\frac{1}{2}\frac{\partial^2\psi(X_{t-})}{\partial x^2}d\langle M^c, M^c\rangle_t - \frac{\partial\psi(X_{t-})}{\partial x}\Delta x_t \tag{6.7.24}$$

3. If $\psi(X_t) = X_tY_t$ where X_t and Y_t are scalar semimartingales given by

$$\begin{aligned} X_t &= M_{X_t}^c + B_{X_t} - A_{X_t} + Z_{X_t}^d \\ Y_t &= M_{Y_t}^c + B_{Y_t} - A_{Y_t} + Z_{Y_t}^d \end{aligned} \tag{6.7.25}$$

then application of the Ito–Doleans-Dade–Meyer rule yields

$$d(X_tY_t) = X_tY_t - X_{t-}Y_{t-} + Y_{t-}\frac{\partial X_t}{\partial x}dX_t + X_{t-}\frac{\partial Y_t}{\partial y}dY_t$$
$$+\tfrac{1}{2}(d\langle M_X^c, M_X^c\rangle_t + d\langle M_X^c, M_Y^c\rangle_t) - (Y_{t-}\,\Delta X_t + X_{t-}\,\Delta Y_t) \tag{6.7.26}$$

Using the fact $\Delta X_t = X_t - X_{t-}$ and $\Delta Y_t = Y_t - Y_{t-}$, we have

$$\begin{aligned}
X_tY_t &- X_{t-}Y_{t-} - (Y_{t-}\,\Delta X_t + X_{t-}\,\Delta Y_t) \\
&= X_tY_t - X_{t-}Y_{t-} - Y_{t-}(X_t - X_{t-}) - X_{t-}(Y_t - Y_{t-}) \\
&= X_tY_t - X_{t-}Y_{t-} - X_tY_{t-} + X_{t-}Y_{t-} - X_{t-}Y_t + X_{t-}Y_{t-} \\
&= X_t(Y_t - Y_{t-}) - X_{t-}(Y_t - Y_{t-}) \\
&= (X_t - X_{t-})(Y_t - Y_{t-}) = \Delta X_t \Delta Y_t
\end{aligned} \tag{6.7.27}$$

Substituting eq. 6.7.27 in eq. 6.7.26, we have

$$d(X_tY_t) = Y_{t-}\,dX_t + X_{t-}\,dY_t + d\langle M_X^c, M_Y^c\rangle_t + \Delta X_t \Delta Y_t \tag{6.7.28}$$

which can also be written as

$$d(X_tY_t) = Y_{t-}\,dX_t + X_{t-}\,dY_t + d[X, Y]_t$$

since

$$\begin{aligned}
[X, Y]_t &= \langle X, Y\rangle_t + \Delta X_t \Delta Y_t \\
&= \langle M_X^c, M_Y^c\rangle_t + \Delta X_t \Delta Y_t
\end{aligned} \tag{6.7.29}$$

a very important result.

If $\mathbf{X}_t$ and $\mathbf{Y}_t$ are n-vector semimartingale processes, the extension of the Ito–Doleans-Dade–Meyer rule for the vector case is given by

$$d(\mathbf{X}_t\mathbf{Y}_t^T) = \mathbf{X}_{t-}(d\mathbf{Y}_t)^T + (d\mathbf{X}_t)\mathbf{Y}_{t-}^T + d\langle \mathbf{M}_X^c, \mathbf{M}_Y^{cT}\rangle_t + \Delta\mathbf{X}_t(\Delta\mathbf{Y}_t)^T \tag{6.7.30}$$

an equally important generalization of eq. 6.7.28.

4. In special case 3 above, if $X_t = Y_t$, then eq. 6.7.28 reduces to

$$\begin{aligned}
dX_t^2 &= 2X_{t-}\,dX_t + d\langle M_X^c, M_X^c\rangle_t + \Delta X_t^2 \\
&= 2X_{t-}\,dX_t + d\langle M_X^c, M_X^c\rangle_t + \Delta M_t^2 \\
&= 2X_{t-}\,dX_t + d[M, M]_t
\end{aligned} \tag{6.7.31}$$

or

$$\int_0^t X_{\xi-}\,dX_\xi = \tfrac{1}{2}\{X_t^2 - [M, M]_t\} \tag{6.7.32}$$

Example 6.7.1

If $X_t = N_t$, a Poisson process, then application of eq. 6.7.32 yields

$$\int_0^t N_{\xi-}\, dN_\xi = \tfrac{1}{2}\{N_t^2 - [M, M]_t\}$$

Since M is a Poisson martingale, $[M, M]_t = N_t$ (note $\langle M, M\rangle_t = \lambda t$), and hence

$$\int_0^t N_{\xi-}\, dN_\xi = \tfrac{1}{2}\{N_t^2 - N_t\} = \tfrac{1}{2}N_t(N_t - 1)$$

a result obtained by other means in Example 6.1.1.

Example 6.7.2

If $X_t = M_t$ is a local $\mathcal{F}_t$-martingale, then

$$\int_0^t M_{\xi-}\, dM_\xi = \tfrac{1}{2}M_t^2 - [M, M]_t$$

is again a local $\mathcal{F}_t$-martingale.

5. If $\mathbf{X}_t$ is a n-vector semimartingale process, eq. 6.7.31 can be generalized to

$$\begin{aligned} d(\mathbf{X}_t\mathbf{X}_t^T) &= \mathbf{X}_{t-}\, d\mathbf{X}_t^T + d\mathbf{X}_t\mathbf{X}_{t-}^T + d\langle \mathbf{M}_X^c, \mathbf{M}_X^{cT}\rangle_t + \Delta\mathbf{X}_t\Delta\mathbf{X}_t^T \\ &= \mathbf{X}_{t-}\, d\mathbf{X}_t^T + d\mathbf{X}_t\mathbf{X}_{t-}^T + d[\mathbf{M}_X^c, \mathbf{M}_X^{cT}]_t \end{aligned} \tag{6.7.33}$$

which is eq. 6.7.30 with $Y_t = X_t$.

Problems

1. Show that the process $\varphi(\omega, t)$ under conditions 6.1.3 is predictable with respect to the filtration σ-field $\{\mathcal{F}_t, t \in T, T = R^+\}$.
2. Let $g(\omega, t)$ be an adapted right continuous simple process given by

$$g(\omega, t) = \sum_{\nu=0}^{n-1} g_\nu(\omega) I_{[t_\nu, t_{\nu+1})}(t)$$

If another process $h(\omega, t)$ is defined by $h(\omega, t) = g(\omega, t-)$, the left limit of the process $g(\omega, t)$, show that $h(\omega, t)$ is predictable.

3. Show that the stochastic integral as defined in eq. 6.1.7

$$I_t(\varphi) = \underset{n\to\infty}{\text{l.i.q.m.}} \int_0^t \varphi_n(\omega, s)\, dW_s$$

is independent (to within stochastic equivalence) of the approximating sequence φ_n.

4. Prove the basic properties of the stochastic integral given by eqs. 6.1.8–6.1.10.

5. Let M_t be a continuous L^2-martingale, and let $\varphi(t, \omega)$ satisfy conditions 6.1.3. Let τ be a stopping time relative to the filtration σ-field $\{\mathcal{F}_t\}$. Show that

$$\int_0^t \varphi(s, \omega)\, dM_{s\wedge\tau} = \int_0^{t\wedge\tau} \varphi(s, \omega)\, dM_s$$

6. Show that the stochastic integral given by

$$I_t(\varphi) = \int_0^t \varphi(s, \omega)\, dW_s$$

is progressively measurable and has continuous trajectories with probability 1.

7. Show that if $\{X_t, t \in T\}$ is an Ito process given by

$$dX_t = a_t(\omega)\, dt + b_t(\omega)\, dW_t$$

then the stochastic integral over the Ito process

$$I_t(\varphi) = \int_0^t \varphi_t(\omega)\, dX_t \qquad t \in T$$

is a continuous semimartingale.

8. The stochastic integral on a Brownian motion is given by

$$I_t(W) = \int_0^t W_\tau\, dW_\tau$$

a. If the integrand W_t is approximated as

$$W\left(\frac{t_i + t_{i+1}}{2}\right)$$

in the interval $[t_i, t_{i+1}]$, show that

$$I_t(W) = \frac{W_t^2}{2}$$

b. If the integrand W_t is approximated as $W((1-\alpha)t_i + \alpha t_{i+1})$ in the interval $[t_i, t_{i+1}]$ for $0 \le \alpha \le 1$, show that

$$I_t(W) = \frac{W_t^2}{2} + \left(\alpha - \frac{1}{2}\right)t$$

9. A stochastic differential equation is given by

$$dX_t = aX_t\,dt + bX_t\,dW_t \qquad t \in T, \quad X_0, \quad a, b \text{ constants}$$

Show that this has a unique solution

$$X_t = X_0 e^{(a-b^2/2)t + bW_t}$$

10. Let $\psi(x)$ be a function having bounded continuous first and second partials, and let $\{W_t, t \in T, T = R^+\}$ be a standard Brownian motion ($\sigma^2 = 1$). Show that

$$X_t = \psi(W_t) - \frac{1}{2}\int_0^t \frac{\partial^2 \psi(W_\tau)}{\partial w^2}\,d\tau$$

is a martingale, and hence show that if

$$\frac{\partial^2 \psi(W_t)}{dw^2} \ge 0$$

then $\psi(W_t)$ is a submartingale.

11. Let $\{\mathbf{X}_t, \mathfrak{F}_t, t \in T\}$ and $\{\mathbf{Y}_t, \mathfrak{F}_t, t \in T\}$ be two n-vector and m-vector Ito processes, respectively, defined by

$$d\mathbf{X}_t = \mathbf{a}_t\,dt + \mathbf{B}_t\,d\mathbf{W}_t$$

$$d\mathbf{Y}_t = \mathbf{c}_t\,dt + \mathbf{D}_t\,d\mathbf{W}_t$$

where $\mathbf{a}_t$ and $\mathbf{c}_t$ are n-vector and m-vector stochastic processes, and $\mathbf{B}_t$ and $\mathbf{D}_t$ are $n \times k$ and $m \times k$ matrices of stochastic processes, all satisfying the conditions in Section 6.4. $\{\mathbf{W}_t, \mathfrak{F}_t, t \in T\}$ is a k-vector standard Brownian motion process with independent components. Let $\mathbf{Z}_t$ be an $n \times m$ matrix defined by $\mathbf{Z}_t = \mathbf{X}_t\mathbf{Y}_t^T$. Show that

$$d\mathbf{Z}_t = \left(\mathbf{X}_t\mathbf{c}_t^T + \mathbf{a}_t\mathbf{Y}_t^T + \mathbf{B}_t\mathbf{D}_t^T\right)dt + \mathbf{B}_t\,d\mathbf{W}_t\mathbf{Y}_t^T + \mathbf{X}_t\,d\mathbf{W}_t^T\mathbf{D}_t^T$$

12. Let $a_t = a_t(\omega)$ be a nonanticipative function such that $\int_T E|a_t(\omega)|^2\,dt < \infty$. Let Y_t be another stochastic process defined by

$$Y_t = \exp\left[\int_0^t a_\tau\,dW_\tau - \tfrac{1}{2}\int_0^t a_\tau^2\,d\tau\right]$$

where W_t is a standard Brownian motion process. Find the stochastic differential equation satisfied by dY_t and $d(1/Y_t)$.

13. Y_t is a stochastic integral given by

$$Y_t = \int_0^t g_\tau(\omega)\, dW_\tau$$

with $g_t(\omega)$ satisfying the usual condition, and W_t is a Brownian motion process with variance parameter σ^2. Show that

$$EY_t^2 = \sigma^2 \int_0^t g_\tau^2\, d\tau$$

14. Let X_t, Y_t belong to the space of continuous $\mathcal{F}_t$-martingales. Then show that the following inequalities hold:

a. $|\langle X, Y\rangle_t|^2 \le \langle X, X\rangle_t \langle Y, Y\rangle_t$

b. $\left|\int_0^t f(s)\, d\langle X, Y\rangle_s\right|^2 \le \int_0^t f^2(s)\, d\langle X, X\rangle_s \langle Y, Y\rangle_t$

15. Prove the Kunita–Watanabe proposition, Proposition 6.5.1.

16. Using the concept of simple functions, prove the following properties of stochastic integrals:

a. $E\int_0^t \varphi_s(\omega)\, dW_s \int_0^t \psi_s(\omega)\, dW_s = E\int_0^t \varphi_s(\omega)\psi_s(\omega)\, ds$

b. $E^{\mathcal{F}_\tau}\int_\tau^t \varphi_s(\omega)\, dW_s \int_\tau^t \psi_s(\omega)\, dW_s = E\int_\tau^t \varphi_s(\omega)\psi_s(\omega)\, ds$

where φ_t and ψ_t are nonanticipative $\mathcal{F}_t$-adapted left continuous functions satisfying conditions 6.1.3.

17. Let W_t and V_t be two standard Brownian motion processes, and let Y_t be the stochastic integral $\int_0^t W_s\, dV_s$. Let $\mathcal{F}_t$ be the σ-field generated by Y_t, $\mathcal{F}_t = \sigma\{Y_s, s \le t\}$. Clearly W_t^2 is $\mathcal{F}_t$-measurable, and $M_t = W_t^2 - t$ is a square integrable $\mathcal{F}_t$-martingale. Show that M_t cannot be represented as a stochastic integral with respect to the martingale Y_t (Kallianpur, 29, p. 204).

18. Let N_t be a standard Poisson process. Let $Y_1, Y_2, \ldots$ be independent identically distributed Bernoulli random variables with $P\{Y_i = 1\} = P\{Y_i = -1\} = \frac{1}{2}$ also independent of N_t. Let $X_t = \sum_{i=0}^{N_t} Y_i$ with $Y_0 = 0$. (X_t is a process which jumps by $+1$ or -1 with probability $\frac{1}{2}$, whenever the standard Poisson process jumps independently of everything.) The process X_t is a square integrable martingale with respect to $\mathcal{F}_t = \sigma\{X_s, s \le t\}$. The processes $M_t^+ = Z_t^+ - t/2$ and $M_t^- = Z_t^- - t/2$ are square integrable $\mathcal{F}_t$-martingales. Show that M_t^+ and M_t^- cannot be expressed as stochastic integrals with respect to X_t.

19. Show that in Theorem 6.6.1, if X_t is measurable with respect to $\mathcal{F}_t^W = \sigma\{W_s, s \le t\}$, then $Z_t = 0$.

20. Let $\{X_t, \mathcal{F}_t, t \in T\}, \{W_t, \mathcal{F}_t, t \in T\}$ be as in Theorem 6.6.2 with $X_0 = 0$. We have then eq. 6.6.11,

$$X_t = \int_0^t \varphi_s(\omega)\, dW_s + Z_t$$

Let $0 < t_1 < t_2 < \cdots < t_n < t$. To show that $Z_t = 0$ it is enough if we establish (eq. 6.6.12)

$$EZ_t \prod_{j=1}^{n} \psi_j(W_{t_j}) = 0 \qquad n = 1, 2, \ldots$$

Using Ito's rule and assuming $n = 1$, $\psi_1(x) = e^{j\lambda x}$, $-\infty < \lambda < \infty$, prove that for all $s \le t$,

$$EZ_t e^{j\lambda W_s} = 0$$

and hence by induction prove eq. 6.6.12.

21. Let $Z_t = e^{V_t} Y_t$ where

$$V_t = X_t - \tfrac{1}{2}\langle X^c, X^c\rangle_t$$

$$Y_t = \prod_{s \le t} (1 + \Delta X_s) e^{-\Delta X_s}$$

and $\{X_t, \mathcal{F}_t, t \in T\}$ is a local semimartingale with jumps ΔX_t. Using the Ito–Doleans-Dade–Meyer formula show that

$$dZ_t = Z_{t-}\, dX_t$$

or

$$Z_t = 1 + \int_0^t Z_{s-}\, dX_s$$

22. In Problem 21 let $X_t = W_t$, a standard Wiener process. Show that

$$Z_t = e^{W_t - t/2}$$

23. In Problem 21 let $X_t = N_t$, a standard Poisson process. Show that

$$Z_t = 2^{N_t}$$

24. Let $\{N_t, \mathcal{F}_t, t \in T\}$ be a process with unity jumps such that $M_t = N_t - t$ is an $\mathcal{F}_t$-martingale. Applying the Ito–Doleans-Dade–Meyer rule to e^{juN_t} show that

a. $N_t - N_s$ is independent of $\mathcal{F}_s$.
b. $N_t - N_s$ is Poisson distributed with intensity $(t - s)$.

7 STOCHASTIC DIFFERENTIAL EQUATIONS

7.1 STOCHASTIC DIFFERENTIAL EQUATION

In the last chapter (Definition 6.2.1) we defined a stochastic differential equation of the form

$$dX_t(\omega) = a_t(\omega)\,dt + b_t(\omega)\,dW_t \qquad t \in T, \quad X_0(\omega) \tag{7.1.1}$$

where $a_t(\omega)$ and $b_t(\omega)$ are nonanticipative $\mathcal{F}_t$-measurable random processes satisfying certain regularity conditions 6.2.1. We called such a process an Ito process. We now extend the concept of a stochastic differential equation given by eq. 7.1.1.

Definition 7.1.1 Stochastic Differential Equation

Let $(\Omega, \mathcal{F}, P)$ be a probability space, and let $\{\mathcal{F}_t, t \in T, T = [a, b]\}$, $a \geq 0$ be a filtration σ-field defined on it. Let $\{W_t, \mathcal{F}_t, t \in T\}$ be a separable Brownian motion process. Let $f_t(\cdot)$ and $g_t(\cdot)$ be $\mathcal{F}_t$-measurable nonanticipative functionals satisfying certain regularity conditions. Then the random process $\{X_t(\omega), t \in T, T = [a, b]\}$ defined on $(\Omega, \mathcal{F}, P)$ is a *strong solution* or *solution* of the stochastic differential equation

$$dX_t(\omega) = f_t(X_t(\omega))\,dt + g_t(X_t(\omega))\,dW_t \qquad t \in T, \quad X_a \tag{7.1.2}$$

with $\mathfrak{F}_a$-measurable initial condition X_a if for each $t \in T$,

1. $X_t(\omega)$ is continuous and $\mathfrak{F}_t$-adapted.
2. $\int_{t \in T} |f_t(X_t)|\, dt < \infty$ (a.s.)

   $\int_{t \in T} |g_t(X_t)|^2\, dt < \infty$ (a.s.)
3. For each $t \in T$, X_t is given by

$$X_t(\omega) = X_a(\omega) + \int_a^t f_\tau(X_\tau(\omega))\, d\tau + \int_a^t g_\tau(X_\tau(\omega))\, dW_\tau \quad \text{(a.s.)}$$

$$t \in T \qquad (7.1.3)$$

The first integral, $\int_a^t f_\tau(X_\tau(\omega))\, d\tau$, is a mean square Riemann integral, and the second integral, $\int_a^t g_\tau(X_\tau(\omega))\, dW_\tau(\omega)$, is an Ito stochastic integral.

In Section 5.4 we interpreted the following differential equation driven by white noise $Z_t(\omega)$:

$$\frac{dX_t(\omega)}{dt} = \alpha(t)X_t(\omega) + \beta(t)Z_t(\omega) \qquad t \in T$$

as equivalent to

$$dX_t(\omega) = \alpha(t)X_t(\omega)\, dt + \beta(t)\, dW_t(\omega) \qquad t \in T$$

where $W_t(\omega)$ is a Brownian motion process, provided that α and β are functions of t only belonging to a class of square integrable functions. We also made a comment that if α and β are stochastic processes themselves (functions of ω and t), then these two representations are not in general equivalent. In light of that comment the stochastic differential equation 7.1.2 *cannot* in general be interpreted as

$$\frac{dX_t(\omega)}{dt} = f_t(X_t(\omega)) + g_t(X_t(\omega))Z_t(\omega) \qquad t \in T \qquad (7.1.4)$$

with $Z_t(\omega)$ being the formal derivative of the Brownian motion process $W_t(\omega)$ since f and g are now functionals of $X_t(\omega)$ and t. In fact, we do not even define eq. 7.1.4 as a stochastic differential equation. We will, however, define it as a white noise differential equation. It has in general an interpretation as a stochastic differential equation different from eq. 7.1.2.

In summary, eq. 7.1.2 can only be interpreted as the integral equation 7.1.3 and not as the differential equation 7.1.4.

We have defined a stochastic differential equation and what its solution means. Now we have to investigate the uniqueness and the existence of the solution to the stochastic differential equation 7.1.2. To guarantee the uniqueness and existence of the solution, we have to make the following assumptions in addition to that given in Definition 7.1.1:

1. There is a positive constant K independent of f, g, and t such that

$$\begin{aligned} f(t, x) &\le K(1 + x^2)^{1/2} \\ g(t, x) &\le K(1 + x^2)^{1/2} \end{aligned} \tag{7.1.5}$$

2. f and g satisfy the uniform Lipschitz condition for $x \in (-\infty, \infty)$,

$$\begin{aligned} |f(t, x_2) - f(t, x_1)| &\le K|x_2 - x_1| \\ |g(t, x_2) - g(t, x_1)| &\le K|x_2 - x_1| \end{aligned} \tag{7.1.6}$$

3. f and g also satisfy the Lipschitz condition for $t \in T$,

$$\begin{aligned} |f(t_2, x) - f(t_1, x)| &\le K|t_2 - t_2| \\ |g(t_2, x) - g(t_1, x)| &\le K|t_2 - t_1| \end{aligned} \tag{7.1.7}$$

We can now state the theorem on the uniqueness and existence of a solution to the stochastic differential equation.

Theorem 7.1.1. Uniqueness and Existence Theorem

Let $(\Omega, \mathfrak{F}, P)$ be a complete probability space, and let $\{\mathfrak{F}_t, t \in T, T = [a, b]\}$ be a filtration σ-field defined on it. Let $\{W_t, \mathfrak{F}_t, t \in T\}$ be a separable Brownian motion process. Let X_a be an $\mathfrak{F}_a$-measurable initial condition random variable with $EX_a < \infty$ and independent of $W_{t+\tau} - W_t$, $\tau > 0$. Let $f_t(x)$ and $g_t(x)$, $t \in T$, $x \in (-\infty, \infty)$, be two nonanticipative $\mathfrak{F}_t$-measurable functionals satisfying in addition to the conditions in Definition 7.1.1 the conditions of eqs. 7.1.5–7.1.7. Then there exists a (strong) solution $\{X_t, t \in T\}$ to the stochastic differential equation

$$dX_t = f_t(X_t)\, dt + g_t(X_t)\, dW_t \qquad t \in T, \quad X_a \tag{7.1.2}$$

having the following properties:

1. For each $t \in T$, X_t is $\mathfrak{F}_t$-measurable
2. $\{X_t, t \in T\}$ is sample continuous almost surely.
3. $\{X_t, t \in T\}$ is unique almost surely.

4. $\{X_t, t \in T\}$ is a Markov process.
5. $\int_{t \in T} EX_t^2 \, dt < \infty$
6. If

$$\mathfrak{F}_t^X = \sigma\{X_s, s \leq t\}$$

and

$$\mathfrak{F}_t^{X_a, W} = \sigma\{X_a, W_s, s \leq t\}$$

then

$$\mathfrak{F}_t^X \subset \mathfrak{F}_t^{X_a, W}$$

The proof is quite involved and is not given. For a proof see De S. Lazaro (12, p. 133), Jazwinski (22, p. 106), Kallianpur (29, p. 97), Lipster and Shiryaev (34, p. 128), and Wong (63, p. 150).

7.2 DIFFERENTIAL EQUATION DRIVEN BY WHITE NOISE

From Section 5.4 a general white noise integral can be defined by

$$Y_t(\omega) = \int_a^t f(\omega, t) Z_\tau(\omega) \, d\tau \qquad t \in T \tag{7.2.1}$$

where $Z_t(\omega)$ is a white noise process, being the formal derivative of the Brownian motion process $W_t(\omega)$, and f is a random process. If f is a function of time only, belonging to a class of square integrable functions, it was seen that eq. 7.2.1 is equivalent to the stochastic integral

$$Y_t(\omega) = \int_a^t f(\tau) \, dW_\tau(\omega) \qquad t \in T, \qquad f \in L^2 \tag{7.2.2}$$

On the other hand, if f is a stochastic process, that is, a function of both ω and t, then eq. 7.2.1 may not be equivalent to eq. 7.2.2.

We first consider the case where $f(\omega, t) = \varphi(W(\omega, t), t) = \varphi_t(W_t(\omega))$. If the white noise integral is given by

$$Y_t(\omega) = \int_a^t \varphi_\tau(W_\tau(\omega)) Z_\tau(\omega) \, d\tau \qquad t \in T \tag{7.2.3}$$

with φ satisfying the usual regularity conditions 6.1.3, then eq. 7.2.3 will not be equivalent to the stochastic integral

$$Y_t(\omega) = \int_a^t \varphi_\tau(W_\tau(\omega)) \, dW_\tau \qquad t \in T \tag{7.2.4}$$

even though $Z_t(\omega) \, dt = dW_t(\omega)$ in a formal sense.

To find the stochastic integral equivalent to the white noise integral of eq. 7.2.3, we consider a sequence of processes $\{Y_{nt}(\omega), t \in T\}$, converging almost surely to $Y_t(\omega)$, defined by

$$Y_{nt}(\omega) = \int_a^t \varphi_\tau(W_{n\tau}(\omega))Z_{n\tau}(\omega)\,d\tau \qquad t \in T \tag{7.2.5}$$

where $\{W_{nt}(\omega), t \in T\}$ is a sequence of random processes well defined in the conventional sense, converging almost surely to the Brownian motion process $\{W_t(\omega), t \in T\}$. The sequence of processes $\{Z_{nt}(\omega), t \in T\}$ is also well defined in the conventional sense, converging in the sense of Definition 5.2.2 to the white noise process $\{Z_t(\omega), t \in T\}$.

Since $W_{nt}(\omega)$ is well defined, it is certainly differentiable, and hence $dW_{nt}(\omega)/dt = Z_{nt}(\omega)$. Therefore eq. 7.2.5 can be written in an equivalent form as

$$Y_{nt}(\omega) = \int_a^t \varphi_\tau(W_{n\tau}(\omega))\,dW_{n\tau}(\omega) \qquad t \in T \tag{7.2.6}$$

The difference between eq. 7.2.5 and eq. 7.2.6 can be stated as follows. Whereas eq. 7.2.5 by its very definition converges almost surely to eq. 7.2.3, eq. 7.2.6 *will not* converge to eq. 7.2.4. We should like to determine the process $Y_t(\omega)$ to which $Y_{nt}(\omega)$ given by eq. 7.2.6 *will* converge in some sense.

Let us now define

$$\psi_t(x) = \int_0^x \varphi_t(z)\,dz \tag{7.2.7}$$

and consider the function $\psi_t(W_{nt}(\omega)) = \psi_t(W_{nt})$. From eq. 7.2.7 we have

$$\begin{aligned} \frac{\partial \psi_t(W_{nt})}{\partial w_n} &= \varphi_t(W_{nt}) \\ \frac{\partial^2 \psi_t(W_{nt})}{\partial^2 w_n} &= \frac{\partial \varphi_t(W_{nt})}{\partial w_n} \end{aligned} \tag{7.2.8}$$

Since $\{W_{nt}, t \in T\}$ is a well-behaved sequence of random processes, the differential of $\psi_t(W_{nt})$ is given by the ordinary calculus and not the Ito calculus,

$$d\psi_t(W_{nt}) = \frac{\partial \psi_t(W_{nt})}{\partial t}dt + \frac{\partial \psi_t(W_{nt})}{\partial w_n}dW_{nt} \tag{7.2.9}$$

Substituting the first equation in eqs. 7.2.8 into eq. 7.2.9,

$$d\psi_t(W_{nt}) = \frac{\partial \psi_t(W_{nt})}{\partial t}dt + \varphi_t(W_{nt})\,dW_{nt} \tag{7.2.10}$$

Integrating eq. 7.2.10 between the limits a to t and substituting eq. 7.2.6,

$$\psi_t(W_{nt}) - \psi_a(W_{na}) - \int_a^t \frac{\partial \psi_\tau(W_{n\tau})}{\partial \tau} d\tau = \int_a^t \varphi_\tau(W_{n\tau})\, dW_{n\tau}$$

$$= Y_{nt} \tag{7.2.11}$$

Since ψ by assumption is a well-behaved function having continuous derivatives, if we assume, for example, that in the limiting process as

$$W_{nt}(\omega) \xrightarrow[n\to\infty]{\text{a.s.}} W_t(\omega)$$

we should expect

$$\psi_t(W_{nt}) \xrightarrow[n\to\infty]{\text{a.s.}} \psi_t(W_t)$$

$$\frac{\partial \psi_t(W_{nt})}{\partial t} \xrightarrow[n\to\infty]{\text{a.s.}} \frac{\partial \psi_t(W_t)}{\partial t}$$

Hence as $n \to \infty$ in eq. 7.2.11, we should also expect

$$Y_{nt}(\omega) \xrightarrow[n\to\infty]{\text{a.s.}} Y_t(\omega) = \psi_t(W_t) - \psi_a(W_a) - \int_a^t \frac{\partial \psi_\tau(W_\tau)}{\partial \tau} d\tau \qquad t \in T$$

$$\tag{7.2.12}$$

or

$$dY_t(\omega) = d\psi_t(W_t) - \frac{d\psi_t(W_t)}{\partial t} dt \qquad t \in T \tag{7.2.13}$$

The differential $d\psi(W_t)$ is now governed by the Ito calculus, with the underlying Ito process defined by

$$dX_t(\omega) = dW_t(\omega) \tag{7.2.14}$$

Substituting $a_t(\omega) = 0$ and $b_t(\omega) = 1$ in eq. 6.2.3, we have from the Ito rule given by eq. 6.3.1,

$$d\psi_t(W_t) = \frac{\partial \psi_t(W_t)}{\partial t} dt + \frac{\partial \psi_t(W_t)}{\partial w} dW_t + \frac{1}{2}\sigma^2 \frac{\partial^2 \psi_t(W_t)}{\partial w^2} \cdot 1 \cdot dt$$

$$\tag{7.2.15}$$

where σ^2 is the variance parameter associated with the Brownian motion process W_t.

By analogy to eqs. 7.2.8 we also have

$$\frac{\partial \psi_t(W_t)}{\partial w} = \varphi_t(W_t)$$
$$\frac{\partial^2 \psi_t(W_t)}{\partial w^2} = \frac{\partial \varphi_t(W_t)}{\partial w} \tag{7.2.16}$$

Substituting eqs. 7.2.16 into eq. 7.2.15, we obtain

$$d\psi_t(W_t) = \frac{\partial \psi_t(W_t)}{\partial t}\,dt + \varphi_t(W_t)\,dW_t + \frac{1}{2}\sigma^2 \frac{\partial \varphi_t(W_t)}{\partial w}\,dt \tag{7.2.17}$$

Substituting for $d\psi_t(W_t)$ in eq. 7.2.13 from eq. 7.2.17,

$$dY_t = \frac{\partial \psi_t(W_t)}{\partial t}\,dt + \varphi_t(W_t)\,dW_t + \frac{1}{2}\sigma^2 \frac{\partial \varphi_t(W_t)}{\partial w}\,dt - \frac{\partial \psi_t(W_t)}{\partial t}$$

or

$$dY_t = \varphi_t(W_t)\,dW_t + \frac{1}{2}\sigma^2 \frac{\partial \varphi_t(W_t)}{\partial w}\,dt \qquad t \in T \tag{7.2.18}$$

However, from eq. 7.2.3 we have

$$dY_t = \varphi_t(W_t) Z_t\,dt \tag{7.2.19}$$

which can also be written as

$$\frac{dY_t}{dt} = \varphi_t(W_t) Z_t \tag{7.2.20}$$

From eqs. 7.2.18 and 7.2.19 we draw the conclusion that the white noise driven differential equation

$$dY_t = \varphi_t(W_t) Z_t\,dt \qquad t \in T$$

has the stochastic differential equation representation

$$dY_t = \varphi_t(W_t)\,dW_t + \frac{1}{2}\sigma^2 \frac{\partial \varphi_t(W_t)}{\partial w}\,dt \qquad t \in T$$

and *not*

$$dY_t = \varphi_t(W_t)\,dW_t$$

even though $Z_t\,dt = dW_t$.

Again integrating eq. 7.2.18 between the limits a to t and with $Y_a = 0$, we obtain

$$Y_t = \int_a^t \varphi_\tau(W_\tau)\, dW_\tau + \frac{1}{2}\sigma^2 \int_a^t \frac{\partial \varphi_\tau(W_\tau)}{\partial w}\, d\tau \qquad t \in T \qquad (7.2.21)$$

Therefore the sequence $\{Y_{nt}, t \in T\}$ given by eq. 7.2.5 or eq. 7.2.6 converges almost surely to $\{Y_t, t \in T\}$ given by eq. 7.2.21. Normally we would have expected only the term $\varphi_t(W_t)\, dW_t$ in eq. 7.2.18 or $\int_a^t \varphi_\tau(W_\tau)\, dW_\tau$ in eq. 7.2.21, but we have an additional term

$$\frac{1}{2}\sigma^2 \frac{\partial \varphi_t(W_t)}{\partial w}\, dt$$

in eq. 7.2.18 or

$$\frac{1}{2}\sigma^2 \int_a^t \frac{\partial \varphi_\tau(W_\tau)}{\partial w}\, d\tau$$

in eq. 7.2.21. This additional term depending upon the variance parameter σ^2 is due to the fact that W_t is a Brownian motion process which is of unbounded variation. The term

$$\frac{1}{2}\sigma^2 \frac{\partial \varphi_t(W_t)}{\partial w}\, dt,$$

or its integral between a to t, is known as the *correction term*.

Hence the white noise integral

$$Y_t(\omega) = \int_a^t \varphi_\tau(W_\tau(\omega)) Z_\tau(\omega)\, d\tau \qquad t \in T \qquad (7.2.3)$$

is equal to the corresponding stochastic integral plus the correction term, that is,

$$\int_a^t \varphi_\tau(W_\tau(\omega)) Z_\tau(\omega)\, d\tau = \int_a^t \varphi_\tau(W_\tau(\omega))\, dW_\tau(\omega) + \frac{1}{2}\sigma^2 \int_a^t \frac{\partial \varphi_\tau(W_\tau(\omega))}{\partial w}\, d\tau$$

$$t \in T \qquad (7.2.22)$$

Similarly the stochastic integral

$$Y_t(\omega) = \int_a^t \varphi_\tau(W_\tau(\omega))\, dW_\tau \qquad t \in T \qquad (7.2.4)$$

is equal to the corresponding white noise integral minus the correction term,

$$\int_a^t \varphi_\tau(W_\tau(\omega))\, dW_\tau(\omega) = \int_a^t \varphi_\tau(W_\tau(\omega)) Z_\tau(\omega)\, d\tau - \frac{1}{2}\sigma^2 \int_a^t \frac{\partial \varphi_\tau(W_\tau(\omega))}{\partial w}\, d\tau \tag{7.2.23}$$

On the other hand if φ_t is independent of W_t, then $\partial\varphi_t/\partial w = 0$, and the stochastic integral is equal to the white noise integral

$$\int_a^t \varphi_\tau\, dW_\tau(\omega) = \int_a^t \varphi_\tau Z_\tau(\omega)\, d\tau$$

a result already derived in the last chapter. If W_t is a deterministic process, then $\sigma^2 = 0$, and we again obtain

$$\int_a^t \varphi_\tau\, dW_\tau = \int_a^t \varphi_\tau Z_\tau\, d\tau$$

The second case we consider is where $f(\omega, t)$ in eq. 7.2.1 is equal to $\varphi(X(\omega, t), t) = \varphi_t(X_t(\omega))$ where $X_t(\omega)$ is related to the Brownian motion process $W_t(\omega)$ via a stochastic differential equation.

The problem is to find the stochastic integral equivalent to the white noise integral given by an equation similar to eq. 7.2.3,

$$Y_t(\omega) = \int_a^t \varphi_\tau(X_\tau(\omega)) Z_\tau(\omega)\, d\tau \qquad t \in T \tag{7.2.24}$$

In a manner similar to the first case we form the sequence $\{Y_{nt}(\omega), t \in T\}$, converging almost surely to $Y_t(\omega)$, given by

$$Y_{nt}(\omega) = \int_a^t \varphi_\tau(X_{n\tau}(\omega)) Z_{n\tau}(\omega)\, d\tau \qquad t \in T \tag{7.2.25}$$

which is equivalent to

$$Y_{nt}(\omega) = \int_a^t \varphi_\tau(X_{n\tau}(\omega))\, dW_{n\tau}(\omega) \qquad t \in T \tag{7.2.26}$$

with $W_{nt}(\omega)$ converging almost surely to $W_t(\omega)$, and $Z_{nt}(\omega)$ converging to the white noise process $Z_t(\omega)$ in the sense of Definition 5.2.2. The sequence $X_{nt}(\omega)$, $t \in T$, in eqs. 7.2.25 and 7.2.26 is defined by

$$dX_{nt}(\omega) = f_t(X_{nt}(\omega))\, dt + g_t(X_{nt}(\omega)) Z_{nt}(\omega)\, dt \qquad t \in T \tag{7.2.27}$$

or

$$dX_{nt}(\omega) = f_t(X_{nt}(\omega))\,dt + g_t(X_{nt}(\omega))\,dW_{nt}(\omega) \qquad t \in T \quad (7.2.28)$$

where the functions f and g are well defined, satisfying conditions 7.1.5–7.1.7.

Clearly as $n \to \infty$, eq. 7.2.25 converges almost surely to eq. 7.2.24 by assumption. We have to find the stochastic integral to which eq. 7.2.26 converges, which is *not*

$$Y_t(\omega) = \int_a^t \varphi_\tau(X_\tau(\omega))\,dW_\tau(\omega) \qquad t \in T$$

Since this problem also involves convergence of the approximants X_{nt} to the Ito process X_t as $n \to \infty$, we have to find first the stochastic differential equation to which eq. 7.2.28 converges. With X_{nt} converging to X_t almost surely, eq. 7.2.27 converges to

$$dX_t(\omega) = f_t(X_t(\omega))\,dt + g_t(X_t(\omega))Z_t(\omega)\,dt \qquad t \in T \quad (7.2.29)$$

which can also be given in an equivalent form as

$$\frac{dX_t(\omega)}{dt} = f_t(X_t(\omega)) + g_t(X_t(\omega))Z_t(\omega) \qquad t \in T \quad (7.2.30)$$

In view of the analysis in the first case we should reasonably expect that eq. 7.2.28 will converge to

$$dX_t(\omega) = f_t(X_t(\omega))\,dt + g_t(X_t(\omega))\,dW_t(\omega) + \text{correction term} \qquad t \in T$$

and we have to determine this correction term.

As before, we define

$$\psi_t(x) = \int_0^x \frac{dz}{g_t(z)} \quad (7.2.31)$$

so that we have the following relationships.

$$\begin{aligned} \frac{\partial \psi_t(X_{nt})}{\partial x_n} &= \frac{1}{g_t(X_{nt})} \\ \frac{\partial^2 \psi_t(X_{nt})}{\partial x_n^2} &= -\frac{(\partial/\partial x_n)g_t(X_{nt})}{g_t^2(X_{nt})} = \frac{-g_t'(X_{nt})}{g_t^2(X_{nt})} \end{aligned} \quad (7.2.32)$$

Since the function $\psi_t(X_{nt})$ is well defined (X_{nt} is not an Ito process), we can use the conventional laws of calculus to write

$$d\psi_t(X_{nt}) = \frac{\partial \psi_t(X_{nt})}{\partial t} dt + \frac{\partial \psi_t(X_{nt})}{\partial x_n} dX_{nt} \qquad (7.2.33)$$

Substituting for dX_{nt} from eq. 7.2.28 and for $\partial \psi_t(X_{nt})/\partial x_n$ from eqs. 7.2.32 into eq. 7.2.33, we obtain

$$d\psi_t(X_{nt}) = \frac{\partial \psi_t(X_{nt})}{\partial t} dt + \frac{1}{g_t(X_{nt})} [f_t(X_{nt})\, dt + g_t(X_{nt})\, dW_{nt}]$$

or

$$d\psi_t(X_{nt}) = \frac{\partial \psi_t(X_{nt})}{\partial t} dt + \frac{f_t(X_{nt})}{g_t(X_{nt})} dt + dW_{nt} \qquad t \in T \quad (7.2.34)$$

Since X_{nt} converges to X_t almost surely and W_{nt} converges to W_t almost surely, we can write

$$d\psi(X_t) = \frac{\partial \psi_t(X_t)}{\partial t} dt + \frac{f_t(X_t)}{g_t(X_t)} dt + dW_t \qquad t \in T \qquad (7.2.35)$$

However, if

$$X_{nt} \xrightarrow[n \to \infty]{\text{a.s.}} X_t$$

Then X_t becomes some Ito process with respect to the Brownian motion W_t and can be given by the usual Ito stochastic differential equation

$$dX_t(\omega) = a_t(\omega)\, dt + b_t(\omega)\, dW_t(\omega) \qquad t \in T \qquad (7.2.36)$$

where the unknown functionals a and b have to be identified in terms of the known functionals f and g.

Since $d\psi_t(X_t)$ is governed by the Ito calculus, we can apply the Ito rule, eq. 6.3.2, to eq. 7.2.35, where the underlying Ito process is given by eq. 7.2.36, and write

$$d\psi_t(X_t) = \frac{\partial \psi_t(X_t)}{\partial t} dt + \frac{\partial \psi_t(X_t)}{\partial x} a_t dt + \frac{\partial \psi_t(X_t)}{\partial x} b_t\, dW_t$$

$$+ \frac{1}{2}\sigma^2 \frac{\partial^2 \psi_t(X_t)}{\partial x^2} b_t^2\, dt \qquad t \in T \qquad (7.2.37)$$

The processes $a_t(\omega)$ and $b_t(\omega)$ can now be identified by equating eq. 7.2.35 to eq. 7.2.37,

$$\left[\frac{\partial\psi_t(X_t)}{\partial t} + \frac{f_t(X_t)}{g_t(X_t)}\right] dt + dW_t$$

$$= \left[\frac{\partial\psi_t(X_t)}{\partial t} + \frac{\partial\psi_t(X_t)}{\partial x} a_t + \frac{1}{2}\sigma^2 \frac{\partial^2\psi_t(X_t)}{\partial x^2} b_t^2\right] dt$$

$$+ \frac{\partial\psi_t(X_t)}{\partial x} b_t\, dW_t \tag{7.2.38}$$

Equating like terms,

$$\frac{\partial\psi_t(X_t)}{\partial x} b_t = 1 \tag{7.2.39}$$

$$\frac{\partial\psi_t(X_t)}{\partial x} a_t + \frac{1}{2}\sigma^2 \frac{\partial^2\psi_t(X_t)}{\partial x^2} b_t^2 = \frac{f_t(X_t)}{g_t(X_t)} \tag{7.2.40}$$

The limiting form of eqs. 7.2.32, as $n \to \infty$, yields

$$\begin{aligned} \frac{\partial\psi_t(X_t)}{\partial x} &= \frac{1}{g_t(X_t)} \\ \frac{\partial^2\psi_t(X_t)}{\partial x^2} &= -\frac{g_t'(X_t)}{g_t^2(X_t)} \end{aligned} \tag{7.2.41}$$

Substituting the first equation of eqs. 7.2.41 into eq. 7.2.39, we obtain

$$b_t = g_t(X_t) \tag{7.2.42}$$

Substituting eqs. 7.2.41 and 7.2.42 into eq. 7.2.40, we obtain

$$\frac{a_t}{g_t(X_t)} - \frac{1}{2}\sigma^2 g_t'(X_t) = \frac{f_t(X_t)}{g_t(X_t)}$$

or

$$a_t = f_t(X_t) + \tfrac{1}{2}\sigma^2 g_t(X_t) g_t'(X_t) \tag{7.2.43}$$

Substituting eqs. 7.2.42 and 7.2.43 into eq. 7.2.36, we find that eq. 7.2.28

converges almost surely as $n \to \infty$ to the stochastic differential equation

$$dX_t = f_t(X_t)\,dt + \frac{1}{2}\sigma^2 g_t(X_t)\frac{\partial}{\partial x}g_t(X_t)\,dt + g_t(X_t)\,dW_t \qquad t \in T \tag{7.2.44}$$

where the correction term is $\frac{1}{2}\sigma^2 g_t(X_t)(\partial/\partial x)g_t(X_t)\,dt$.

Equation 7.2.44 is also the stochastic differential equation corresponding to the white noise differential equations, eq. 7.2.29 or eq. 7.2.30. Conversely, given the stochastic differential equation

$$dX_t = f_t(X_t)\,dt + g_t(X_t)\,dW_t \qquad t \in T \tag{7.2.45}$$

the corresponding white noise differential equation is

$$dX_t = f_t(X_t)\,dt + g_t(X_t)Z_t\,dt - \frac{1}{2}\sigma^2 g_t(X_t)\frac{\partial}{\partial x}g_t(X_t)\,dt \qquad t \in T \tag{7.2.46}$$

or

$$\frac{dX_t}{dt} = f_t(X_t) + g_t(X_t)Z_t - \frac{1}{2}\sigma^2 g_t(X_t)\frac{\partial}{\partial x}g_t(X_t) \qquad t \in T \tag{7.2.47}$$

Here again, if g_t is independent of X_t, then $\partial g/\partial x = 0$, and if X_t is independent of W_t or W_t is deterministic, then $\sigma^2 = 0$, and there are no correction terms resulting in the equivalence of stochastic and white noise differential equations.

The correction terms play an important role in converting the rules of stochastic differential equations into the rules of ordinary differential equations for computer simulation in estimation problems.

Having found the stochastic differential equation to which X_{nt} converges, we go back to the problem of finding the stochastic integral corresponding to the white noise integral given by eq. 7.2.24. We should expect that the stochastic integral to which eq. 7.2.26 converges will be of the form

$$Y_t(\omega) = \int_a^t \varphi_\tau(X_\tau(\omega))\,dW_\tau(\omega) + \text{correction term} \tag{7.2.48}$$

To find the correction term we define a function $\psi_t(x)$ in a manner similar to what we defined in the first case,

$$\psi_t(x) = \int_0^x \frac{\varphi_t(z)}{g_t(z)}\,dz \tag{7.2.49}$$

so that we have

$$\frac{\partial \psi_t(X_{nt})}{\partial x_n} = \frac{\varphi_t(X_{nt})}{g_t(X_{nt})}$$

$$\frac{\partial^2 \psi_t(X_{nt})}{\partial x_n^2} = \frac{\partial}{\partial x_n} \frac{\varphi_t(X_{nt})}{g_t(X_{nt})} \tag{7.2.50}$$

$$= \frac{g_t(X_{nt})\varphi_t'(X_{nt}) - \varphi_t(X_{nt})g_t'(X_{nt})}{g_t^2(X_{nt})}$$

Since ψ_t and X_{nt} are well-behaved functions, we can use ordinary calculus to write

$$d\psi_t(X_{nt}) = \frac{\partial \psi_t(X_{nt})}{\partial t} dt + \frac{\partial \psi_t(X_{nt})}{\partial x_n} dX_{nt} \tag{7.2.51}$$

Substituting for dX_{nt} from eq. 7.2.27 and using the first equation of eqs. 7.2.50, we obtain

$$d\psi_t(X_{nt}) = \frac{\partial \psi_t(X_{nt})}{\partial t} dt + \frac{\varphi_t(X_{nt})}{g_t(X_{nt})} [f_t(X_{nt})\, dt + g_t(X_{nt})\, dW_{nt}]$$

$$= \frac{\partial \psi_t(X_{nt})}{\partial t} dt + \frac{f_t(X_{nt})}{g_t(X_{nt})} \varphi_t(X_{nt})\, dt + \varphi_t(X_{nt})\, dW_{nt} \tag{7.2.52}$$

However, from eq. 7.2.26,

$$dY_{nt} = \varphi_t(X_{nt})\, dW_{nt} \tag{7.2.53}$$

Substituting dY_{nt} for $\varphi_t(X_{nt})\, dW_{nt}$ in eq. 7.2.52 and rearranging terms,

$$dY_{nt} = d\psi_t(X_{nt}) - \frac{\partial \psi_t(X_{nt})}{\partial t} dt - \frac{f_t(X_{nt})}{g_t(X_{nt})} \varphi_t(X_{nt}) dt \tag{7.2.54}$$

As $n \to \infty$, eq. 7.2.54 converges almost surely to

$$dY_t = d\psi_t(X_t) - \frac{\partial \psi_t(X_t)}{\partial t} dt - \frac{f_t(X_t)}{g_t(X_t)} \varphi_t(X_t)\, dt \tag{7.2.55}$$

However, as $n \to \infty$, the differential $d\psi_t(X_t)$ is governed by the Ito calculus, where the underlying Ito process dX_t is governed by the stochastic differential equation 7.2.44. Hence using Ito calculus, eq. 6.3.2, for $d\psi_t(X_t)$, we have

$$d\psi_t(X_t) = \frac{\partial\psi_t(X_t)}{\partial t}dt + \frac{\partial\psi_t(X_t)}{\partial x}\left[f_t(X_t) + \frac{1}{2}\sigma^2 g_t(X_t)g_t'(X_t)\right]dt$$
$$+ \frac{\partial\psi_t(X_t)}{\partial x}g_t(X_t)\,dW_t + \frac{1}{2}\sigma^2 g_t^2(X_t)\frac{\partial^2\psi_t(X_t)}{\partial x^2}dt \qquad (7.2.56)$$

The limiting form of eqs. 7.2.50 as $n \to \infty$ yields

$$\frac{\partial\psi_t(X_t)}{\partial x} = \frac{\varphi_t(X_t)}{g_t(X_t)}$$
$$\frac{\partial^2\psi_t(X_t)}{\partial x^2} = \frac{g_t(X_t)\varphi_t'(X_t) - \varphi_t(X_t)g_t'(X_t)}{g_t^2(X_t)} \qquad (7.2.57)$$

Substituting eq. 7.2.57 into eq. 7.2.56 yields

$$d\psi_t(X_t) = \frac{\partial\psi_t(X_t)}{\partial t}dt + \frac{\varphi_t(X_t)}{g_t(X_t)}\left[f_t(X_t) + \frac{1}{2}\sigma^2 g_t(X_t)g_t'(X_t)\right]dt$$
$$+ \frac{\varphi_t(X_t)}{g_t(X_t)}g_t(X_t)\,dW_t$$
$$+ \frac{1}{2}\sigma^2 g_t^2(X_t)\frac{g_t(X_t)\varphi_t'(X_t) - \varphi_t(X_t)g_t'(X_t)}{g_t^2(X_t)}dt$$
$$= \frac{\partial\psi_t(X_t)}{\partial t} + \frac{f_t(X_t)}{g_t(X_t)}\varphi_t(X_t)\,dt + \varphi_t(X_t)\,dW_t$$
$$+ \frac{1}{2}\sigma^2 g_t(X_t)\varphi_t'(X_t)\,dt \qquad (7.2.58)$$

Substituting for $d\psi_t(X_t)$ from eq. 7.2.58 into eq. 7.2.55, we obtain

$$dY_t = \varphi_t(X_t)\,dW_t + \frac{1}{2}\sigma^2 g_t(X_t)\frac{\partial}{\partial x}\varphi_t(X_t)\,dt \qquad t \in T \qquad (7.2.59)$$

Integrating between the limits a to t with $Y_a = 0$ we arrive at

$$Y_t = \int_a^t \varphi_\tau(X_\tau)\,dW_\tau + \frac{1}{2}\sigma^2\int_a^t g_\tau(X_\tau)\frac{\partial}{\partial x}\varphi_\tau(X_\tau)\,d\tau \qquad t \in T \qquad (7.2.60)$$

As in eq. 7.2.21, here also we get an additional term,

$$\frac{1}{2}\sigma^2\int_a^t g_\tau(X_\tau)\frac{\partial\varphi_\tau(X_\tau)}{\partial x}\,d\tau$$

called correction term.

Thus the white noise integral, eq. 7.2.24, is equal to the corresponding stochastic integral plus the correction term. Conversely the stochastic integral is equal to the corresponding white noise integral minus the correction term. We have therefore established the relationship between the white noise integral and the corresponding stochastic integral for the cases where f in eq. 7.2.1 is given by either $\varphi_t(W_t)$ or $\varphi_t(X_t)$ where X_t is the Ito process connected to W_t via the stochastic differential equation 7.2.44.

We have shown the existence of correction terms when we go from the white noise integral to the corresponding stochastic integral and from the white noise differential equation to the corresponding stochastic differential equation. We have also seen that all these convergences are in the almost sure sense. We shall now state the assumptions (Wong and Zakai, 64) on the approximating sequence $\{W_{nt}, t \in T\}$ of a Brownian motion process W_t, $t \in T$.

1. For all $t \in T$ the process $W_{nt}(\omega)$ is sample continuous, and for each n and almost all ω it is of bounded variation and

$$W_{nt}(\cdot)\xrightarrow[n\to\infty]{\text{a.s.}} W_t(\cdot)$$

Note that $W_t(\omega)$ is of unbounded variation.

2. For all $t \in T$ and for almost all ω, W_{nt} is uniformly bounded,

$$\sup_n \sup_{t\in T}|W_{nt}(\omega)| < \infty$$

3. For each n and almost all ω, $W_{nt}(\omega)$ has a continuous first derivative with respect to time,

$$\dot{W}_{nt}(\omega) = \frac{dW_{nt}(\omega)}{dt}$$

4. For each n and almost all ω, $W_{nt}(\omega)$ is a polygonal approximation of $W_t(\omega)$, defined by

$$W_{nt}(\omega) = W_{t_\nu^{(n)}}(\omega) + \left[W_{t_{\nu+1}^{(n)}}(\omega) - W_{t_\nu^{(n)}}(\omega)\right]\frac{t - t_\nu^{(n)}}{t_{\nu+1}^{(n)} - t_\nu^{(n)}}$$

$$t_\nu^{(n)} \le t < t_{\nu+1}^{(n)}, \quad \nu = 0,1,\ldots,N(n) \qquad (7.2.61)$$

where $\{t_\nu^{(n)}, \nu = 0, 1, \ldots, N(n)\}$ are the partitions of the interval $T = [a, b]$ such that

$$a = t_0^{(n)} < t_1^{(n)} < \cdots < t_{N(n)}^{(n)} = b$$

and

$$\lim_{n\to\infty} \max_{\nu} \left(t_{\nu+1}^{(n)} - t_\nu^{(n)} \right) \to 0$$

We are now in a position to state the following propositions on the convergences of

$$Y_{nt}(\omega) = \int_a^t \varphi_\tau(W_{n\tau}(\omega))\, dW_{n\tau}(\omega) \qquad t \in T \tag{7.2.6}$$

$$dX_{nt}(\omega) = f_t(X_{nt}(\omega))\, dt + g_t(X_{nt}(\omega))\, dW_{nt}(\omega) \qquad t \in T \tag{7.2.28}$$

$$Y_{nt}(\omega) = \int_a^t \varphi_\tau(X_{n\tau}(\omega))\, dW_{n\tau}(\omega) \qquad t \in T \tag{7.2.26}$$

Proposition 7.2.1 (Wong and Zakai, 63, p. 160, 64)

Let $\varphi_t(x)$ have continuous partial derivatives $\partial\varphi_t(x)/\partial t$ and $\partial\varphi_t(x)/\partial x$ for $t \in T$ and $x \in (-\infty, \infty)$, where $T = [a, b]$. Let the approximating sequence $W_{nt}(\omega)$, $t \in T$, satisfy assumptions 1 and 2. Then

$$\int_a^b \varphi_\tau(W_{n\tau}(\omega))\, dW_{n\tau}(\omega) \xrightarrow[n\to\infty]{\text{a.s.}} \int_a^b \varphi_\tau(W_\tau(\omega))\, dW_\tau(\omega) + \frac{1}{2}\sigma^2 \int_a^b \frac{\partial\varphi_\tau(W_\tau(\omega))}{\partial w}\, d\tau \tag{7.2.62}$$

Proposition 7.2.2 (Wong and Zakai, 63, p. 160, 64)

Let $f_t(x)$, $g_t(x)$, $\partial g_t(x)/\partial t$, and $\partial g_t(x)/\partial x$ be continuous in $x \in (-\infty, \infty)$ and $t \in T$. Further, let $f_t(x)$, $g_t(x)$, and $g_t(x)\, \partial g_t(x)/\partial x$ satisfy the uniform Lipschitz conditions 7.1.5–7.1.7. Let $\{X_{nt}(\omega), t \in T\}$ satisfy the differential equation 7.2.28,

$$dX_{nt}(\omega) = f_t(X_t(\omega))\, dt + g_t(X_{nt}(\omega))\, dW_{nt}(\omega) \qquad t \in T \tag{7.2.28}$$

and let $X_t(\omega)$, $t \in T$, satisfy the stochastic differential equation 7.2.44,

$$dX_t(\omega) = f_t(X_t(\omega))\, dt + \frac{1}{2}\sigma^2 g_t(X_t(\omega)) \frac{\partial}{\partial x} g_t(X_t(\omega))\, dt + g_t(X_t(\omega))\, dW_t(\omega) \qquad t \in T \tag{7.2.44}$$

Let the initial condition $X_{na}(\omega) = X_a(\omega)$, with $EX_a^2 < \infty$, be independent of $|W_t - W_a|$, $t \in T$.

1. If in addition $|g_t(x)| > 0$ and $|g_t(x)| < Kg_t^2(x)$, then with $\{W_{nt}(\omega)\}$ satisfying assumptions 1, 2, and 3,

$$X_{nt}(\omega) \xrightarrow[n\to\infty]{\text{a.s.}} X_t(\omega) \qquad t \in T$$

2. If, however, $W_{nt}(\omega)$ satisfies assumption 4 and with $EX_t^4 < \infty$, then

$$X_{nt}(\omega) \xrightarrow[n\to\infty]{\text{l.i.q.m.}} X_t(\omega) \qquad t \in T$$

Proposition 7.2.3

Let $\varphi_t(x)$ have continuous partial derivatives $\partial\varphi_t(x)/\partial t$ and $\partial\varphi_t(x)/\partial x$ for $t \in T$ and $x \in (-\infty, \infty)$. Let the sequence $\{X_{nt}(\omega), t \in T\}$ and the process $\{X_t(\omega), t \in T\}$ satisfy the conditions of Proposition 7.2.2. Then

$$\int_a^b \varphi_\tau(X_{n\tau}(\omega))\, dW_{n\tau} \xrightarrow[n\to\infty]{\text{a.s.}} \int_a^b \varphi_\tau(X_\tau(\omega))\, dW_\tau + \frac{1}{2}\sigma^2 \int_a^b g_\tau(X_\tau) \frac{\partial\varphi_\tau(X_\tau)}{\partial x}\, \partial\tau$$

if $\{W_{nt}(\omega), t \in T\}$ and $g_t(x)$ satisfy condition 1 of Proposition 7.2.2. If, however, $\{W_{nt}(\omega), t \in T\}$ and X_t satisfy condition 2 of Proposition 7.2.2, then the convergence is in the quadratic mean.

7.3 VECTOR FORMULATION

In many applications involving white noise differential equations we frequently encounter signal equation given in vector form as

$$\frac{d\mathbf{X}_t}{dt} = \mathbf{f}_t(\mathbf{X}_t) + \mathbf{G}_t(\mathbf{X}_t)\mathbf{Z}_t \qquad t \in T \tag{7.3.1}$$

or

$$d\mathbf{X}_t = \mathbf{f}_t(\mathbf{X}_t)\, dt + \mathbf{G}_t(\mathbf{X}_t)\mathbf{Z}_t\, dt \qquad t \in T \tag{7.3.2}$$

where $\mathbf{X}_t$ and $\mathbf{f}_t$ are n-vectors, $\mathbf{Z}_t$ is a p-vector of independent Gaussian white noise processes with parameters $\boldsymbol{\sigma}^2$, and $\mathbf{G}_t$ is an $n \times p$ rectangular matrix. **Boldface** will be used throughout to represent both vectors and matrices. The stochastic differential equation corresponding to eqs. 7.3.1 and 7.3.2 is

$$d\mathbf{X}_t = \mathbf{f}_t(\mathbf{X}_t)\, dt + \mathbf{G}_t(\mathbf{X}_t)\, d\mathbf{W}_t + \text{correction terms} \tag{7.3.3}$$

in a manner similar to eq. 7.2.44.

To find these correction terms is not that trivial, and these terms have been given by Wong (63, p. 162).

To obtain an expression for the correction terms we reformulate the problem by writing eq. 7.3.2 in component form as

$$dX_{it} = f_{it}(\mathbf{X}_t)\,dt + \mathbf{g}_{it}(\mathbf{X}_t)\mathbf{Z}_t\,dt \qquad i = 1,2,\ldots,n, \quad t \in T \qquad (7.3.4)$$

where $\mathbf{g}_{it}$ is the *row* p-vector $\{g_{i1t} \quad g_{i2t} \quad \cdots \quad g_{ipt}]$. Corresponding to the white noise differential equation 7.3.4, the stochastic differential equation is

$$dX_{it} = f_{it}(\mathbf{X}_t)\,dt + \mathbf{g}_{it}(\mathbf{X}_t)\,d\mathbf{W}_t + \frac{1}{2}dt\sum_{l=1}^{p}\left[\frac{\partial g_{ilt}(\mathbf{X}_t)}{\partial \mathbf{x}}\right]^T \mathbf{g}_{lt}(\mathbf{X}_t)\sigma_l^2$$

$$i = 1,2,\ldots,n, \quad t \in T \qquad (7.3.5)$$

where $\mathbf{g}_{lt}$ is the *column* n-vector given by

$$\mathbf{g}_{lt} = \begin{bmatrix} g_{1lt} \\ g_{2lt} \\ \vdots \\ g_{nlt} \end{bmatrix}$$

and g_{ilt} is the element corresponding to the ith row and the lth column of the $\mathbf{G}_t$-matrix of eq. 7.3.2.

The correction terms for dX_{it} are given by

$$\frac{1}{2}dt\sum_{l=1}^{p}\left[\frac{\partial g_{ilt}(\mathbf{X}_t)}{\partial \mathbf{x}}\right]^T \mathbf{g}_{lt}(\mathbf{X}_t)\sigma_l^2 \qquad i = 1,2,\ldots,n, \quad t \in T \qquad (7.3.6)$$

Equation 7.3.5 can also be given in scalar form as

$$dX_{it} = f_{it}(\mathbf{X}_t)\,dt + \sum_{k=1}^{p} g_{ikt}(\mathbf{X}_t)\,dW_{kt} + \frac{1}{2}dt\sum_{m=1}^{n}\sum_{l=1}^{p}\frac{\partial g_{ilt}(\mathbf{X}_t)}{\partial x_m} g_{mlt}(\mathbf{X}_t)\sigma_l^2$$

$$i = 1,2,\ldots,n, \quad t \in T \qquad (7.3.7)$$

and the correction terms for dX_{it} are

$$\frac{1}{2}dt\sum_{m=1}^{n}\sum_{l=1}^{p}\frac{\partial g_{ilt}(\mathbf{X}_t)}{\partial x_m} g_{mlt}(\mathbf{X}_t)\sigma_l^2 \qquad (7.3.8)$$

where σ_l^2 is the variance parameter associated with the Brownian motion process W_{lt}.

7.4 STRATONOVICH INTEGRAL

We recall that the Ito integral

$$I_t(\varphi) = \int_a^t \varphi_\tau(\omega)\, dW_\tau(\omega) \qquad t \in T \tag{7.4.1}$$

with $\varphi_t(\cdot)$ satisfying the regularity conditions 6.1.3 was defined in Chapter 6 by

$$\int_a^t \varphi_\tau(\omega)\, dW_\tau(\omega) = \underset{n\to\infty}{\text{l.i.q.m.}} \sum_{\nu=0}^{N(n)-1} \varphi_{t_\nu^{(n)}}(\omega)\left[W_{t_{\nu+1}^{(n)}}(\omega) - W_{t_\nu^{(n)}}(\omega)\right] \qquad t \in T \tag{7.4.2}$$

where the partitions $\{t_\nu^{(n)}\}$ of $[a, t]$ satisfy

$$a = t_0^{(n)} < t_1^{(n)} < t_2^{(n)} < \cdots < t_{N(n)}^{(n)} = t \qquad t \in T$$

with $\max_\nu(t_{\nu+1}^{(n)} - t_\nu^{(n)}) \to 0$ as $n \to \infty$. The function sequence $\varphi_{t_\nu^{(n)}}(\omega)$ are (t, ω) approximants converging in the quadratic mean to $\varphi_t(\omega)$ as $n \to \infty$. We note in particular that the stochastic integral is defined by the forward difference $(W_{t_{\nu+1}^{(n)}} - W_{t_\nu^{(n)}})$. If the function $\varphi(\cdot)$ is a function of the Brownian motion process W_t, eq. 7.2.4, then the Ito integral is defined by

$$\int_a^t \varphi_\tau(W_\tau)\, dW_\tau = \underset{n\to\infty}{\text{l.i.q.m.}} \sum_{\nu=0}^{N(n)-1} \varphi_{t_\nu^{(n)}}(W_{t_\nu^{(n)}})(W_{t_{\nu+1}^{(n)}} - W_{t_\nu^{(n)}}) \qquad t \in T \tag{7.4.3}$$

A symmetrized definition has been given by Stratonovich (53) for the stochastic integral of eq. 7.4.3.

Definition 7.4.1 Stratonovich Stochastic Integral

Let the partitions of $\{t_\nu^{(n)}\}$ of $[a, t]$ satisfy

$$a = t_0^{(n)} < t_1^{(n)} < \cdots < t_{N(n)}^{(n)} = t \qquad t \in T$$

with $\max_\nu(t_{\nu+1}^{(n)} - t_\nu^{(n)}) \to 0$ as $n \to \infty$. The Stratonovich stochastic integral (notation: $\int_a^t \varphi_\tau(W_\tau) \circ dW_\tau$) is denoted by

$$\int_a^t \varphi_\tau(W_\tau) \circ dW_\tau = \underset{n\to\infty}{\text{l.i.q.m.}} \sum_{\nu=0}^{N(n)-1} \frac{1}{2}\left(\varphi_{t_\nu^{(n)}}(W_{t_\nu^{(n)}}) + \varphi_{t_{\nu+1}^{(n)}}(W_{t_{\nu+1}^{(n)}})\right) \times (W_{t_{\nu+1}^{(n)}} - W_{t_\nu^{(n)}}) \tag{7.4.4}$$

Like the Ito integral the Stratonovich integral is also defined by the forward difference $(W_{t_{\nu+1}^{(n)}} - W_{t_\nu^{(n)}})$ but the function φ is given by the average of the forward $(t_{\nu+1}^{(n)})$ and present $(t_\nu^{(n)})$ values.

It can be shown that the Stratonovich integral defined by eq. 7.4.4 satisfies all the formal rules of calculus including the chain rule of differentiation (see Ito and Watanabe, 12, p. xi) and thus behaves like an ordinary integral. However, the Stratonovich integral loses the martingale property. A relationship between the integrals can be established just like the relationship (eq. 7.2.22) between the white noise integral and the Ito integral. Thus we come to the following proposition given without proof.

Proposition 7.4.1 Stratonovich (53)

Let $(\Omega, \mathfrak{F}, P)$ be a complete probability space and let $\{\mathfrak{F}_t, t \in T\}$ be a filtration σ-field defined on it. Let φ_t be a nonanticipatory continuous function satisfying the conditions 6.1.3. Under these conditions the limit in the quadratic mean exists for eq. 7.4.4 and the integral is related to the Ito integral by

$$\int_a^t \varphi_\tau(W_\tau) \circ dW_\tau = \int_a^t \varphi_\tau(W_\tau)\, dW_\tau + \frac{1}{2}\int_a^t d\varphi_\tau(W_\tau)\, dW_\tau \qquad t \in T \quad (7.4.5)$$

More generally, if $\{X_t, \mathfrak{F}_t, t \in T\}$ and $\{Y_t, \mathfrak{F}_t, t \in T\}$ are two continuous semimartingales, the Stratonovich integral $\int_a^t Y_\tau \circ dX_\tau$ can be given by (see Ito and Watanabe, 72)

$$\int_a^t Y_\tau \circ dX_\tau = \int_a^t Y_\tau\, dX_\tau + \frac{1}{2}\int_a^t dY_\tau \cdot dX_\tau \qquad t \in T \qquad (7.4.6)$$

However, from the results of the last chapter (eq. 6.7.10) $dY_t \cdot dX_t = \langle dM_Y, dM_X \rangle_t$ where M_Y and M_X are the martingales associated with the continuous semimartingales Y and X. Hence eq. 7.4.6 can also be given in an equivalent form as

$$\int_a^t Y_\tau \circ dX_\tau = \int_a^t Y_\tau\, dX_\tau + \frac{1}{2}\int_a^t \langle dM_Y, dM_X \rangle_\tau \qquad t \in T \qquad (7.4.7)$$

By using eq. 7.4.7, eq. 7.4.5 can be given as (see Davis, 19, p. 509)

$$\int_a^t \varphi_\tau(W_\tau) \circ dW_\tau = \int_a^t \varphi_\tau(W_\tau)\, dW_\tau + \tfrac{1}{2}\int_a^t d\langle \varphi(W), W \rangle_\tau \qquad t \in T \qquad (7.4.8)$$

If partial derivatives of φ exist, then

$$d\langle \varphi(W), W\rangle_t = \frac{\partial \varphi_t(W_t)}{\partial w} \cdot \sigma^2 \, dt$$

and eq. 7.4.8 reduces to

$$\int_a^t \varphi_\tau(W_\tau) \circ dW_\tau = \int_a^t \varphi_\tau(W_\tau) \, dW_\tau + \frac{1}{2}\sigma^2 \int_a^t \frac{\partial \varphi_\tau(W_\tau)}{\partial w} \, d\tau \qquad t \in T \tag{7.4.9}$$

Thus we see the equivalence between the white noise integral $\int_a^t \varphi_\tau(W_\tau) Z_\tau \, d\tau$ (eq. 7.2.22) and the Stratonovich integral $\int_a^t \varphi_\tau(W_\tau) \circ dW_\tau$ given above. Both these integrals obey the ordinary laws of calculus.

The form for the Stratonovich differential equation analogous to the Ito differential equation (7.1.2) is given by

$$dX_t = f_t(X_t) \, dt + g_t(X_t) \circ dW_t \qquad t \in T \tag{7.4.10}$$

By using eq. 7.4.8 the Ito integral corresponding to the Stratonovich integral $\int_a^t g_\tau(X_\tau) \circ dW_\tau$ can be found.

Assuming partial derivatives of g exist, the quadratic covariance process

$$d\langle g(X), W\rangle_t = \frac{\partial g_t(X_t)}{\partial x} g_t(X_t) \sigma^2 t$$

and the Ito stochastic differential equation corresponding to eq. 7.4.10 is

$$dX_t = f_t(X_t) \, dt + g_t(X_t) \, dW_t + \frac{1}{2}\sigma^2 \frac{\partial g_t(X_t)}{\partial x} g_t(X_t) \, dt \quad t \in T$$

which is the same as eq. 7.2.44.

Thus the Stratonovich differential equation (7.4.10) is the same as the white noise differential equation (7.2.29) and Proposition 7.2.2 applies.

We now give several examples to illustrate the differences between Stratonovich and Ito differential equations and their solutions.

Example 7.4.1

With $W_t - W_a = \varphi_t(W_t)$ we evaluate

$$I_t(\varphi) = \int_a^t \varphi_\tau(W_\tau) \, dW_\tau \qquad t \in T \tag{7.4.11}$$

both in the Ito and the Stratonovich senses.

Ito Solution. With $a = t_0^{(n)} < t_1^{(n)} < \cdots < t_{N(n)}^{(n)} = t$ we have by the Ito definition (eq. 7.4.3)

$$\int_a^t (W_\tau - W_a)\, dW_\tau = \underset{n\to\infty}{\text{l.i.q.m.}} \sum_{\nu=0}^{N(n)-1} \left(W_{t_\nu^{(n)}} - W_a\right)\left(W_{t_{\nu+1}^{(n)}} - W_{t_\nu^{(n)}}\right)$$

$$= \underset{n\to\infty}{\text{l.i.q.m.}} \Big(W_{t_1^{(n)}} W_{t_2^{(n)}} - W_a W_{t_2^{(n)}} - W_{t_1^{(n)}}^2 + W_a W_{t_1^{(n)}}$$

$$+ W_{t_2^{(n)}} W_{t_3^{(n)}} - W_a W_{t_3^{(n)}} - W_{t_2^{(n)}}^2 + W_a W_{t_2^{(n)}} + \cdots$$

$$+ W_{t_{N(n)-1}^{(n)}} W_t - W_a W_t - W_{t_{N(n)-1}^{(n)}}^2 + W_a W_{t_{N(n)-1}^{(n)}} \Big)$$

$$= \underset{n\to\infty}{\text{l.i.q.m.}} \Big(W_a W_{t_1^{(n)}} - \tfrac{1}{2} W_a^2 - \tfrac{1}{2} W_{t_1^{(n)}}^2$$

$$+ W_{t_1^{(n)}} W_{t_2^{(n)}} - \tfrac{1}{2} W_{t_1^{(n)}}^2 - \tfrac{1}{2} W_{t_2^{(n)}}^2$$

$$\cdots$$

$$+ W_{t_{N(n)-1}^{(n)}} W_t - \tfrac{1}{2} W_{t_{N(n)-1}^{(n)}}^2 - \tfrac{1}{2} W_t^2$$

$$+ \tfrac{1}{2} W_a^2 + \tfrac{1}{2} W_t^2 - W_a W_t \Big)$$

which on simplification yields

$$\int_a^t (W_\tau - W_a)\, dW_\tau = \underset{n\to\infty}{\text{l.i.q.m.}} \left[\tfrac{1}{2}(W_t - W_a)^2 - \tfrac{1}{2} \sum_{\nu=0}^{N(n)-1} \left(W_{t_{\nu+1}^{(n)}} - W_{t_\nu^{(n)}}\right)^2 \right]$$

$$= \tfrac{1}{2}(W_t - W_a)^2 - \lim_{n\to\infty} \tfrac{1}{2} E \sum_{\nu=0}^{N(n)-1} \left(W_{t_{\nu+1}^{(n)}} - W_{t_\nu^{(n)}}\right)^2$$

$$= \tfrac{1}{2}(W_t - W_a)^2 - \tfrac{1}{2}\sigma^2(t - a) \tag{7.4.12}$$

which corresponds to the result

$$\int_0^t W_\tau\, dW_\tau = \frac{W_t^2}{2} - \frac{\sigma^2 t}{2}$$

already derived.

Stratonovich Solution. Let us now calculate the stochastic integral eq. 7.4.11 in the Stratonovich sense, namely,

$$I_t(\varphi) = \int_a^t \varphi_\tau(W_\tau) \circ dW_\tau \qquad t \in T$$

$$\int_a^t (W_\tau - W_a) \circ dW_\tau$$

$$= \underset{n\to\infty}{\text{l.i.q.m.}} \sum_{\nu=0}^{N(n)-1} \left(\frac{W_{t_{\nu+1}^{(n)}} + W_{t_\nu^{(n)}}}{2} - W_a \right) \left(W_{t_{\nu+1}^{(n)}} - W_{t_\nu^{(n)}} \right)$$

$$= \underset{n\to\infty}{\text{l.i.q.m.}} \sum_{\nu=0}^{N(n)-1} \left[\left(W_{t_\nu^{(n)}} - W_a \right) \left(W_{t_{\nu+1}^{(n)}} - W_{t_\nu^{(n)}} \right) + \tfrac{1}{2} \left(W_{t_{\nu+1}^{(n)}} - W_{t_\nu^{(n)}} \right)^2 \right]$$

$$= \tfrac{1}{2}(W_t - W_a)^2 - \tfrac{1}{2}\sigma^2(t-a) + \tfrac{1}{2}\sigma^2(t-a) \qquad \text{from eq. 7.4.12}$$

$$= \tfrac{1}{2}(W_t - W_a)^2 \tag{7.4.13}$$

Instead of going through the fundamental definition of the Stratonovich integral we can also find the Stratonovich solution from eq. 7.4.8 by calculating the quadratic variance $d\langle W - W_a, W\rangle_t$ and adding $\int_a^t d\langle W - W_a, W\rangle_\tau$ to the Ito solution. Since $\int_a^t d\langle W - W_a, W\rangle_\tau = \sigma^2(t-a)$, the Stratonovich solution is again eq. 7.4.13.

The result of eq. 7.4.13 could have been derived by the usual laws of calculus, whereas eq. 7.4.12 could not have been derived by that method. However, the integral defined in the Stratonovich sense loses the martingale property. In the above example, $\frac{1}{2}(W_t - W_a)^2 - \frac{1}{2}\sigma^2(t-a)$ is a martingale, whereas $\frac{1}{2}(W_t - W_a)^2$ is not.

Example 7.4.2

Let the underlying Ito process be

$$dX_t = dW_t \qquad t \in T, \quad T = R^+$$

and if the process Y_t is given by

$$Y_t = e^{W_t} \tag{7.4.14}$$

then dY_t obtained by using the Ito calculus,

$$dY_t = e^{W_t}\,dW_t + \tfrac{1}{2}\sigma^2 e^{W_t}\,dt$$

or

$$dY_t = Y_t\,dW_t + \tfrac{1}{2}\sigma^2 Y_t\,dt \qquad t \in T, \quad Y_0 = 1 \tag{7.4.15}$$

The corresponding integral form for eq. 7.4.15 is

$$\int_0^t dY_\tau = 1 + \int_0^t Y_\tau\,dW_\tau + \tfrac{1}{2}\sigma^2 \int_0^t Y_\tau\,d\tau \qquad t \in T \tag{7.4.16}$$

where $\int_0^t Y_\tau\,dW_\tau$ is the Ito integral.

Clearly the solution to the stochastic differential equation (7.4.15) interpreted in the Ito sense is $Y_t = e^{W_t}$. We now find the solution to the same stochastic differential equation interpreted in the Stratonovich sense.

By using eq. 7.4.7 the Stratonovich equivalent of the Ito differential $Y_t\,dW_t$ is given by

$$Y_t \circ dW_t = Y_t\,dW_t + \tfrac{1}{2}d\langle Y, W\rangle_t \tag{7.4.17}$$

where the quadratic covariance $d\langle Y, W\rangle_t$ can be calculated as

$$d\langle Y, W\rangle_t = \frac{dY_t}{dw}d\langle W, W\rangle_t = \sigma^2 Y_t\,dt$$

By substituting eq. 7.4.17 into eq. 7.4.15 the Stratonovich stochastic differential equation is given by

$$dY_t = Y_t \circ dW_t \qquad t \in T, \quad Y_0 = 1 \tag{7.4.18}$$

with the corresponding integral representation

$$\int_0^t dY_\tau = 1 + \int_0^t Y_\tau \circ dW_\tau \qquad t \in T \tag{7.4.19}$$

Since the Stratonovich differential equation can be manipulated by the ordinary rules of calculus we obtain the solution to eq. 7.4.18 as $Y_t = e^{W_t}$, the same as the Ito solution.

Thus in many computational problems involving Ito stochastic differential equations, the solutions can be more readily obtained by converting them into Stratonovich form and applying ordinary laws of calculus. This is particularly advantageous when computers are employed since the Runge–Kutta algorithms used to solve differential equations converge to the Stratonovich solution.

Example 7.4.3

Equation 7.4.18 will now be interpreted in the Ito sense

$$dY_t = Y_t\,dW_t \qquad t \in T \tag{7.4.20}$$

The corresponding Stratonovich differential equation can be obtained from eq. 7.4.17 as

$$dY_t = Y_t \circ dW_t - \tfrac{1}{2}\sigma^2 Y_t\,dt \qquad t \in T, \quad Y_0 = 1 \tag{7.4.21}$$

The formal solution to this differential equation using ordinary calculus is

$$Y_t = \exp\left(W_t - \tfrac{1}{2}\sigma^2 t\right)$$

In summary, we have the following:

1. $dY_t = Y_t\,dW_t$ ↗ Ito solution; $\exp\left(W_t - \tfrac{1}{2}\sigma^2 t\right)$ ↘ Stratonovich solution; e^{W_t}
2. $dY_t = Y_t\,dW_t + \tfrac{1}{2}\sigma^2 Y_t\,dt$ ↗ Ito solution; e^{W_t} ↘ Stratonovich solution; $\exp\left(W_t + \tfrac{1}{2}\sigma^2 t\right)$

Example 7.4.4

As a final example we investigate the effects of forward difference, central difference, and any general difference for $Y_t = e^{W_t}$ where W_t is the Brownian motion process (Varadhan, 54, p. 72).

Forward Difference. If

$$\begin{aligned} dY_t &= e^{W_{t+dt}} - e^{W_t} \\ &= e^{W_t}\left(1 + dW_t + \frac{dW_t^2}{2} + \frac{dW_t^3}{3!} + \cdots\right) - e^{W_t} \\ &= Y_t\left(dW_t + \frac{dW_t^2}{2}\right) + o\left(dW_t^2\right) \end{aligned}$$

or

$$dY_t = Y_t\,dW_t + \frac{\sigma^2}{2} Y_t\,dt \qquad \text{Ito equation}$$

Central Difference

$$\begin{aligned} dY_t &= e^{W_{t+dt/2}} - e^{W_{t-dt/2}} \\ &= e^{W_t}\left(1 + \frac{dW_t}{2} + \frac{dW_t^2}{2.2} + \cdots\right) - e^{W_t}\left(1 - \frac{dW_t}{2} + \frac{dW_t^2}{2.2} + \cdots\right) \\ &= e^{W_t}\,dW_t + 0 \end{aligned}$$

or

$$dY_t = Y_t \circ dW_t \qquad \text{Stratonovich equation}$$

General Difference. For any general difference we can write with $0 \leq \lambda \leq 1$

$$\begin{aligned} d_\lambda Y_t &= Y_{t+\lambda\,dt} - Y_{t-(1-\lambda)\,dt} \\ &= e^{W_{t+\lambda\,dt}} - e^{W_{t-(1-\lambda)\,dt}} \\ &= Y_t\left[1 + \lambda\,dW_t + \frac{\lambda^2\,dW_t^2}{2} + o\left(dW_t^3\right)\right] \\ &\quad - Y_t\left[1 - (1-\lambda)\,dW_t + (1-\lambda)^2\frac{dW_t^2}{2} + o\left(dW_t^3\right)\right] \\ &= Y_t\left\{[\lambda + (1-\lambda)]\,dW_t + \tfrac{1}{2}dW_t^2(2\lambda - 1) + o\left(dW_t^3\right)\right\} \\ &= Y_t\left[dW_t + \left(\lambda - \tfrac{1}{2}\right)dW_t^2 + o\left(dW_t^3\right)\right] \end{aligned}$$

or

$$d_\lambda Y_t = Y_t\,dW_t + Y_t\left(\lambda - \tfrac{1}{2}\right)dW_t^2 \tag{7.4.22}$$

In equation 7.4.22

if $\lambda = 1$ (forward difference),

$$dY_t = Y_t\,dW_t + \tfrac{1}{2}Y_t\,dW_t^2 \qquad \text{Ito}$$

if $\lambda = \frac{1}{2}$ (central difference),

$$dY_t = Y_t \circ dW_t \qquad \text{Stratonovich}$$

if $\lambda = 0$ (backward difference),

$$dY_t = Y_t\,dW_t - \tfrac{1}{2}Y_t\,dW_t^2$$

As a consequence of $\lambda = \frac{1}{2}$, the Stratonovich integral satisfies the ordinary differential calculus in this case and it can be shown to be true in the general case also. However, as already stated before, the martingale property of the stochastic integral is lost.

Problems

1. Let $\{X_t, t \in T, T = [0, b]\}$ be a solution to the stochastic differential equation

$$dX_t = f_t X_t\,dt + g_t X_t\,dW_t \qquad t > 0$$

where f_t and g_t are square integrable nonrandom functions. Show that the solution X_t is given by

$$X_t = X_0 \exp\left[\int_0^t g_s\, dW_s + \int_0^t \left(f_s - \frac{g_s^2}{2}\right) ds\right] \qquad t \in T$$

2. Let $\{X_t, t \in T,\ T = [0, b]\}$ be a solution to the stochastic differential equation

$$dX_t = f_t(X_t)\, dt + g_t(X_t)\, dW_t$$

with f and g satisfying the conditions in Theorem 7.1.1. Show that for $k > 0$

$$EX_t^2 \le 3\left[EX_0^2 + K(1 + t)\int_0^t (1 + EX_s^2)\, ds\right] \qquad t \in T$$

3. Let $\{X_t, t \in T,\ T = [a, b]\}$ be a sample continuous second-order stochastic process. Let $\mathscr{F}_t$ be the σ-field generated by X_t, that is, $\mathscr{F}_t = \sigma\{X_s, s \le t\}$. Let $\{X_t, t \in T\}$ further satisfy the following conditions:
   a. There exists a $\{Z_t, t \in T\}$ with $Z_t > 0$ and $EZ_t < \infty$ such that $\sup_{t>s} E^{\mathscr{F}_s} X_t^2 \le Z_s$
   b. There exists a function $q(h) > 0$ with $\lim_{h \downarrow 0} q(h) = 0$ such that for $a \le t \le t + h \le b$,

$$\left|E^{\mathscr{F}_t}(X_{t+h} - X_t) - \int_t^{t+h} f_s(X_s)\, ds\right| \le hq(h)(1 + X_t^2)$$

$$\left|E^{\mathscr{F}_t}(X_{t+h} - X_t)^2 - \int_t^{t+h} g_s^2(X_s)\, ds\right| \le hq(h)(1 + X_t^2)$$

   where f and g are nonanticipative $\mathscr{F}_t$-measurable functions satisfying

$$f_t(x) \le K\sqrt{1 + x^2}$$

$$0 \le g_t(x) \le K\sqrt{1 + x^2}$$

   Show that $\{X_t, t \in T\}$ is a Markov process satisfying the stochastic differential equation

$$X_t = X_a + \int_a^t f_\tau(X_\tau)\, d\tau + \int_a^t g_\tau(X_\tau)\, dW_\tau \qquad t \in T$$

   Is the solution unique?

4. $\{X_t, t \in T\}$ satisfies the following stochastic differential equation:

$$dX_t = -X_t\,dt + \sqrt{2(1 + X_t^2)}\,dW_t$$

where $\{W_t, t \in T\}$ is a Brownian motion process with parameter σ^2. Find the corresponding white noise differential equation.

5. A stochastic differential equation is given by

$$dX_t = 2\,dt + \sqrt{X_t}\,dW_t$$

where $\{W_t, t \in T\}$ is a standard Brownian motion process. Does $\sqrt{X_t}$ satisfy the uniform Lipschitz condition? Find the corresponding white noise differential equation with $X_0 = 0$.

6. $\{Y_t, t \in T\}$ and $\{Z_t, t \in T\}$ are two standard Brownian motion processes. Let

$$X_t = Y_t^2 + Z_t^2$$

Find the stochastic differential equation satisfied by X_t.

7. A white noise differential equation is given by

$$dX_t = f_t(X_t)\,dt + \mathbf{g}_t^T(X_t)\mathbf{Z}_t\,dt$$

where $\mathbf{g}_t^T$ is the row p-vector $[g_{1t} \quad g_{2t} \quad \cdots \quad g_{pt}]$ and $\mathbf{Z}_t$ is a p-vector of independent Gaussian white noise processes with parameter $\boldsymbol{\sigma}^2$. Show that the corresponding stochastic differential equation is

$$dX_t = f_t(X_t)\,dt + \mathbf{g}_t^T(X_t)\,d\mathbf{W}_t + \tfrac{1}{2}dt\frac{\partial}{\partial x}\mathbf{g}_t^T(X_t)\boldsymbol{\alpha}_t(X_t)$$

where $\boldsymbol{\alpha}_t$ is a p-vector consisting of components $g_{1t}\sigma_1^2, g_{2t}\sigma_2^2, \ldots, g_{pt}\sigma_p^2$.

8. A white noise differential equation is given by

$$d\mathbf{X}_t = \mathbf{f}_t(\mathbf{X}_t)\,dt + \mathbf{g}_t(\mathbf{X}_t)Z_t\,dt$$

where **X**, **f**, and **g** are n-vectors and Z is a scalar white noise process with parameter σ^2. Show that the corresponding stochastic differential equation is

$$d\mathbf{X}_t = \mathbf{f}_t(\mathbf{X}_t)\,dt + \mathbf{g}_t(\mathbf{X}_t)\,dW_t + \frac{1}{2}\sigma^2\,dt\left(\frac{\partial}{\partial \mathbf{x}}\right)^T \mathbf{g}_t(\mathbf{X}_t)\cdot\mathbf{g}_t(\mathbf{X}_t)$$

9. Rederive the Ito formula, eq. 6.3.2, using the Stratonovich definition, eq. 7.4.4, of the stochastic integral. Does the correction term disappear in the Ito formula?

10. Let $\mathbf{X}_t$ be the vector

$$\mathbf{X}_t = \begin{bmatrix} W_t^2 \\ e^{W_t} \end{bmatrix}$$

Show that $\mathbf{X}_t$ is the solution of the vector Ito stochastic differential equation

$$d\mathbf{X}_t = \mathbf{f}(\mathbf{X}_t)\, dt + \mathbf{g}(\mathbf{X}_t)\, dW_t$$

where

$$\mathbf{f}(x) = \begin{bmatrix} 1 \\ \frac{1}{2}e^x \end{bmatrix} \qquad \mathbf{g}(x) = \begin{bmatrix} 2x \\ e^x \end{bmatrix}$$

11. In Problem 10 derive the corresponding vector Stratonovich stochastic differential equation. Solve for the Stratonovich solution if the vector stochastic differential equation in Problem 10 is interpreted in the Stratonovich sense.

12. The stochastic differential equation

$$dX_t = aX_t\, dt + bX_t\, dW_t \qquad a, b \text{ constants}, \quad X_0$$

is interpreted in the Stratonovich sense.

a. Find the corresponding Ito differential equation.
b. Solve the differential equation.

8 OPTIMAL NONLINEAR FILTERING

8.1 DIFFUSION PROCESSES

Before we go into the detailed representation of the nonlinear filtering problem, we shall cover some preliminaries. We defined the Ito process in Chapter 6 as

$$dX_t(\omega) = a_t(\omega)\,dt + b_t(\omega)\,dW_t(\omega) \qquad t \in T, \quad X_0(\omega) \tag{8.1.1}$$

where $a_t(\omega)$ and $b_t(\omega)$ satisfy the conditions of Definition 6.2.1, with $W_t(\omega)$ being a Brownian motion process. Note that $a_t(\omega)$ and $b_t(\omega)$ are not necessarily functions of the Ito process X_t. We also defined a general stochastic differential equation in Chapter 7 as

$$dX_t(\omega) = f_t(X_t(\omega))\,dt + g_t(X_t(\omega))\,dW_t(\omega) \qquad t \in T, \quad X_0(\omega) \tag{8.1.2}$$

with f_t and g_t satisfying regularity conditions of Theorem 7.1.1. Note here that f_t and g_t are explicit functions of the process X_t. Such processes are known as diffusion processes. There are many definitions for a diffusion process, but we give the following definition.

Definition 8.1.1 Diffusion Process

Let $(\Omega, \mathfrak{F}, P)$ be a complete probability space, and let $\{\mathfrak{B}_t, t \in T\}$ be a filtration σ-field defined on it. The Ito process $\{X_t, \mathfrak{B}_t, t \in T\}$ given by eq.

8.1.1 is called a *diffusion process* relative to the Brownian motion process $\{W_t, \mathfrak{B}_t, t \in T\}$ if the functionals $a_t(\omega)$ and $b_t(\omega)$, for all $t \in T$, are measurable with respect to the right continuous σ-field $\mathfrak{F}_t$ generated by $\{X_s, s \leq t, t \in T\}$,

$$a_t(\omega),\, b_t(\omega) \in \sigma\{X_s, s \leq t, t \in T\} = \mathfrak{F}_t \tag{8.1.3}$$

Note. The σ-field $\{\mathfrak{F}_t, t \in T\}$ is a subfield of $\{\mathfrak{B}_t, t \in T\}$, $\mathfrak{B}_t \supset \mathfrak{F}_t$, and the stochastic differential equation 8.1.2 is a diffusion process.

It can be shown (Lipster and Shiryaev, 34, p. 114) by construction that if $\{X_t, t \in T\}$ is a diffusion process with coefficients $a_t(\omega)$ and $b_t(\omega)$, then there will be diffusion coefficients $f_t(X_t)$ and $g_t(X_t)$ measurable with respect to the right continuous σ-field $\{\mathfrak{F}_t, t \in T\}$ generated by $\{X_s, s \leq t, t \in T\}$ such that for all $t \in T$,

$$f_t(X_t(\omega)) = a_t(\omega) \quad \text{(a.s.)}, \qquad g_t(X_t(\omega)) = b_t(\omega) \quad \text{(a.s.)} \tag{8.1.4}$$

Hence given that the process is of the diffusion type, the Ito process representation of eq. 8.1.1 and the diffusion process representation of eq. 8.1.2 are equivalent.

A question now arises as to whether *any* Ito process can be represented as a diffusion process relative to the innovations process $\{\nu_t, t \in T\}$. The answer is given in the following theorem due to Kailath (27, 28). See also Lipster and Shiryaev (34, p. 258).

Theorem 8.1.1 Ito Process as a Diffusion Process Relative to Innovations

Let $\{X_t, \mathfrak{B}_t, t \in T\}$ be an Ito process defined on a complete probability space $(\Omega, \mathfrak{F}, P)$ represented by the stochastic differential equation

$$dX_t = a_t(\omega)\,dt + dW_t(\omega) \qquad t \in T, \quad X_0(\omega) = 0 \tag{8.1.5}$$

where

$$\int_{t\in T} E|a_t(\omega)|\,dt < \infty$$

with $\mathfrak{B}_t$ being the σ-field generated by $\{a_s, W_s, s \leq t, t \in T\}$. σ^2 is the variance parameter associated with W_t. Let $\{\mathfrak{F}_t, t \in T\}$ be the right continuous σ-field generated by $\{X_s, s \leq t, t \in T\}$ with $\mathfrak{F}_t \subset \mathfrak{B}_t \subset \mathfrak{F}$, and define a functional $\alpha_t(X_t(\omega)) = \hat{a}_t(\omega)$ as the projection of $a_t(\omega)$ on the σ-field $\{\mathfrak{F}_t, t \in T\}$,

$$\alpha_t(X_t(\omega)) = \hat{a}_t(\omega) = E^{\mathfrak{F}_t} a_t(\omega) \tag{8.1.6}$$

Then the innovations process ν_t given by

$$d\nu_t = dX_t - \alpha_t(X_t)\,dt \quad t \in T \tag{8.1.7}$$

is an $\mathcal{F}_t$-measurable Brownian motion process, and the Ito process $\{X_t\}$ is a diffusion process relative to $\{\nu_t\}$,

$$dX_t = \alpha_t(X_t)\,dt + d\nu_t \qquad t \in T \tag{8.1.8}$$

Proof. The $\mathcal{F}_t$-measurability of ν_t is quite clear since both X_t and α_t are $\mathcal{F}_t$-measurable by assumption. To prove the Brownian motion nature of ν_t we show that the characteristic equation of ν_t is that of an independent increment Gaussian process with the same statistics as W_t. Or

$$E^{\mathcal{F}_s} e^{ju(\nu_t - \nu_s)} = \exp\left[-\tfrac{1}{2}u^2\sigma^2(t-s)\right] \qquad s \le t, \quad t \in T \tag{8.1.9}$$

From eqs. 8.1.5 and 8.1.7 $\{\nu_t\}$ is another Ito process characterized by the stochastic differential equation

$$d\nu_t = \left[a_t(\omega) - \alpha_t(X_t)\right]dt + dW_t \qquad t \in T, \quad \nu_0 = 0 \tag{8.1.10}$$

To find an expression for the characteristic function of ν_t, we apply Ito's rule given by eq. 6.3.2 to $e^{ju\nu_t}$ with eq. 8.1.10 as the Ito process and obtain

$$de^{ju\nu_t} = jue^{ju\nu_t}(a_t - \alpha_t)\,dt + jue^{ju\nu_t}\,dW_t - \frac{u^2\sigma^2}{2}e^{ju\nu_t}\,dt \tag{8.1.11}$$

Taking conditional expectation of both sides of eq. 8.1.11 with respect to the σ-field $\{\mathcal{F}_s, s \le t, t \in T\}$, we have

$$dE^{\mathcal{F}_s} e^{ju\nu_t} = -\frac{u^2\sigma^2}{2}E^{\mathcal{F}_s}e^{ju\nu_t}\,dt \qquad s \le t, \quad t \in T \tag{8.1.12}$$

since

$$\begin{aligned} E^{\mathcal{F}_s} e^{ju\nu_t}(a_t - \alpha_t)\,dt &= E^{\mathcal{F}_s}E^{\mathcal{F}_t}e^{ju\nu_t}(a_t - \alpha_t)\,dt \\ &= E^{\mathcal{F}_s}e^{ju\nu_t}E^{\mathcal{F}_t}(a_t - \alpha_t)\,dt \\ &= 0 \qquad \text{from eq. 8.1.6} \end{aligned}$$

and

$$\begin{aligned} E^{\mathcal{F}_s} e^{ju\nu_t}\,dW_t &= E^{\mathcal{F}_s}E^{\mathcal{F}_t}E^{\mathcal{B}_t}e^{ju\nu_t}\,dW_t \\ &= E^{\mathcal{F}_s}E^{\mathcal{F}_t}e^{ju\nu_t}E^{\mathcal{B}_t}\,dW_t \\ &= 0 \qquad \text{since } W_t \text{ is a } \mathcal{B}_t\text{-martingale} \end{aligned}$$

The differential equation 8.1.12 can be rewritten as

$$\frac{dE^{\mathcal{F}_s}e^{ju\nu_t}}{E^{\mathcal{F}_s}e^{ju\nu_t}} = -\frac{u^2\sigma^2}{2}dt \qquad s \le t, \quad t \in T$$

which, when integrated between the limits s and t, yields the result

$$E^{\mathfrak{F}_s} e^{ju(\nu_t - \nu_s)} = \exp\left[-\tfrac{1}{2}u^2\sigma^2(t-s)\right] \qquad s \leq t, \quad t \in T \qquad (8.1.13)$$

As a result, the process $\{\nu_t, t \in T\}$ has the same characteristic function as $\{W_t, t \in T\}$ and hence is a Brownian motion process. This was discussed briefly in Example 4.4.6. □

The innovations process ν_t is of particular importance in deriving the representation for the nonlinear filtering problem.

8.2 INNOVATIONS PROCESS

As already indicated in eq. 3.5.20, the process ν_t given by eq. 8.1.7 is the innovations process, which is formally defined below.

Definition 8.2.1 Innovations Process

Let $\{X_t, \mathfrak{B}_t, t \in T\}$, $\{\mathfrak{B}_t, t \in T\}$, $\mathfrak{F}_t = \sigma\{X_s, s \leq t, \ t \in T\}$, $\{\alpha_t(X_t), \mathfrak{F}_t, t \in T\}$, $\{a_t, \mathfrak{B}_t, t \in T\}$, and $\{W_t, \mathfrak{B}_t, t \in T\}$ be as defined in Theorem 8.1.1. Then the process $\{\nu_t, \mathfrak{F}_t, t \in T\}$ given by eq. 8.1.7 is called the *innovations process*.

The reason why it is called innovations is because it contains new information, and this point was made clear in Chapter 3. The process $\{\nu_t, \mathfrak{F}_t, t \in T\}$ is an $\mathfrak{F}_t$-martingale as given by the following proposition.

Proposition 8.2.1

Let the innovations process $\{\nu_t, \mathfrak{F}_t, t \in T\}$ be as defined in eq. 8.1.7. Then the process is an $\mathfrak{F}_t$-martingale.

The proof has already been indicated in Chapter 3, where the uniqueness of the Doob decomposition theorem has been utilized to show that $\{\nu_t, \mathfrak{F}_t\}$ is a martingale. Further, according to Theorem 8.1.1, $\{\nu_t, \mathfrak{F}_t\}$ has the same characteristic function as $\{W_t, \mathfrak{B}_t\}$, and hence it is also a martingale. The general treatment of the innovations process has been discussed in detail by Kailath (25, 28) and Kallianpur (29, pp. 192–204).

By the very definition of the innovations process $\{\nu_t, \mathfrak{F}_t, t \in T\}$ we can certainly say that the σ-field generated by $\{\nu_s, s \leq t, t \in T\}$ is included in the σ-field generated by $\{X_s, s \leq t, t \in T\} = \mathfrak{F}_t$, that is,

$$\sigma\{\nu_s, s \leq t, t \in T\} = \mathfrak{F}_t^{\nu} \subset \mathfrak{F}_t$$

In many cases of applications the reverse inclusion, namely,

$$\mathcal{F}_t \subset \mathcal{F}_t^{\nu}$$

may be valid. This is certainly valid in the case of linear systems. The conditions under which the reverse inclusion is valid have been the subject of intense investigation by many authors [Clark (8), Kallianpur (29, 72), Lipster and Shiryaev (34), Allinger and Mitter (65)].

One condition for the equivalence of these two σ-fields is contained in the following theorem.

Theorem 8.2.1 Equivalence of σ-Fields

Let $\{X_t, \mathcal{B}_t, \mathcal{F}_t, \mathcal{B}_t \supseteq \mathcal{F}_t, t \in T\}$ be an Ito process defined on a complete probability space $\{\Omega, \mathcal{F}, P\}$ with the representation

$$dX_t(\omega) = a_t(\omega)\,dt + dW_t(\omega) \qquad t \in T, \quad X_0(\omega) = 0$$

where the process $\{a_t(\omega), \mathcal{B}_t, t \in T\}$ is a Gaussian process satisfying the condition

$$\int_{t \in T} E|a_t|^2(\omega)\,dt < \infty$$

with $\mathcal{B}_t = \sigma\{a_s, W_s, s \leq t, t \in T\}$ and $\mathcal{F}_t = \sigma\{X_s, s \leq t, t \in T\}$.

If the system $\{a_t, W_t, \mathcal{B}_t, t \in T\}$ is also jointly Gaussian for all $t \in T$, then

$$\sigma\{\nu_s, s \leq t, t \in T\} = \sigma\{X_s, s \leq t, t \in T\} = \mathcal{F}_t$$

where $\{\nu_t, t \in T\}$ is the innovations process defined by

$$d\nu_t = dX_t - \alpha_t(X_t)\,dt$$

and $\alpha_t(X_t) = E^{\mathcal{F}_t} a_t(\omega) = \hat{a}_t(\omega)$.

For a proof see Lipster and Shiryaev (34, p. 264).

Other conditions of equivalence have also been discussed in Lipster and Shiryaev (34, II, pp. 27, 68) and Kallianpur (29, p. 283; 72, p. 128). It has been shown by Allinger and Mitter (65) that if $a_t(\omega)$ and W_t are independent, then the equivalence of σ-fields also holds.

8.3 ESTIMATION PROBLEM

The *estimation problem* is the estimation of a *signal*, or *system*, or *state* process $\{X_t, t \in T\}$ measurable with respect to some σ-field. The process cannot be observed directly. Instead we observe another process $\{Y_t, t \in T\}$ which is related to the process $\{X_t, t \in T\}$ and estimate the signal process in an optimal manner using some criterion of optimality. It turns out that for a broad class of criterion functions, including the mean square error function, the conditional expectation of the process $\{X_t, t \in T\}$ given the observation process $\{Y_t, t \in T\}$ minimizes the expected value of these criterion functions. Hence the problem of estimating the signal process is essentially that of finding the expectation of X_t conditioned on the observation process $\{Y_t\}$. This estimate, in general, will be a complicated nonlinear function of the observations. The problem is further complicated by the fact that both the system and the observation processes are governed by stochastic differential equations, and thus the conditional expectation will be governed by another stochastic differential equation. In most engineering problems we also have the problem of updating the estimates continuously when observations are arriving continuously.

The conditional mean, which is the first moment of the conditional density of the signal process, will depend upon all higher order moments in the general nonlinear case. In the linear case only the second moments will be involved. The martingale approach to the estimation problem developed by Fujisaki, Kallianpur, and Kunita (15) and by Lipster and Shiryaev (34) gives a representation of the estimator for the general nonlinear problem in a closed form. The preceding chapters contained the tools for this closed form representation.

To get a general feeling for the estimation problem, we state the problem loosely as follows.

The signal process $\{X_t, t \in T\}$ is given by the Ito stochastic differential equation

$$dX_t(\omega) = f_t(\omega)\,dt + dW_t(\omega) \qquad t \in T \tag{8.3.1}$$

where $\{W_t, t \in T\}$ is a *general martingale* process (not necessarily a Brownian motion process). The observation process $\{Y_t, \tau \in T\}$ is given by another Ito stochastic differential equation,

$$dY_\tau(\omega) = h_\tau(\omega)\,d\tau + dV_\tau(\omega) \quad \tau \in T \tag{8.3.2}$$

where $\{V_\tau, \tau \in T\}$ is a Brownian motion process.

The estimation problem is a *filtering problem* if $\tau = t$, a *smoothing problem* if $\tau > t$, and a *prediction problem* if $\tau < t$. The filtering and prediction problems are amenable to real-time operations where estimates are required based on the data available up to the present. In the case of smoothing, more data are allowed to accumulate so that improved estimates can be obtained by off-line processing.

8.4 OPTIMAL NONLINEAR FILTERING

Next we pose the nonlinear filtering problem more precisely for the scalar case and extend it to the vector case later.

Let $(\Omega, \mathfrak{F}, P)$ be a complete probability space. The signal process $\{X_t, \mathfrak{B}_t, t \in T\}$ is an Ito process defined on the complete probability space by

$$dX_t(\omega) = f_t(\omega)\, dt + dW_t(\omega) \qquad t \in T, \quad X_0(\omega) \tag{8.4.1}$$

or by the corresponding integral equation

$$X_t(\omega) = X_0(\omega) + \int_0^t f_\tau(\omega)\, d\tau + W_t(\omega) \qquad t \in T \tag{8.4.2}$$

The observations process $\{Y_t, \mathfrak{B}_t, t \in T\}$ is another Ito process defined on the complete probability space by

$$dY_t(\omega) = h_t(\omega)\, dt + dV_t(\omega) \qquad t \in T, \quad Y_0(\omega) = 0 \tag{8.4.3}$$

or by the corresponding integral equation

$$Y_t(\omega) = \int_0^t h_\tau(\omega)\, d\tau + V_t(\omega) \qquad t \in T \tag{8.4.4}$$

We make the following assumptions concerning eqs. 8.4.1–8.4.4:

1. $\{\mathfrak{B}_t, t \in T\}$ is the filtration σ-field of the probability space $(\Omega, \mathfrak{F}, P)$ containing sets from $\mathfrak{F}$ of zero probability measure and is defined by

$$\mathfrak{B}_t \supset \sigma\{X_0, X_s, W_s, Y_s, V_s, s \le t, t \in T\}$$

2. $\{\mathfrak{F}_t, t \in T\}$ is the natural filtration σ-field generated by the observation process $\{Y_t, t \in T\}$ containing sets from $\mathfrak{F}$ of zero probability measure and is defined by

$$\mathfrak{F}_t = \sigma\{Y_s, s \le t, t \in T\}$$

Clearly $\mathfrak{F}_t \subset \mathfrak{B}_t$.

3. The signal process $\{X_t(\omega), t \in T\}$, not necessarily sample continuous, and the observation process $\{Y_t(\omega), t \in T\}$ with sample continuous trajectories are semimartingales on the σ-field $\{\mathfrak{B}_t, t \in T\}$.

4. Unique solutions $\{X_t(\omega), t \in T\}$ satisfying $\sup_{t \in T} E|X_t|^2(\omega) < \infty$ exist for eqs. 8.4.1 or 8.4.2, and $\{Y_t(\omega), t \in T\}$ satisfying $\sup_{t \in T} E|Y_t|^2(\omega) < \infty$ exist for eqs. 8.4.3 or 8.4.4.

5. $X_0(\omega)$ is an arbitrary initial condition for the stochastic differential equation 8.4.1 with $E|X_0|^2(\omega) < \infty$ and is independent of $\{\mathfrak{F}_t, t \in T\}$, $\sigma\{W_s, s \le t, t \in T\}$, and $\sigma\{V_s, s \le t, t \in T\}$.

6. The random processes $f_t(\omega)$ and $h_t(\omega)$—may be functions of $X_t(\omega)$—are $\mathfrak{B}_t$-measurable nonanticipative functionals satisfying the condi-

tions

$$\int_{t\in T} E|f_t|^2(\omega)\,dt < \infty \qquad \int_{t\in T} E|h_t|^2(\omega)\,dt < \infty$$

7. $\{W_t, \mathcal{B}_t, t \in T\}$ is a *general right-continuous L^2-martingale* (not necessarily a Brownian motion process) with $\sigma\{W_t - W_s, s < t, t \in T\}$ independent of $\{\mathcal{B}_s, s < t\}$.

8. $\{V_t, \mathcal{B}_t, t \in T\}$ is a Brownian motion process with parameter σ_v^2, and $\sigma\{V_t - V_s, s < t, t \in T\}$ is independent of $\{\mathcal{B}_s, s < t\}$ and $\{\mathcal{F}_s, s < t\}$.

9. If $g_t(\omega)$ is some measurable random process satisfying $E|g_t(\omega)| < \infty$, then the conditional expectation $E^{\mathcal{F}_t}g_t(\omega)$ represented by $\hat{g}_t(\omega)$ has a measurable modification.

Under assumptions 8 and 9 and Theorem 8.1.1, the innovations process $\{\nu_t, t \in T\}$ defined by

$$d\nu_t(\omega) = dY_t(\omega) - \hat{h}_t(\omega)\,dt \qquad t \in T \tag{8.4.5}$$

is an $\mathcal{F}_t$-measurable Brownian motion process having the same statistics as $\{V_t, t \in T\}$, namely, parameter σ_v^2 and independence of σ-fields $\sigma\{\nu_t - \nu_s, s < t, t \in T\}$ and $\{\mathcal{F}_s, s < t\}$.

10. The σ-field generated by the innovations process is equal to the σ-field generated by the observation process

$$\mathcal{F}_t^{\nu} = \sigma\{\nu_s, s \le t, t \in T\} = \sigma\{Y_s, s \le t, t \in T\} = \mathcal{F}_t$$

In the classic work of Fujisaki, Kallianpur, and Kunita (15) on nonlinear filtering representation this equivalence of σ-fields has *not* been invoked.

Note. In eqs. 8.4.1–8.4.4 we have assumed that the coefficients of $\{W_t\}$ and $\{V_t\}$ are 1, and thus they do not represent the general Ito process.

The problem now is to compute the least-squares estimate of the signal process $\{X_t, t \in T\}$ given the entire past observations $\{Y_s, s \le t, t \in T\}$. As a consequence of the least-squares estimate we have to find the conditional expectation of $\{X_t, t \in T\}$ given the observation σ-field $\{\mathcal{F}_t, t \in T\}$. In addition, we would like to determine the conditional expectation recursively, if possible, so that the estimates can be updated using only new observations.

We shall now state an important theorem, similar to Theorem 6.6.2, whereby a square integrable martingale can be represented as a stochastic integral with respect to the innovations process.

Theorem 8.4.1 (Fujisaki, Kallianpur, and Kunita, 15)

Let the observation process Y_t be governed by eq. 8.4.3 and the innovations process ν_t by eq. 8.4.5. Then under assumptions 2, 6, and 8, every separable square integrable martingale $\{Y_t, \mathcal{F}_t, t \in T\}$ is sample continuous and has the representation

$$Y_t - EY_0 = \int_0^t \varphi_\tau(\omega)\, d\nu_\tau \quad t \in T \tag{8.4.6}$$

where $\varphi_t(\omega)$ is a nonanticipative random process satisfying conditions 6.1.3.

If assumption 10, namely, $\mathcal{F}_t^\nu = \mathcal{F}_t$ holds, then the above result follows from Kunita and Watanabe (32). However, only the forward inclusion $\mathcal{F}_t^\nu \subset \mathcal{F}_t$ holds in general. But Fujisaki, Kallianpur, and Kunita (15) use Girsanov's theorem (69) and a sequence of delicate arguments to show that the representation theorem holds even when the equivalence of σ-fields does not hold.

For details of proof see Kallianpur (29, p. 208).

We now formulate the nonlinear filtering theorem in a slightly different form from that postulated by Fujisaki, Kallianpur, and Kunita (15).

Theorem 8.4.2 Nonlinear Filtering Theorem

Let $(\Omega, \mathcal{F}, P)$ be a complete probability space, and let $\{\mathcal{B}_t, t \in T\}$ be a filtration σ-field defined on it. Let $\{X_t, \mathcal{B}_t, t \in T\}$ be the signal process given by eq. 8.4.1 or eq. 8.4.2, and let $\{Y_t, \mathcal{B}_t, t \in T\}$ be the observation process given by eq. 8.4.3 or eq. 8.4.4. Then under assumptions 1 through 10, the estimate $\hat{X}_t = E^{\mathcal{F}_t} X_t$ is given by

$$d\hat{X}_t = \hat{f}_t\, dt + \frac{1}{\sigma_v^2}\left[E^{\mathcal{F}_t}\frac{d}{dt}\langle W, V\rangle_t + E^{\mathcal{F}_t}(X_{t-}h_t) - E^{\mathcal{F}_t}X_{t-}E^{\mathcal{F}_t}h_t\right] d\nu_t$$

$$t \in T, \quad \hat{X}_0(\omega) \tag{8.4.7}$$

or in integral form,

$$\hat{X}_t = \hat{X}_0 + \int_0^t \hat{f}_\tau(\omega)\, d\tau + \frac{1}{\sigma_v^2}\int_0^t \left[E^{\mathcal{F}_\tau}\frac{d}{d\tau}\langle W, V\rangle_\tau + E^{\mathcal{F}_\tau}(X_{\tau-}h_\tau) - E^{\mathcal{F}_\tau}X_{\tau-}E^{\mathcal{F}_\tau}h_\tau\right] d\nu_\tau \quad t \in T \tag{8.4.8}$$

where $\langle W, V\rangle_t$ is the quadratic covariance process between $\{W_t, \mathcal{B}_t, t \in T\}$ and $\{V_t, \mathcal{B}_t, t \in T\}$, with $\{\nu_t, \mathcal{F}_t, t \in T\}$ being the innovations process. X_{t-} is the left-hand limit of the process X_t at the point t of its jump.

Proof. The proof is reasonably involved and we shall proceed in steps.

Since the conditional expectation of $X_t(\omega)$ with respect to $\mathcal{F}_t$ is needed, we take the conditional expectation on both sides of eq. 8.4.2 and write

$$E^{\mathcal{F}_t}X_t(\omega) = E^{\mathcal{F}_t}X_0(\omega) + E^{\mathcal{F}_t}\int_0^t f_\tau(\omega)\, d\tau + E^{\mathcal{F}_t}W_t(\omega) \quad t \in T \tag{8.4.9}$$

Since $X_0(\omega)$, the initial condition, is independent of $\mathfrak{F}_t$ by assumption 5, we have

$$\hat{X}_t(\omega) = EX_0(\omega) + E^{\mathfrak{F}_t}\int_0^t f_\tau(\omega)\,d\tau + E^{\mathfrak{F}_t}W_t(\omega) \qquad t \in T \qquad (8.4.10)$$

We now state the following lemmas to prove Theorem 8.4.2.

Lemma 8.4.1

The stochastic process

$$E^{\mathfrak{F}_t}\int_0^t f_\tau(\omega)\,d\tau - \int_0^t E^{\mathfrak{F}_\tau} f_\tau(\omega)\,d\tau \qquad t \in T$$

is a square integrable $\mathfrak{F}_t$-martingale.

Proof. Using Fubini's theorem, we have for $s \le t$,

$$\begin{aligned}
E^{\mathfrak{F}_s}&\left[E^{\mathfrak{F}_t}\int_0^t f_\tau(\omega)\,d\tau - \int_0^t E^{\mathfrak{F}_\tau} f_\tau(\omega)\,d\tau\right] \\
&= E^{\mathfrak{F}_s}\int_0^t f_\tau(\omega)\,d\tau - \int_0^t E^{\mathfrak{F}_s}E^{\mathfrak{F}_\tau} f_\tau(\omega)\,d\tau \\
&= E^{\mathfrak{F}_s}\int_0^s f_\tau(\omega)\,d\tau + E^{\mathfrak{F}_s}\int_s^t f_\tau(\omega)\,d\tau \\
&\quad - \int_0^s E^{\mathfrak{F}_s}E^{\mathfrak{F}_\tau} f_\tau(\omega)\,dt - \int_s^t E^{\mathfrak{F}_s}E^{\mathfrak{F}_\tau} f_\tau(\omega)\,d\tau
\end{aligned} \qquad (8.4.11)$$

In eq. 8.4.11 the following relationships hold:

$$E^{\mathfrak{F}_s}E^{\mathfrak{F}_\tau} f_\tau(\omega) = \begin{cases} E^{\mathfrak{F}_\tau} f_\tau(\omega) & \tau \le s \\ E^{\mathfrak{F}_s} f_\tau(\omega) & \tau > s \end{cases} \qquad (8.4.12)$$

Using eq. 8.4.12 in eq. 8.4.11 and again using Fubini's theorem,

$$\begin{aligned}
E^{\mathfrak{F}_s}&\left[E^{\mathfrak{F}_t}\int_0^t f_\tau(\omega)\,d\tau - \int_0^t E^{\mathfrak{F}_\tau} f_\tau(\omega)\,d\tau\right] \\
&= E^{\mathfrak{F}_s}\int_0^s f_\tau(\omega)\,d\tau - \int_0^s E^{\mathfrak{F}_\tau} f_\tau(\omega)\,d\tau \\
&\quad + \int_s^t E^{\mathfrak{F}_s} f_\tau(\omega)\,d\tau - \int_s^t E^{\mathfrak{F}_s} f_\tau(\omega)\,d\tau \\
&= E^{\mathfrak{F}_s}\int_0^s f_\tau(\omega)\,d\tau - \int_0^s E^{\mathfrak{F}_\tau} f_\tau(\omega)\,d\tau
\end{aligned} \qquad (8.4.13)$$

thus showing the $\mathcal{F}_t$-martingale property. The square integrability follows from assumption 6. □

Lemma 8.4.2

The stochastic process $E^{\mathcal{F}_t}W_t(\omega)$, $t \in T$, is a square integrable $\mathcal{F}_t$-martingale.

Proof. Since W_t is a $\mathcal{B}_t$-martingale, we have for $s \leq t$,

$$E^{\mathcal{F}_s}E^{\mathcal{F}_t}W_t = E^{\mathcal{F}_s}W_t = E^{\mathcal{F}_s}E^{\mathcal{B}_s}W_t = E^{\mathcal{F}_s}W_s$$

The square integrability follows from assumption 7. □

Lemma 8.4.3

The random process

$$\mu_t(\omega) = \hat{X}_t(\omega) - EX_0(\omega) - \int_0^t E^{\mathcal{F}_\tau}f_\tau(\omega)\,d\tau$$

is a square integrable $\mathcal{F}_t$-martingale.

Proof. Equation 8.4.10 can be rewritten as

$$\hat{X}_t(\omega) = EX_0(\omega) + E^{\mathcal{F}_t}\int_0^t f_\tau(\omega)\,d\tau - \int_0^t E^{\mathcal{F}_t}f_\tau(\omega)\,d\tau$$

$$+ \int_0^t E^{\mathcal{F}_\tau}f_\tau(\omega)\,d\tau + E^{\mathcal{F}_t}W_t(\omega) \tag{8.4.14}$$

Applying Lemmas 8.4.1 and 8.4.2 to eq. 8.4.14, we find that

$$\mu_t(\omega) = \hat{X}_t(\omega) - EX_0(\omega) - \int_0^t E^{\mathcal{F}_\tau}f_\tau(\omega)\,d\tau \tag{8.4.15}$$

equals the sum of two square integrable martingales, which is again a square integrable martingale. □

In Section 6.6 we discussed the general conditions under which any martingale can be given as a stochastic integral. We stated in theorem 8.4.1 that a square integrable martingale can be given as a stochastic integral with respect to the innovations process. In fact it is this ability that makes the representation in closed form of the nonlinear filtering problem feasible. Hence the square integrable $\mathcal{F}_t$-martingale μ_t given by eq. 8.4.15 can be represented as a stochastic integral with respect to the innovations process $\{\nu_t, \mathcal{F}_t\}$, or

$$\mu_t(\omega) = \int_0^t \varphi_\tau(\omega)\,d\nu_\tau(\omega) \tag{8.4.16}$$

where $\varphi_t(\omega)$ is some $\mathcal{F}_t$-adapted predictable process satisfying conditions 6.1.3. In order to identify the process $\varphi_t(\omega)$, we note that since both μ_t and ν_t are square integrable $\mathcal{F}_t$-martingales, and we can write the quadratic covariance process $\langle \mu, \nu \rangle_t$ from eq. 6.5.20 as

$$\langle \mu, \nu \rangle_t = \left\langle \int \varphi_\tau(\omega)\, d\nu_\tau, \nu \right\rangle_t = \int_0^t \varphi_\tau(\omega)\, d\langle \nu, \nu \rangle_\tau$$

Since $\{\nu_t\}$ is the innovations process, having the same statistics as $\{V_t\}$, we have

$$\langle \mu, \nu \rangle_t = \int_0^t \varphi_\tau(\omega)\, d\langle \nu, \nu \rangle_\tau = \int_0^t \varphi_\tau(\omega) \sigma_v^2\, d\tau$$

and the function $\varphi_t(\omega)$ can be given in terms $\langle \mu, \nu \rangle_t$ as

$$\varphi_t(\omega) = \frac{1}{\sigma_v^2} \frac{d}{dt} \langle \mu, \nu \rangle_t \tag{8.4.17}$$

Substituting eq. 8.4.17 into eq. 8.4.16 and using eq. 8.4.15, we have

$$\mu_t(\omega) = \int_0^t \frac{1}{\sigma_v^2} \frac{d}{d\tau} \langle \mu, \nu \rangle_t\, d\nu_\tau$$

$$= \hat{X}_t(\omega) - \int_0^t \hat{f}_\tau(\omega)\, d\tau - EX_0(\omega) \tag{8.4.18}$$

From eq. 8.4.18 we arrive at the basic nonlinear filtering equation

$$\hat{X}_t(\omega) = EX_0(\omega) + \int_0^t \hat{f}_\tau(\omega)\, d\tau + \int_0^t \frac{1}{\sigma_v^2} \frac{d}{d\tau} \langle \mu, \nu \rangle_\tau\, d\nu_\tau \qquad t \in T \tag{8.4.19}$$

where the quadratic covariance process $\langle \mu, \nu \rangle_t$ is yet to be determined.

Evaluation of $\langle \mu, \nu \rangle_t$. Applying the Ito–Doleans-Dade–Meyer rule of eq. 6.7.29 to the semimartingale product $\hat{X}_t Y_t$ and using the fact that Y_t has sample continuous trajectories, we arrive at

$$\hat{X}_t Y_t = \int_0^t \hat{X}_{\tau-}\, dY_\tau + \int_0^t Y_\tau\, d\hat{X}_\tau + [\mu, \nu]_t \qquad t \in T \tag{8.4.20}$$

where $\hat{X}_{\tau-}$ represents the left-hand limit of the semimartingale process $\hat{X}_t$ at the point τ of its jump. From lemma 8.4.3 μ_t is the $\mathcal{F}_t$-martingale associated with the $\mathcal{F}_t$-semimartingale $\hat{X}_t$, and eq. 8.4.18 can be rewritten as

$$\hat{X}_t = EX_0 + \int_0^t \hat{f}_\tau\, d\tau + \mu_t \qquad t \in T \tag{8.4.21}$$

ν_t is the $\mathcal{F}_t$-martingale associated with the $\mathcal{F}_t$-semimartingale Y_t, and eq. 8.4.5 can be rewritten as

$$Y_t = \int_0^t \hat{h}_t \, d\tau + \nu_t \qquad t \in T \tag{8.4.22}$$

$[\mu, \nu]_t$ is the quadratic covariation process between the two square integrable $\mathcal{F}_t$-martingales μ_t and ν_t.

In a similar manner we can apply eq. 6.7.29 to the semimartingale product $X_t Y_t$ and write

$$X_t Y_t = \int_0^t X_{\tau-} \, dY_\tau + \int_0^t Y_\tau \, dX_\tau + [W, V]_t \qquad t \in T \tag{8.4.23}$$

In eq. 8.4.23 W_t is the $\mathcal{B}_t$-martingale associated with the $\mathcal{B}_t$-semimartingale X_t, which is given by

$$X_t = X_0 + \int_0^t f_\tau \, d\tau + W_t \qquad t \in T \tag{8.4.24}$$

and V_t is the $\mathcal{B}_t$-martingale associated with the $\mathcal{B}_t$-semimartingale Y_t (also an $\mathcal{F}_t$-semimartingale), which is given by

$$Y_t = \int_0^t h_\tau \, d\tau + V_t \qquad t \in T \tag{8.4.25}$$

Using eqs. 8.4.20 and 8.4.23 we can write the following equations:

$$\hat{X}_t Y_t - \hat{X}_s Y_s = \int_s^t \hat{X}_{\tau-} \, dY_\tau + \int_s^t Y_\tau \, d\hat{X}_\tau + [\mu, \nu]_t - [\mu, \nu]_s \qquad t \in T \tag{8.4.26}$$

$$X_t Y_t - X_s Y_s = \int_s^t X_{\tau-} \, dY_\tau + \int_s^t Y_\tau \, dX_\tau + [W, V]_t - [W, V]_s \qquad t \in T \tag{8.4.27}$$

We now subtract eq. 8.4.26 from eq. 8.4.27 and take the conditional expectation with respect to the σ-field $\mathcal{F}_s$,

$$\begin{aligned} E^{\mathcal{F}_s}\{X_t Y_t - X_s Y_s - (\hat{X}_t Y_t - \hat{X}_s Y_s)\} &= E^{\mathcal{F}_s}\left\{\int_s^t X_{\tau-} \, dY_\tau - \int_s^t \hat{X}_{\tau-} \, dY_\tau\right\} \\ &\quad + E^{\mathcal{F}_s}\left\{\int_s^t Y_\tau \, dX_\tau - \int_s^t Y_\tau \, d\hat{X}_\tau\right\} \\ &\quad + E^{\mathcal{F}_s}\{[W, V]_t - [W, V]_s\} \\ &\quad - E^{\mathcal{F}_s}\{[\mu, \nu]_t - [\mu, \nu]_s\} \end{aligned} \tag{8.4.28}$$

We now evaluate eq. 8.4.28 term by term. First we evaluate the term $E^{\mathcal{F}_s}\{X_tY_t - X_sY_s\}$ in the left-hand side of eq. 8.4.28:

$$\begin{aligned} E^{\mathcal{F}_s}\{X_tY_t - X_sY_s\} &= E^{\mathcal{F}_s}X_tY_t - E^{\mathcal{F}_s}X_sY_s \\ &= E^{\mathcal{F}_s}E^{\mathcal{F}_t}X_tY_t - E^{\mathcal{F}_s}X_sY_s \\ &= E^{\mathcal{F}_s}\hat{X}_tY_t - E^{\mathcal{F}_s}\hat{X}_sY_s \\ &= E^{\mathcal{F}_s}\{\hat{X}_tY_t - \hat{X}_sY_s\} \end{aligned}$$

Substituting the above result in the left-hand side of eq. 8.4.28 yields

$$E^{\mathcal{F}_s}\{X_tY_t - X_sY_s - (\hat{X}_tY_t - \hat{X}_sY_s)\} = 0 \tag{8.4.29}$$

Since

$$dY_t = h_t\,dt + dV_t$$

and also

$$dY_t = \hat{h}_t\,dt + d\nu_t$$

we can write the first term in the right-hand side of eq. 8.4.28 as

$$\begin{aligned} &E^{\mathcal{F}_s}\left\{\int_s^t X_{\tau-}\,dY_\tau - \int_s^t \hat{X}_{\tau-}\,dY_\tau\right\} \\ &\quad = E^{\mathcal{F}_s}\left\{\int_s^t X_{\tau-}h_\tau\,d\tau + \int_s^t X_{\tau-}\,dV_\tau - \int_s^t \hat{X}_{\tau-}\hat{h}_\tau\,d\tau - \int_s^t \hat{X}_{\tau-}\,d\nu_\tau\right\} \\ &\quad = E^{\mathcal{F}_s}\left\{\int_s^t (X_{\tau-}h_\tau - \hat{X}_{\tau-}\hat{h}_\tau)\,d\tau + \int_s^t X_{\tau-}\,dV_\tau - \int_s^t \hat{X}_{\tau-}\,d\nu_\tau\right\} \end{aligned} \tag{8.4.30}$$

In eq. 8.4.30 the term $\int_s^t X_{\tau-}\,dV_\tau$ is a $\mathcal{B}_s$-martingale difference, and the term $\int_s^t \hat{X}_{\tau-}\,d\nu_\tau$ is an $\mathcal{F}_s$-martingale difference (see Proposition 6.1.2). Hence they are both zero when conditioned on the σ-field $\mathcal{F}_s$ (since $\mathcal{F}_s \subset \mathcal{B}_s$). Hence eq. 8.4.30 reduces to

$$\begin{aligned} E^{\mathcal{F}_s}\left\{\int_s^t X_{\tau-}\,dY_\tau - \int_s^t \hat{X}_{\tau-}\,dY_\tau\right\} &= E^{\mathcal{F}_s}\left\{\int_s^t (X_{\tau-}h_\tau - \hat{X}_{\tau-}\hat{h}_\tau)\,d\tau\right\} \\ &= E^{\mathcal{F}_s}\left\{\int_s^t E^{\mathcal{F}_\tau}(X_{\tau-}h_\tau - \hat{X}_{\tau-}\hat{h}_\tau)\,d\tau\right\} \end{aligned}$$

by Fubini's theorem. (8.4.31)

Since

$$dX_t = f_t\,dt + dW_t$$

and

$$d\hat{X}_t = \hat{f}_t\,dt + d\mu_t$$

we can write the second term in the right-hand side of eq. 8.4.28 as

$$E^{\mathcal{F}_s}\left\{\int_s^t Y_\tau\,dX_\tau - \int_s^t Y_\tau\,d\hat{X}_\tau\right\}$$

$$= E^{\mathcal{F}_s}\left\{\int_s^t Y_\tau f_\tau\,d\tau + \int_s^t Y_\tau\,dW_\tau - \int_s^t Y_\tau \hat{f}_\tau\,d\tau - \int_s^t Y_\tau\,d\mu_\tau\right\}$$

$$= E^{\mathcal{F}_s}\int_s^t (f_\tau - \hat{f}_\tau)Y_\tau\,d\tau$$

because $E^{\mathcal{F}_s}\int_s^t Y_\tau\,dW_\tau$ and $E^{\mathcal{F}_s}\int_s^t Y_\tau\,d\mu_\tau$ are both equal to zero, being $\mathcal{B}_s$ and $\mathcal{F}_s$-martingale differences respectively. But by Fubini's theorem

$$E^{\mathcal{F}_s}\int_s^t (f_\tau - \hat{f}_\tau)Y_\tau\,d\tau = E^{\mathcal{F}_s}\int_s^t E^{\mathcal{F}_\tau}(f_\tau - \hat{f}_\tau)Y_\tau\,d\tau = 0$$

Hence

$$E^{\mathcal{F}_s}\left\{\int_s^t Y_\tau\,dX_\tau - \int_s^t Y_\tau\,d\hat{X}_\tau\right\} = 0 \tag{8.4.32}$$

We now determine the third term in the right-hand side of eq. 8.4.28. Since W_t and V_t are square integrable $\mathcal{B}_t$-martingales (assumption 7), we have by Remark 1 under Theorem 4.4 that $[W,V]_t - \langle W,V\rangle_t$ is also a square integrable $\mathcal{B}_t$-martingale. Hence

$$E^{\mathcal{B}_s}\{[W,V]_t - \langle W,V\rangle_t\} = [W,V]_s - \langle W,V\rangle_s$$

or

$$E^{\mathcal{F}_s}E^{\mathcal{B}_s}\{[W,V]_t - \langle W,V\rangle_t\} = E^{\mathcal{F}_s}\{[W,V]_s - \langle W,V\rangle_s\}$$

Since $\mathcal{F}_s \subset \mathcal{B}_s$, we have

$$E^{\mathcal{F}_s}\{[W,V]_t - [W,V]_s\} = E^{\mathcal{F}_s}\{\langle W,V\rangle_t - \langle W,V\rangle_s\} \tag{8.4.33}$$

Since $\{V_t, t \in T\}$ is a continuous martingale, we can assume that $\langle W,V\rangle_t$ is absolutely continuous from eq. 4.4.8 and write

$$E^{\mathcal{F}_s}\{\langle W,V\rangle_t - \langle W,V\rangle_s\} = E^{\mathcal{F}_s}\int_s^t \frac{d}{d\tau}\langle W,V\rangle_\tau\,d\tau$$

$$= E^{\mathcal{F}_s}\int_s^t E^{\mathcal{F}_\tau}\frac{d}{d\tau}\langle W,V\rangle_\tau\,d\tau \qquad \text{by Fubini's theorem} \tag{8.4.34}$$

In a similar manner, in the fourth term in the right-hand side of eq. 8.4.28, since μ_t and ν_t are square integrable $\mathcal{F}_t$-martingales, we have

$$E^{\mathcal{F}_s}\{[\mu, \nu]_t - [\mu, \nu]_s\} = E^{\mathcal{F}_s}\{\langle \mu, \nu \rangle_t - \langle \mu, \nu \rangle_s\} \tag{8.4.35}$$

Combining eqs. 8.4.29, 8.4.31, 8.4.32, 8.4.34, and 8.4.35, there results

$$E^{\mathcal{F}_s}\left\{\int_s^t E^{\mathcal{F}_\tau}\left(X_{\tau-}h_\tau - \hat{X}_{\tau-}\hat{h}_\tau + \frac{d}{d\tau}\langle W, V\rangle_\tau\right) d\tau - \langle \mu, \nu\rangle_t + \langle \mu, \nu\rangle_s\right\} = 0 \tag{8.4.36}$$

and since $\mu_0 = 0 = \nu_0$, we have the final result

$$\langle \mu, \nu\rangle_t = \int_0^t E^{\mathcal{F}_\tau}\left(X_{\tau-}h_\tau - \hat{X}_{\tau-}\hat{h}_\tau + \frac{d}{d\tau}\langle W, V\rangle_\tau\right) d\tau \qquad t \in T \tag{8.4.37}$$

Having determined $\langle \mu, \nu\rangle_t$, we substitute this value in eq. 8.4.19 and arrive at the final nonlinear filtering representation

$$\hat{X}_t = EX_0 + \int_0^t \hat{f}_\tau d\tau + \frac{1}{\sigma_v^2}\int_0^t \left[E^{\mathcal{F}_\tau}\left(X_{\tau-}h_\tau - \hat{X}_{\tau-}\hat{h}_\tau + \frac{d}{d\tau}\langle W, V\rangle_\tau\right)\right] d\nu_\tau \qquad t \in T \tag{8.4.38}$$ □

By noting

$$\begin{aligned} E^{\mathcal{F}_\tau}\{(\hat{X}_{\tau-} - X_{\tau-})(\hat{h}_\tau - h_\tau)\} &= E^{\mathcal{F}_\tau}\{X_{\tau-}h_\tau - \hat{X}_{\tau-}h_\tau - X_{\tau-}\hat{h}_\tau + \hat{X}_{\tau-}\hat{h}_\tau\} \\ &= E^{\mathcal{F}_\tau}\{X_{\tau-}h_\tau - \hat{X}_{\tau-}\hat{h}_\tau\} \end{aligned} \tag{8.4.39}$$

and defining the error quantities $\tilde{X}_\tau = \hat{X}_{\tau-} - X_{\tau-}$ and $\tilde{h}_\tau = \hat{h}_\tau - h_\tau$, eq. 8.4.38 can be rewritten in the following alternate form:

$$\hat{X}_t = EX_0 + \int_0^t \hat{f}_\tau d\tau + \frac{1}{\sigma_v^2}\int_0^t \left[E^{\mathcal{F}_\tau}\left(\tilde{X}_\tau\tilde{h}_\tau + \frac{d}{d\tau}\langle W, V\rangle_\tau\right)\right] d\nu_\tau \qquad t \in T \tag{8.4.40}$$

or

$$d\hat{X}_t = \hat{f}_t\, dt + \frac{1}{\sigma_v^2}\left[E^{\mathcal{F}_t}\left(\tilde{X}_t\tilde{h}_t + \frac{d}{dt}\langle W, V\rangle_t\right)\right] d\nu_t \qquad t \in T, \quad EX_0 \tag{8.4.41}$$

Remarks

1. If W_t and V_t are independent L^2-martingales, then $\langle W, V \rangle_t = 0$ and eq. 8.4.41 simplifies to

$$d\hat{X}_t = \hat{f}_t\,dt + \frac{1}{\sigma_v^2} E^{\mathcal{F}_t}\left(\tilde{X}_t \tilde{h}_t\right) d\nu_t \qquad t \in T, \quad EX_0 \tag{8.4.42}$$

2. Theorem 8.4.1 also holds if W_t and V_t are locally square integrable $\mathcal{B}_t$-martingales instead of square integrable $\mathcal{B}_t$-martingales. In this case if τ_n is $\mathcal{F}_\tau$ stopping time, we have to use $t \wedge \tau_n$ instead of t and $s \wedge \tau_n$ instead of s. For details see Kallianpur (29, pp. 210–219).

3. The case when V_t is also a general square integrable $\mathcal{B}_t$-martingale is discussed in Segall, Davis, and Kailath (48) and Segall (50).

8.5 VECTOR FORMULATION

We now formulate the nonlinear filtering theorem for the vector case. Let $\{\Omega, \mathcal{F}, P\}$ be the probability space. The signal process $\{\mathbf{X}_t, \mathcal{B}_t, t \in T\}$ is an n-vector Ito process defined by

$$\mathbf{X}_t(\omega) = \mathbf{X}_0(\omega) + \int_0^t \mathbf{f}_\tau(\omega)\,d\tau + \mathbf{W}_t(\omega) \qquad t \in T \tag{8.5.1}$$

and the observation process $\{\mathbf{Y}_t, \mathcal{B}_t, t \in T\}$ is an m-vector Ito process defined by

$$\mathbf{Y}_t(\omega) = \int_0^t \mathbf{h}_\tau(\omega)\,d\tau + \mathbf{V}_t(\omega) \qquad t \in T \tag{8.5.2}$$

The following assumptions are made concerning eqs. 8.5.1 and 8.5.2:

1. $\{\mathcal{B}_t, t \in T\}$ is the filtration σ-field of the probability space $(\Omega, \mathcal{F}, P)$ containing sets from $\mathcal{F}$ of zero probability measure and is defined by

$$\mathcal{B}_t \supset \sigma\{\mathbf{X}_0, \mathbf{X}_s, \mathbf{W}_s, \mathbf{Y}_s, \mathbf{V}_s, s \leq t, t \in T\}$$

2. $\{\mathcal{F}_t, t \in T\}$ is the natural filtration σ-field generated by the observation process $\{\mathbf{Y}_t, t \in T\}$ containing sets from $\mathcal{F}$ of zero probability and is defined by

$$\mathcal{F}_t = \sigma\{\mathbf{Y}_s, s \leq t, t \in T\}$$

with $\mathcal{F}_t \subseteq \mathcal{B}_t$.

3. The n-vector signal process $\{\mathbf{X}_t, t \in T\}$, not necessarily sample continuous, and the m-vector observation process $\{\mathbf{Y}_t, t \in T\}$ with sample continuous trajectories are semimartingales on the σ-field $\{\mathcal{B}_t, t \in T\}$.

4. Unique solutions $\{\mathbf{X}_t(\omega), t \in T\}$ satisfying $\sup_{t \in T} E|X_{it}|^2(\omega) < \infty$, $i = 1, \ldots, n$, exist for eq. 8.5.1, and $\{\mathbf{Y}_t(\omega), t \in T\}$ satisfying $\sup E|Y_{it}|^2(\omega) < \infty$, $i = 1, \ldots, m$, exist for eq. 8.5.2.

5. The n-vector initial condition process $\mathbf{X}_0(\omega)$ is arbitrary with $\{E|X_{0i}|^2(\omega), i = 1,\cdots,n\} < \infty$ and is independent of $\{\mathcal{F}_t, t \in T\}$, $\sigma\{\mathbf{W}_s, s \leq t, t \in T\}$ and $\sigma\{\mathbf{V}_s, s \leq t, t \in T\}$.

6. The n-vector random process $\mathbf{f}_t(\omega)$ and the m-vector random process $\mathbf{h}_t(\omega)$—may be a functions of $\mathbf{X}_t(\omega)$—are $\mathcal{B}_t$-measurable nonanticipative functionals satisfying

$$\int_{t\in T} E|f_{it}|^2(\omega)\,dt < \infty \qquad i = 1,2,\ldots,n$$

$$\int_{t\in T} E|h_{it}|^2(\omega)\,dt < \infty \qquad i = 1,2,\ldots,m$$

7. $\{\mathbf{W}_t, \mathcal{B}_t, t \in T\}$ is an n-vector of general L^2-martingales with $\sigma\{W_{it} - W_{is}, i = 1,\ldots,n, s < t, t \in T\}$ independent of $\{\mathcal{B}_s, s < t\}$.

8. $\{\mathbf{V}_t, \mathcal{B}_t, t \in T\}$ is an m-vector of Brownian motion processes with $m \times m$ positive definite covariance parameter matrix $\mathbf{R}$, and $\sigma\{V_{it} - V_{is}, i = 1,\ldots,m, s < t, t \in T\}$ is independent of $\{\mathcal{B}_s, s < t\}$ or $\{\mathcal{F}_s, s < t\}$.

The other two assumptions are the same as in Theorem 8.4.1.

The m-vector innovations process $\{\boldsymbol{\nu}_t, t \in T\}$ given by

$$d\boldsymbol{\nu}_t(\omega) = d\mathbf{Y}_t(\omega) - \hat{\mathbf{h}}_t(\omega)\,dt \qquad t \in T, \quad \boldsymbol{\nu}_0 = 0 \tag{8.5.3}$$

is an $\mathcal{F}_t$-measurable Brownian motion process with $m \times m$ positive definite covariance parameter matrix $\mathbf{R}$, the same as that of $\mathbf{V}_t$.

Under the above assumptions we can now formulate the vector form of the nonlinear filtering representation.

Theorem 8.5.1 Vector Form of Nonlinear Filtering Theorem

Let $\{\Omega, \mathcal{F}, P\}$ be a complete probability space, and let $\{\mathcal{B}_t, t \in T\}$ be a filtration σ-field defined on it. Let the n-vector signal process $\mathbf{X}_t(\omega)$ and the m-vector observation process $\mathbf{Y}_t(\omega)$ be as given in eqs. 8.5.1 and 8.5.2, respectively. Then under assumptions 1 through 10, the n-vector filtered estimate $\hat{\mathbf{X}}_t$ is given by

$$d\hat{\mathbf{X}}_t = \hat{\mathbf{f}}_t\,dt + \left[E^{\mathcal{F}_t}\frac{d}{dt}\langle \mathbf{W}, \mathbf{V}^T\rangle_t + E^{\mathcal{F}_t}(\mathbf{X}_{t-}\mathbf{h}_t^T) - E^{\mathcal{F}_t}\mathbf{X}_{t-}E^{\mathcal{F}_t}\mathbf{h}_t^T\right]\mathbf{R}^{-1}\,d\boldsymbol{\nu}_t$$

$$t \in T, \quad E\mathbf{X}_0 \tag{8.5.4}$$

or

$$\hat{\mathbf{X}}_t = E\mathbf{X}_0 + \int_0^t \hat{\mathbf{f}}_\tau\,d\tau + \int_0^t\left[E^{\mathcal{F}_\tau}\frac{d}{d\tau}\langle \mathbf{W}, \mathbf{V}^T\rangle_\tau + E^{\mathcal{F}_\tau}(\mathbf{X}_{\tau-}\mathbf{h}_\tau^T)\right.$$

$$\left. - E^{\mathcal{F}_\tau}\mathbf{X}_{\tau-}E^{\mathcal{F}_\tau}\mathbf{h}_\tau^T\right]\mathbf{R}^{-1}\,d\boldsymbol{\nu}_\tau \tag{8.5.5}$$

The proof follows the lines exactly similar to that of Theorem 8.4.1, except that scalar quantities are replaced by vector quantities.

We can also represent eqs. 8.5.4 and 8.5.5 in terms of the n-vector error $\tilde{\mathbf{X}}_t$ and the m-vector error $\tilde{\mathbf{h}}_t$ given by

$$\tilde{\mathbf{X}}_t = \hat{\mathbf{X}}_{t-} - \mathbf{X}_{t-}$$

$$\tilde{\mathbf{h}}_t = \hat{\mathbf{h}}_{t-} - \mathbf{h}_{t-}$$

$$\hat{\mathbf{X}}_t = E\mathbf{X}_0 + \int_0^t \hat{\mathbf{f}}_\tau \, d\tau + \int_0^t \left[E^{\mathcal{F}_\tau}\left(\tilde{\mathbf{X}}_\tau \tilde{\mathbf{h}}_\tau^T + \frac{d}{d\tau}\langle \mathbf{W}, \mathbf{V}^T \rangle_\tau \right) \right] \mathbf{R}^{-1}\, d\nu_\tau \qquad t \in T \tag{8.5.6}$$

or

$$d\hat{\mathbf{X}}_t = \hat{\mathbf{f}}_t \, dt + \left[E^{\mathcal{F}_t}\left(\tilde{\mathbf{X}}_t \tilde{\mathbf{h}}_t^T + \frac{d}{dt}\langle \mathbf{W}, \mathbf{V}^T \rangle_t \right) \right] \mathbf{R}^{-1}\, d\nu_t \tag{8.5.7}$$

Note. The $n \times m$ error matrix $E^{\mathcal{F}_t}\tilde{\mathbf{X}}_t \tilde{\mathbf{h}}_t^T$ is known as the optimum random gain matrix and is represented by $\mathbf{K}_t$.

Remark. If the random vectors $\mathbf{W}_t$ and $\mathbf{V}_t$ are independent, then $\langle \mathbf{W}, \mathbf{V}^T \rangle_t = 0$ and eq. 8.5.7 becomes

$$d\hat{\mathbf{X}}_t = \hat{\mathbf{f}}_t \, dt + \mathbf{K}_t \mathbf{R}^{-1}\, d\nu_t \tag{8.5.8}$$

and this equation will be used in deriving the Kalman filter from the nonlinear filtering representation.

The nonlinear filter equations 8.4.38 and 8.5.6 are only closed form representations, and they are not closed form solutions for the conditional mean. Since $\mathbf{h}_t(\omega)$ is a function of $\mathbf{X}_t$ as well, we need higher order moments to solve these equations. In other words, the first-order moment involves the second-order moment, and the second-order moment will involve the third-order moment, and so on. In the linear Gaussian case (known as Kalman filter) we obtain a closed form solution where the first moment depends upon the second moment and the second moment stands by itself. In addition, Benes (66) has proposed finite dimensional solutions for a class of nonlinear filtering problems. In order to solve explicitly for the general optimal nonlinear filter equations, we necessarily have to take recourse to approximations to obtain closed form solutions resulting in a suboptimal filter. For other approaches to nonlinear filtering see Davis (68) and Yavin (75). In the next chapter we derive the Kalman filter and show its relationship to the general optimal nonlinear filter.

Problems

1. A stochastic process $\{X_t, \mathcal{F}_t, t \in T\}$ is a *strong* Markov process if for every stopping time $\tau(\omega)$ ($\{\tau(\omega) \leq t\}$ is $\mathcal{F}_t$-measurable)

$$P\{X_{\tau+s} \in A | \mathcal{F}_{\tau+}\} = P\{X_{\tau+s} \in A | X_\tau\}$$

Show that a strong Markov process satisfies the ordinary Markov property

$$P\{X_{t+s} \in A | \mathcal{F}_t\} = P\{X_{t+s} \in A | X_t\}$$

2. A stochastic process $\{X_t, \mathcal{F}_t, t \in T\}$ is defined by

$$X_t(\omega) = 0 \wedge (t - \tau(\omega)) = \max(0, t - \tau(\omega)) \qquad t \in T$$

where $\tau(\omega)$ is a stopping time relative to the right continuous filtration σ-field $\{\mathcal{F}_t, t \in T\}$ having the probability distribution function

$$P\{\tau(\omega) \leq t\} = 1 - e^{-t} \qquad t \in T$$

Show that the process X_t is a Markov process but not a strong Markov process.

3. Let $\{X_t, \mathcal{F}_t, t \in T\}$ be an Ito process given by

$$dX_t = a\,dt + dW_t \qquad t \in T, \quad X_0 = 0$$

where a is an $\mathcal{F}_0$-measurable normally distributed random variable with mean μ and variance σ^2. The Brownian motion process $\{W_t, \mathcal{F}_t, t \in T\}$ and a are assumed independent. Let $\mathcal{F}_t^X$ be the σ-field generated by $\{X_s, s \leq t, t \in T\}$. Show that

$$E^{\mathcal{F}_t^X} a = \frac{\mu + \sigma^2 X_t}{1 + \sigma^2 t}$$

and hence show that the diffusion equation representation is

$$dX_t = \frac{\mu + \sigma^2 X_t}{1 + \sigma^2 t} dt + d\nu_t$$

4. Let $\{X_t, \mathcal{B}_t, t \in T\}$ be an Ito process given by

$$dX_t = a_t X_t\,dt + b_t\,dW_t \qquad t \in T, \quad X_0$$

where a_t and b_t are functions of time only. Find an expression for the innovations process $\{\nu_t\}$ and show that

$$\sigma\{\nu_s, s \leq t, t \in T\} = \sigma\{X_s, s \leq t, t \in T\}$$

5. Let $\{W_t, \mathfrak{F}_t, t \in T\}$ and $\{V_t, \mathfrak{F}_t, t \in T\}$ be standard Brownian motion processes defined on a complete probability space $(\Omega, \mathfrak{F}, P)$ with $W_0 = V_0 = 0$. Let $X_t = W_t^2 + V_t^2$. Express X_t as a diffusion process.

6. Let an observation process be given in the form

$$Z_t = Z_0 + \int_0^t g_\tau(\omega)\, d\tau + M_t$$

where $g_t(\omega)$ is a nonanticipative process with respect to $\{\mathfrak{F}_t\}$ and M_t is an $\mathfrak{F}_t$-martingale. Let S_t be a signal process, and let W_t be an $\mathfrak{F}_t$ Brownian motion process. If

$$Y_t = Y_0 + \int_0^t S_\tau(\omega)\, d\tau + W_t$$

clearly $g_t(\omega) = S_t(\omega)$ and $M_t = W_t$ for the process Y_t. If h is a twice differentiable function and if $Z_t = h(Y_t)$, find $g_t(\omega)$ and M_t.

7. A signal process is given by

$$dX_t = f_t(\omega) + g_t(\omega)\, dW_t \qquad t \in T, \quad X_0$$

and the observation process by

$$dY_t = h_t(\omega)\, dt + dV_t \qquad t \in T, \quad Y_0 = 0$$

with the usual assumptions. Formulate the nonlinear filtering representation in the form of eqs. 8.4.7 and 8.4.41.

8. A signal process is given by

$$dX_t = fX_t\, dt + g\, dW_t \qquad t \in T, \quad X_0$$

and the observation process by

$$dY_t = hX_t\, dt + dV_t \qquad t \in T, \quad Y_0 = 0$$

where f, g, h are constants. Formulate the corresponding linear filtering representation. Can this equation be solved in closed form?

9. Let an observation process be given by

$$dY_t = h_t(\omega)\, dt + dV_t \qquad t \in T, \quad Y_0 = 0$$

Let the σ-field generated by $\{Y_s, s \leq t\}$ be $\mathcal{F}_t$. Show that every square integrable martingale $\{M_t, \mathcal{F}_t, t \in T\}$ has the representation

$$M_t = EM_0 + \int_0^t \varphi_s(\omega)\, d\nu_s$$

where

$$\int_{t \in T} E|\varphi_s|^2(\omega)\, ds < \infty$$

and $\varphi_t(\omega)$ is measurable and adapted to $\{\mathcal{F}_t, t \in T\}$. Note that φ_t is not necessarily adapted to $\{\mathcal{F}_t^\nu, t \in T\}$ (Fujisaki, Kallianpur, and Kunita, 15).

9 OPTIMAL LINEAR NONSTATIONARY FILTERING (KALMAN – BUCY FILTER)

In the previous chapter we derived the optimal nonlinear filter. Kalman and Bucy (31) had proposed a linear nonstationary filter where the signal and observation processes are driven by Gaussian white noise. We first derive the Kalman–Bucy filter purely from statistical considerations, and later we show that it is a special case of the nonlinear filter given by eq. 8.5.7. The discrete filter is derived first, and the results are extended to the continuous filter.

9.1 RECURSIVE ESTIMATION

We motivate the derivation of the Kalman filter from statistical considerations by means of a simple example. Let us assume that $\{X_i, i = 1, 2, \ldots, k\}$ is a signal process and $X_i = X$ a constant. Let $\{Y_i, i = 1, 2, \ldots, k\}$ be an observation process related to the signal process $\{X_i\}$ by the equation

$$Y_i = X_i + V_i \qquad i = 1, 2, \ldots, k \tag{9.1.1}$$

where $\{V_i, i = 1, 2, \ldots, k\}$ is a white noise sequence with $EV_i = 0$, $i = 1, 2, \ldots, k$, and $E(V_i V_j) = \sigma_v^2 \delta_{ij}$, $i, j = 1, 2, \ldots, k$. δ_{ij} is the familiar Kronecker delta.

We have to estimate the process $\{X_i\}$ given the process $\{Y_i\}$. Let $\hat{X}_k$ be the estimate of the signal process X given k observations or measurements $\{Y_i, i = 1, 2, \ldots, k\}$. A suitable estimator $\hat{X}_k$ is the weighted sum of the observations given by

$$\hat{X}_k = \frac{1}{k} \sum_{i=1}^{k} Y_i \tag{9.1.2}$$

The estimator $\hat{X}_k$ is an unbiased estimator in the sense

$$E\hat{X}_k = \frac{1}{k}\sum_{i=1}^{k} EY_i = X$$

and also a minimum variance estimator in the sense $E(\hat{X}_k - X)^2$ is a minimum.

Let us now assume that an additional observation Y_{k+1} is available at time $k + 1$. How does this affect the estimate $\hat{X}_k$? Clearly the new estimate from eq. 9.1.2 is

$$\hat{X}_{k+1} = \frac{1}{k+1}\sum_{i=1}^{k+1} Y_i \tag{9.1.3}$$

However, eq. 9.1.3 does not in any way involve the prior estimate $\hat{X}_k$. We have processed the entire information $\{Y_i, i = 1, 2, \ldots, k + 1\}$. In order to show explicitly the prior estimate $\hat{X}_k$, we rewrite eq. 9.1.3 as follows:

$$\hat{X}_{k+1} = \frac{k}{k+1}\,\frac{1}{k}\sum_{i=1}^{k} Y_i + \frac{Y_{k+1}}{k+1}$$

$$= \frac{k}{k+1}\hat{X}_k + \frac{1}{k+1}Y_{k+1} \tag{9.1.4}$$

Equation 9.1.4 can also be written as

$$\hat{X}_{k+1} = \left(1 - \frac{1}{k+1}\right)\hat{X}_k + \frac{1}{k+1}Y_{k+1}$$

$$= \hat{X}_k + \frac{1}{k+1}(Y_{k+1} - \hat{X}_k) \tag{9.1.5}$$

The term $(Y_{k+1} - \hat{X}_k)$ can be recognized as the discrete version of the innovations process given by Definition 8.2.1. In eqs. 9.1.4, 9.1.5, and 9.1.6 we have achieved a recursive action, namely, utilization of the past estimate to update the present estimate.

More generally, eq. 9.1.4 can be expressed as

$$\hat{X}_{k+1} = K_k'\hat{X}_k + K_kY_{k+1} \tag{9.1.6}$$

where K_k' and K_k are weighting coefficients which have to be determined using some optimality criteria. In the present case the optimality criteria are *unbiasedness* and *minimum variance*.

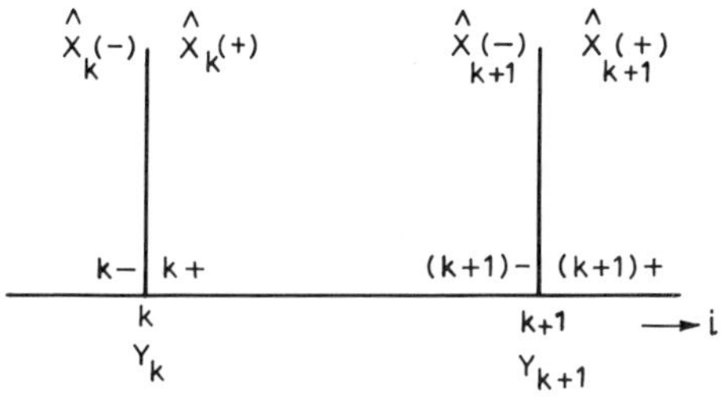

FIGURE 9.1.1

Let us now reformulate the above problem a little bit more precisely. Let us denote by $(k+1)-$ the time just *before the observation* Y_{k+1}, and by $(k+1)+$ the time just *after the observation*. $\hat{X}_{k+1}(-)$ is the estimate just before the observation Y_{k+1} and $\hat{X}_{k+1}(+)$ is the estimate just after the observation. These are illustrated in Figure 9.1.1.

The evolution of the state between $k+$ and $(k+1)-$ is governed by the dynamics of the system. In the present case there are no dynamics since X_k is a constant X for all times. Hence

$$X_k(+) = X \qquad X_{k+1}(-) = X \tag{9.1.7}$$

As a consequence we also have

$$\hat{X}_{k+1}(-) = \hat{X}_k(+) \tag{9.1.8}$$

We have thus two zones, namely, *between observations* where the estimate is governed by the dynamics of the system and *across observations* where the estimate is updated by means of the new observation available. We can therefore write the recursive action of eq. 9.1.5 in two stages as

$$\text{between observations} \qquad \hat{X}_{k+1}(-) = \hat{X}_k(+)$$

$$\text{across observations} \qquad \hat{X}_{k+1}(+) = \hat{X}_{k+1}(-) + \frac{1}{k+1}\left(Y_{k+1} - \hat{X}_{k+1}(-)\right) \tag{9.1.9}$$

Combining both equations we can write a single equation for the recursive estimator (filter),

$$\hat{X}_{k+1}(+) = \hat{X}_k(+) + \frac{1}{k+1}\left(Y_{k+1} - \hat{X}_k(+)\right) \tag{9.1.10}$$

which is eq. 9.1.5, in a precise form.

9.2 DISCRETE KALMAN FILTER

Next we formulate the linear discrete nonstationary filtering problem. As usual **boldface** represents both vectors and matrices. The discrete linear signal process is represented by the vector difference equation

$$\mathbf{X}_k = \mathbf{\Phi}_{k,k-1}\mathbf{X}_{k-1} + \mathbf{\Gamma}_{k-1}\mathbf{W}_{k-1} \qquad k \in N, \quad \mathbf{X}_0 \tag{9.2.1}$$

where N stands for the discrete interval $[0, 1, 2, \ldots, N]$. The observation process is again another discrete linear process represented by

$$\mathbf{Y}_k = \mathbf{H}_k\mathbf{X}_k + \mathbf{V}_k \qquad k \in N, \quad \mathbf{Y}_0 = 0 \tag{9.2.2}$$

The following assumptions are made regarding eqs. 9.2.1 and 9.2.2:

1. The signal process $\{\mathbf{X}_k, k \in N\}$ is an n-vector, and the observation process $\{\mathbf{Y}_k, k \in N\}$ is an m-vector, both evaluated at time t_k.
2. $\mathbf{\Phi}_{k,k-1}$ is an $n \times n$ nonsingular signal transition matrix from time t_{k-1} to t_k.
3. $\mathbf{\Gamma}_k$ is an $n \times r$ nonrandom rectangular matrix evaluated at time t_k.
4. $\mathbf{W}_k$ is an r-vector of white Gaussian noise sequence with $E\mathbf{W}_k = 0$ and $E\mathbf{W}_k\mathbf{W}_k^T = \mathbf{Q}_k$.
5. $\mathbf{V}_k$ is an m-vector of white Gaussian noise sequence with $E\mathbf{V}_k = 0$ and $E\mathbf{V}_k\mathbf{V}_k^T = \mathbf{R}_k$.
6. $\mathbf{H}_k$ is an $m \times n$ nonrandom weighting matrix evaluated at time t_k.
7. The Gaussian initial condition vector $\mathbf{X}_0$, the signal noise vector $\{\mathbf{W}_k, k \in N\}$, and the observation noise vector $\{\mathbf{V}_k, k \in N\}$ are all assumed independent.
8. If $\mathbf{g}_k$ is some random vector sequence, the conditional expectation of $\mathbf{g}_k$ given the observations $\{\mathbf{Y}_k, k \in N\}$ is represented by $\hat{\mathbf{g}}_k = E^k\mathbf{g}_k = E(\mathbf{g}_k | \mathbf{Y}_i, i = 0, 1, \ldots, k)$.
9. The noise vectors $\{\mathbf{W}_k\}$ and $\{\mathbf{V}_k\}$ and the estimation error vector $\{\tilde{\mathbf{X}}_k\} = \{(\hat{\mathbf{X}}_k - \mathbf{X}_k)\}$ are uncorrelated, that is,

$$E\tilde{\mathbf{X}}_k\mathbf{W}_k^T = E\mathbf{W}_k\tilde{\mathbf{X}}_k^T = \mathbf{0} = E\tilde{\mathbf{X}}_k\mathbf{V}_k^T = E\mathbf{V}_k\tilde{\mathbf{X}}_k^T.$$

10. The innovations sequence $\{\boldsymbol{\nu}_k, k \in N\}$ is also an m-vector given by

$$\boldsymbol{\nu}_k = \mathbf{Y}_k - \mathbf{H}_k\hat{\mathbf{X}}_k \qquad k \in N \tag{9.2.3}$$

11. The $n \times n$ error covariance matrix $\mathbf{P}_k = E(\hat{\mathbf{X}}_k - \mathbf{X}_k)(\hat{\mathbf{X}}_k - \mathbf{X}_k)^T$ is positive definite.

We can now state the discrete Kalman filter by means of the following theorem.

Theorem 9.2.1 Discrete Kalman Filter

Let the linear discrete signal process $\{\mathbf{X}_k, k \in N\}$ be as given in eq. 9.2.1, and let the linear discrete observation process $\{\mathbf{Y}_k, k \in N\}$ be as given in eq. 9.2.2. Then under assumptions 1 through 11 the minimum variance unbiased filter (optimal) consists of the following difference equations for the conditional mean and the unconditional covariance matrix.

Across Observations

$$\hat{\mathbf{X}}_k(+) = \hat{\mathbf{X}}_k(-) + \mathbf{K}_k(\mathbf{Y}_k - \mathbf{H}_k\hat{\mathbf{X}}_k(-)) \qquad k \in N \tag{9.2.4a}$$

$$\mathbf{P}_k(+) = (\mathbf{I} - \mathbf{K}_k\mathbf{H}_k)\mathbf{P}_k(-) \qquad k \in N \tag{9.2.4b}$$

where

$$\mathbf{K}_k = \mathbf{P}_k(-)\mathbf{H}_k^T(\mathbf{H}_k\mathbf{P}_k(-)\mathbf{H}_k^T + \mathbf{R}_k)^{-1} \qquad k \in N \tag{9.2.5}$$

is the $n \times m$ Kalman gain matrix.

Between Observations

$$\hat{\mathbf{X}}_{k+1}(-) = \mathbf{\Phi}_{k+1,k}\hat{\mathbf{X}}_k(+) \qquad k \in N \tag{9.2.6a}$$

$$\mathbf{P}_{k+1}(-) = \mathbf{\Phi}_{k+1,k}\mathbf{P}_k\mathbf{\Phi}_{k+1,k}^T + \mathbf{\Gamma}_k\mathbf{Q}_k\mathbf{\Gamma}_k^T \qquad k \in N \tag{9.2.6b}$$

Proof. We give a heuristic proof for this theorem. First we prove the theorem for across observations. We denote by $t_k(-)$ the time just before the observation time t_k and by $t_k(+)$ the time just after the observation time t_k. Let us assume that the estimate $\hat{\mathbf{X}}_k(-)$ at $t_k(-)$ has been found. At $t_k(+)$, an observation $\mathbf{Y}_k$ is available. We have to use this observation $\mathbf{Y}_k$ and the prior estimate $\hat{\mathbf{X}}_k(-)$ to get a new estimate $\hat{\mathbf{X}}_k(+)$. In a manner similar to what was done in the motivating example, eq. 9.1.6, we can write

$$\hat{\mathbf{X}}_k(+) = \mathbf{K}'_k\hat{\mathbf{X}}_k(-) + \mathbf{K}_k\mathbf{Y}_k \tag{9.2.7}$$

where the weighting matrices $\mathbf{K}'_k(n \times n)$ and $\mathbf{K}_k(n \times m)$ have to be determined according to unbiasedness and minimum variance as the two criteria.

We convert all estimates to estimation errors by defining

$$\begin{aligned} \tilde{\mathbf{X}}_k(+) &= \hat{\mathbf{X}}_k(+) - \mathbf{X}_k \\ \tilde{\mathbf{X}}_k(-) &= \hat{\mathbf{X}}_k(-) - \mathbf{X}_k \end{aligned} \tag{9.2.8}$$

where $\mathbf{X}_k$ is the true value of the signal process at time t_k. Clearly $\mathbf{X}_k$ is unaffected by the observations. $\tilde{\mathbf{X}}_k(+)$ is the error estimate at $t_k(+)$, and $\tilde{\mathbf{X}}_k(-)$ is the error estimate at $t_k(-)$. Subtracting $\mathbf{X}_k$ from both sides of eq. 9.2.7,

$$\hat{\mathbf{X}}_k(+) - \mathbf{X}_k = \mathbf{K}'_k(\hat{\mathbf{X}}_k(-) - \mathbf{X}_k) + \mathbf{K}'_k\mathbf{X}_k - \mathbf{X}_k + \mathbf{K}_k\mathbf{Y}_k \tag{9.2.9}$$

Substituting for $\mathbf{Y}_k$ from eq. 9.2.2 into eq. 9.2.9, there results

$$\hat{\mathbf{X}}_k(+) - \mathbf{X}_k = \mathbf{K}'_k(\hat{\mathbf{X}}_k(-) - \mathbf{X}_k) + (\mathbf{K}'_k + \mathbf{K}_k\mathbf{H}_k - \mathbf{I})\mathbf{X}_k + \mathbf{K}_k\mathbf{V}_k \tag{9.2.10}$$

Substituting the error equations 9.2.8 into eq. 9.2.10, we have

$$\tilde{\mathbf{X}}_k(+) = \mathbf{K}'_k\tilde{\mathbf{X}}_k(-) + (\mathbf{K}'_k + \mathbf{K}_k\mathbf{H}_k - \mathbf{I})\mathbf{X}_k + \mathbf{K}_k\mathbf{V}_k \tag{9.2.11}$$

If the estimator is to be unbiased, we must have

$$E\tilde{\mathbf{X}}_k(+) = \mathbf{0} = E\tilde{\mathbf{X}}_k(-) \tag{9.2.12}$$

Taking expectation on both sides of eq. 9.2.11,

$$E\tilde{\mathbf{X}}_k(+) = \mathbf{K}'_kE\tilde{\mathbf{X}}_k(-) + (\mathbf{K}'_k + \mathbf{K}_k\mathbf{H}_k - \mathbf{I})E\mathbf{X}_k + \mathbf{K}_kE\mathbf{V}_k \tag{9.2.13}$$

Substituting eq. 9.2.12 in eq. 9.2.13 and from assumption 5, $E\mathbf{V}_k = 0$, we have

$$\mathbf{K}'_k + \mathbf{K}_k\mathbf{H}_k - \mathbf{I} = 0$$

or

$$\mathbf{K}'_k = \mathbf{I} - \mathbf{K}_k\mathbf{H}_k \tag{9.2.14}$$

Thus we have found the unknown $\mathbf{K}'_k$ in terms of $\mathbf{K}_k$. Substituting for $\mathbf{K}'_k$ in eq. 9.2.7 from eq. 9.2.14 we arrive at

$$\hat{\mathbf{X}}_k(+) = \hat{\mathbf{X}}_k(-) + \mathbf{K}_k(\mathbf{Y}_k - \mathbf{H}_k\hat{\mathbf{X}}_k(-)) \qquad k \in N \tag{9.2.15}$$

which is eq. 9.2.4a with the unknown quantity $\mathbf{K}_k$ yet to be determined.

Equation 9.2.15 is the vector version similar to eq. 9.1.9 of the motivating example. The estimation error equation 9.2.11 can be rewritten using the value of $\mathbf{K}'_k$ from eq. 9.2.14:

$$\begin{aligned}\tilde{\mathbf{X}}_k(+) &= (\mathbf{I} - \mathbf{K}_k\mathbf{H}_k)\tilde{\mathbf{X}}_k(-) + \mathbf{K}_k\mathbf{V}_k \\ &= \tilde{\mathbf{X}}_k(-) + \mathbf{K}_k\big(\mathbf{V}_k - \mathbf{H}_k\tilde{\mathbf{X}}_k(-)\big)\end{aligned} \tag{9.2.16}$$

Equation 9.2.15 represents the estimate update from $\hat{\mathbf{X}}_k(-)$ to $\hat{\mathbf{X}}_k(+)$ due to an observation at t_k, and eq. 9.2.16 represents the corresponding estimation error update from $\tilde{\mathbf{X}}_k(-)$ to $\tilde{\mathbf{X}}_k(+)$. We still have to determine the unknown gain matrix $\mathbf{K}_k$.

We now define the error covariance matrices $\mathbf{P}_k(+)$ and $\mathbf{P}_k(-)$ as

$$\begin{aligned}\mathbf{P}_k(+) &= E\tilde{\mathbf{X}}_k(+)\tilde{\mathbf{X}}_k^T(+) \\ \mathbf{P}_k(-) &= E\tilde{\mathbf{X}}_k(-)\tilde{\mathbf{X}}_k^T(-)\end{aligned} \tag{9.2.17}$$

From eq. 9.2.16 we have

$$\begin{aligned}\mathbf{P}_k(+) &= E\Big\{\big[\tilde{\mathbf{X}}_k(-) + \mathbf{K}_k\big(\mathbf{V}_k - \mathbf{H}_k\tilde{\mathbf{X}}_k(-)\big)\big] \\ &\qquad \times \big[\tilde{\mathbf{X}}_k(-) + \mathbf{K}_k\big(\mathbf{V}_k - \mathbf{H}_k\tilde{\mathbf{X}}_k(-)\big)\big]^T\Big\} \\ &= E\Big\{\tilde{\mathbf{X}}_k(-)\tilde{\mathbf{X}}_k^T(-) + \mathbf{K}_k\big(\mathbf{V}_k - \mathbf{H}_k\tilde{\mathbf{X}}_k(-)\big)\big(\mathbf{V}_k - \mathbf{H}_k\tilde{\mathbf{X}}_k(-)\big)^T\mathbf{K}_k^T \\ &\qquad + \tilde{\mathbf{X}}_k(-)\big(\mathbf{V}_k - \mathbf{H}_k\tilde{\mathbf{X}}_k(-)\big)^T\mathbf{K}_k^T + \mathbf{K}_k\big(\mathbf{V}_k - \mathbf{H}_k\tilde{\mathbf{X}}_k(-)\big)\tilde{\mathbf{X}}_k^T(-)\Big\}\end{aligned} \tag{9.2.18}$$

Since $E\mathbf{V}_k\mathbf{V}_k^T = \mathbf{R}_k$ and using assumption 9 and eq. 9.2.17 in eq. 9.2.18, we obtain

$$\mathbf{P}_k(+) = (\mathbf{I} - \mathbf{K}_k\mathbf{H}_k)\mathbf{P}_k(-)(\mathbf{I} - \mathbf{K}_k\mathbf{H}_k)^T + \mathbf{K}_k\mathbf{R}_k\mathbf{K}_k^T \tag{9.2.19}$$

The unknown Kalman gain matrix $\mathbf{K}_k$ can now be determined by using the minimum variance criterion. The diagonal elements of the matrix $\mathbf{P}_k(+)$ represent the variance of $\tilde{\mathbf{X}}_k(+)$. Thus the variance function that should be minimized is

$$E\tilde{\mathbf{X}}_k^T(+)\tilde{\mathbf{X}}_k(+) = \operatorname{tr}\mathbf{P}_k(+) \tag{9.2.20}$$

where $\operatorname{tr}\mathbf{P}_k(+)$ is the trace of the matrix $\mathbf{P}_k(+)$. $\mathbf{K}_k$ can now be obtained by solving for

$$\frac{\partial}{\partial\mathbf{K}_k}\operatorname{tr}\mathbf{P}_k(+) = 0 \tag{9.2.21}$$

Since $\mathbf{P}_k(+)$ is a quadratic form, we use the result

$$\frac{\partial}{\partial \mathbf{A}} \operatorname{tr}(\mathbf{ABA}^T) = 2\mathbf{AB} \qquad \text{if } \mathbf{B} \text{ is symmetric}$$

to obtain for eq. 9.2.21

$$\frac{\partial}{\partial \mathbf{K}_k} \operatorname{tr}\left[(\mathbf{I} - \mathbf{K}_k\mathbf{H}_k)\mathbf{P}_k(-)(\mathbf{I} - \mathbf{K}_k\mathbf{H}_k)^T + \mathbf{K}_k\mathbf{R}_k\mathbf{K}_k^T\right]$$

$$= -2(\mathbf{I} - \mathbf{K}_k\mathbf{H}_k)\mathbf{P}_k(-)\mathbf{H}_k^T + 2\mathbf{K}_k\mathbf{R}_k = 0 \qquad (9.2.22)$$

Solving for $\mathbf{K}_k$ from eq. 9.2.22 we obtain

$$\mathbf{K}_k = \mathbf{P}_k(-)\mathbf{H}_k^T\left(\mathbf{H}_k\mathbf{P}_k(-)\mathbf{H}_k^T + \mathbf{R}_k\right)^{-1} \qquad k \in N \qquad (9.2.23)$$

which is eq. 9.2.5 of Theorem 9.2.1.

Substituting the value of $\mathbf{K}_k$ given in eq. 9.2.23 in the error covariance equation 9.2.19, there results

$$\mathbf{P}_k(+) = (\mathbf{I} - \mathbf{K}_k\mathbf{H}_k)\mathbf{P}_k(-) \qquad k \in N \qquad (9.2.24)$$

which is eq. 9.2.4b.

The signal estimate is of course given by eq. 9.2.15 where $\mathbf{K}_k$, the Kalman gain matrix, is given by eq. 9.2.23.

We must now prove the theorem for between observations. We take the conditional expectation of eq. 9.2.1 conditioned on the observations,

$$\hat{\mathbf{X}}_{k+1}(+) = \mathbf{\Phi}_{k+1,k}\hat{\mathbf{X}}_k(+) + \mathbf{\Gamma}_k\hat{\mathbf{W}}_k \qquad (9.2.25)$$

Since $\{\mathbf{W}_k\}$ is independent of the observations, $\hat{\mathbf{W}}_k = E\mathbf{W}_k = 0$. Hence eq. 9.2.25 reduces to

$$\hat{\mathbf{X}}_{k+1}(-) = \mathbf{\Phi}_{k+1,k}\hat{\mathbf{X}}_k(+) \qquad k \in N \qquad (9.2.26)$$

which is eq. 9.2.6a.

The signal process at time t_{k+1} can be written from eq. 9.2.1:

$$\mathbf{X}_{k+1} = \mathbf{\Phi}_{k+1,k}\mathbf{X}_k + \mathbf{\Gamma}_k\mathbf{W}_k \qquad (9.2.27)$$

Subtracting eq. 9.2.27 from eq. 9.2.26 yields the estimation error at $t_{k+1}(-)$

$$\tilde{\mathbf{X}}_{k+1}(-) = \mathbf{\Phi}_{k+1,k}\tilde{\mathbf{X}}_k(+) - \mathbf{\Gamma}_k\mathbf{W}_k \qquad (9.2.28)$$

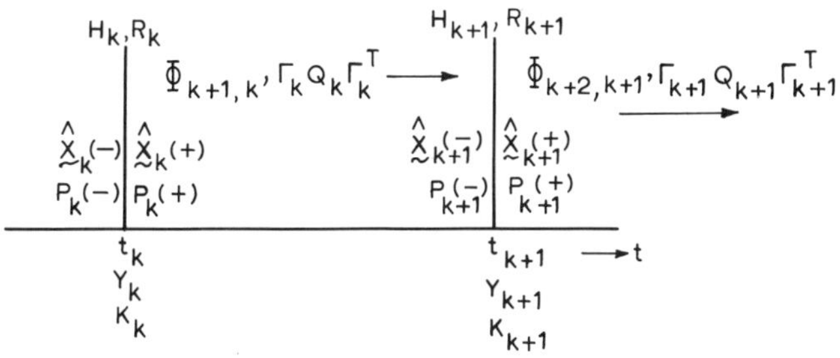

FIGURE 9.2.1

The error covariance matrix $\mathbf{P}_{k+1}(-)$ is

$$\begin{aligned}
\mathbf{P}_{k+1}(-) &= E\tilde{\mathbf{X}}_{k+1}(-)\tilde{\mathbf{X}}_{k+1}^T(-) \\
&= E\left\{\left(\mathbf{\Phi}_{k+1,k}\tilde{\mathbf{X}}_k(+) - \mathbf{\Gamma}_k\mathbf{W}_k\right)\left(\mathbf{\Phi}_{k+1,k}\tilde{\mathbf{X}}_k(+) - \mathbf{\Gamma}_k\mathbf{W}_k\right)^T\right\} \\
&= E\left\{\mathbf{\Phi}_{k+1,k}\tilde{\mathbf{X}}_k(+)\tilde{\mathbf{X}}_k^T(+)\mathbf{\Phi}_{k+1,k}^T + \mathbf{\Gamma}_k\mathbf{W}_k\mathbf{W}_k^T\mathbf{\Gamma}_k^T\right. \\
&\quad \left. -\mathbf{\Phi}_{k+1,k}\tilde{\mathbf{X}}_k(+)\mathbf{W}_k^T\mathbf{\Gamma}_k^T - \mathbf{\Gamma}_k\mathbf{W}_k\mathbf{X}_k^T(+)\mathbf{\Phi}_{k+1,k}^T\right\} \qquad (9.2.29)
\end{aligned}$$

Since the estimation errors are uncorrelated with the noise vector $\mathbf{W}_k$, eq. 9.2.29 reduces to

$$\mathbf{P}_{k+1}(-) = \mathbf{\Phi}_{k+1,k}\mathbf{P}_k(+)\mathbf{\Phi}_{k+1,k}^T + \mathbf{\Gamma}_k\mathbf{Q}_k\mathbf{\Gamma}_k^T \qquad k \in N \qquad (9.2.30)$$

which is precisely eq. 9.2.6b. □

The timing diagram similar to Figure 9.1.1 for eqs. 9.2.4, 9.2.5, and 9.2.6 is presented in Figure 9.2.1. The block diagram implementation of eqs. 9.2.1, 9.2.2, 9.2.4, 9.2.5, and 9.2.6 is shown in Figure 9.2.2.

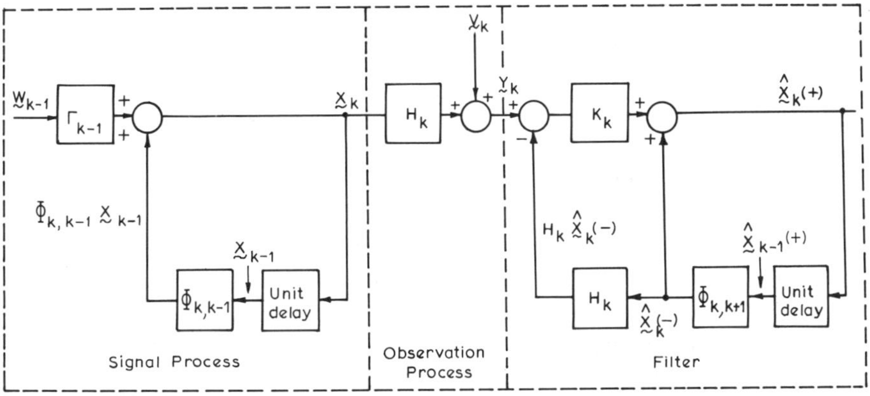

FIGURE 9.2.2

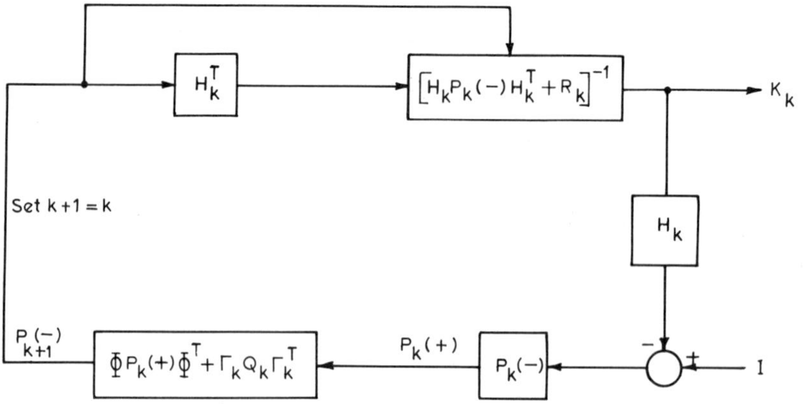

FIGURE 9.2.3

The block diagram implementation of the Kalman gain matrix $\mathbf{K}_k$ and the error covariance matrix $\mathbf{P}_k$ is shown in Figure 9.2.3.

Remarks

1. The equations for across and between measurements can be combined to yield one equation for conditional mean and unconditional variance:

$$\hat{\mathbf{X}}_{k+1}(-) = \mathbf{\Phi}_{k+1,k}\hat{\mathbf{X}}_k(-) + \mathbf{\Phi}_{k+1,k}\mathbf{P}_k(-)\mathbf{H}_k^T \times\left(\mathbf{H}_k\mathbf{P}_k(-)\mathbf{H}_k^T + \mathbf{R}_k\right)^{-1}\left(\mathbf{Y}_k - \mathbf{H}_k\hat{\mathbf{X}}_k(-)\right) \qquad k \in N \tag{9.2.31}$$

$$\mathbf{P}_{k+1}(-) = \mathbf{\Phi}_{k+1,k}\mathbf{P}_k(-)\mathbf{\Phi}_{k+1,k}^T - \mathbf{\Phi}_{k+1,k}\mathbf{P}_k(-)\mathbf{H}_k^T \times\left(\mathbf{H}_k\mathbf{P}_k(-)\mathbf{H}_k^T + \mathbf{R}_k\right)^{-1}\mathbf{H}_k\mathbf{P}_k(-)\mathbf{\Phi}_k^T + \mathbf{\Gamma}_k\mathbf{Q}_k\mathbf{\Gamma}_k^T \qquad k \in N \tag{9.2.32}$$

2. The signal estimate equations 9.2.31 and the error covariance equations 9.2.32 are not coupled. Hence the error covariance matrix can be calculated separately from the initial error covariance matrix and the corresponding Kalman gain matrix $\mathbf{K}_k$ calculated. This is fed into the signal estimate update. This fortuitous circumstance occurs only for the linear Gaussian case.

3. The error covariance update equation

$$\mathbf{P}_k(+) = (\mathbf{I} - \mathbf{K}_k\mathbf{H}_k)\mathbf{P}_k(-)$$

can be expressed in an alternate form by

$$\mathbf{P}_k^{-1}(+) = \mathbf{P}_k^{-1}(-) + \mathbf{H}_k^T\mathbf{R}_k^{-1}\mathbf{H}_k \tag{9.2.33}$$

4. The Kalman gain matrix $\mathbf{K}_k$ can also be expressed in an alternate form as

$$\mathbf{K}_k = \mathbf{P}_k(+)\mathbf{H}_k^T\mathbf{R}_k^{-1} \tag{9.2.34}$$

Next we illustrate the discrete Kalman filter by examples.

Example 9.2.1

The observation process is given by the scalar equation

$$Y_{k-1} = X_{k-1} + V_{k-1} \qquad k \in N$$

We want to investigate the effect of an additional observation Y_k on the error covariance. We assume $\mathbf{R}_k = \sigma_v^2$, $\mathbf{P}_k(+) = p_k(+)$, and $\mathbf{P}_k(-) = p_k(-)$. Using eq. 9.2.33, we obtain

$$\frac{1}{p_k(+)} = \frac{1}{p_k(-)} + \frac{1}{\sigma_v^2}$$

or

$$p_k(+) = \frac{p_k(-)}{1 + p_k(-)/\sigma_v^2}$$

Thus an additional observation Y_k reduces the estimation error variance from $p_k(-)$ to $p_k(-)/(1 + p_k(-)/\sigma_v^2)$. On the other hand, if the measurement uncertainty σ_v^2 is low, then even if there is a high initial error variance, it is drastically reduced by the good measurement. However, if the measurement uncertainty σ_v^2 is high, an extra measurement does not appreciably reduce the error variance.

Example 9.2.2

The signal process is given by

$$X_k = X_{k-1}$$

and the observation process is given by

$$Y_k = X_k + V_k$$

where V_k is distributed as $N(0, \sigma_v^2)$. The initial error variance is $p_0 = E(\hat{X}_0 - X_0)^2$.

We use Theorem 9.2.1 to obtain the equations for across and between observations.

Across Observations. The Kalman gain matrix is obtained from eq. 9.2.5 with $\mathbf{H}_k = 1$,

$$k_k = p_k(-) \cdot 1 \cdot \left(1 \cdot p_k(-) \cdot 1 + \sigma_v^2\right)^{-1}$$

$$= \frac{p_k(-)}{p_k(-) + \sigma_v^2}$$

Using eq. 9.2.34, the Kalman gain matrix can also be given by

$$k_k = \frac{p_k(+)}{\sigma_v^2}$$

The signal estimate is obtained from eq. 9.2.4a,

$$\hat{X}_k(+) = \hat{X}_k(-) + \frac{p_k(+)}{\sigma_v^2}\left(Y_k - \hat{X}_k(-)\right)$$

From eq. 9.2.4b we obtain the variance

$$p_k(+) = \left(1 - \frac{p_k(-)}{p_k(-) + \sigma_v^2}\right) p_k(-)$$

$$= \frac{p_k(-)\sigma_v^2}{p_k(-) + \sigma_v^2}$$

$$= \frac{p_k(-)}{1 + p_k(-)/\sigma_v^2} \tag{9.2.35}$$

Between Observations

$$\hat{X}_{k+1}(-) = \hat{X}_k(+)$$

$$p_{k+1}(-) = p_k(+)$$

Since $p_k(-) = p_{k-1}(+)$, eq. 9.2.35 can be rewritten as

$$p_k(+) = \frac{p_{k-1}(+)}{1 + p_{k-1}(+)/\sigma_v^2}$$

If the above difference equation is solved, there results

$$p_k(+) = \frac{p_0}{1 + kp_0/\sigma_v^2}$$

Therefore the Kalman gain k_k is given by

$$k_k = \frac{p_0}{\sigma_v^2 + kp_0}$$

The signal estimate equation for $\hat{X}_k(+)$ can now be given by

$$\hat{X}_k(+) = \hat{X}_k(-) + \frac{p_0}{\sigma_v^2 + kp_0}(Y_k - \hat{X}_k(-))$$

Substituting $\hat{X}_{k+1}(-) = \hat{X}_k(+)$ in the above equation, we obtain

$$\hat{X}_{k+1}(-) = \hat{X}_k(-) + \frac{p_0}{\sigma_v^2 + kp_0}(Y_k - \hat{X}_k(-))$$

Since $p_{k+1}(-) = p_k(+)$, the variance equation for $p_k(+)$ can now be rewritten as

$$p_{k+1}(-) = \frac{p_0}{1 + kp_0/\sigma_v^2}$$

Remarks

1. As the number of observations increases, that is, k increases, $p_{k+1}(-)$ decreases, and hence there is an improvement in the signal estimate $\hat{X}_{k+1}(-)$.
2. Since the rate at which $p_{k+1}(-)$ decreases with respect to k is given by

$$\frac{-p_0^2}{\sigma_v^2(1 + kp_0/\sigma_v^2)^2}$$

or,

$$\frac{\partial p_{k+1}(-)}{\partial k} \propto -\frac{1}{k^2}$$

for large k, there is no drastic improvement in the signal estimate beyond a certain k.

9.3 CONTINUOUS KALMAN FILTER

We now pose the continuous Kalman filter problem. The continuous linear signal process is represented by the n-vector stochastic differential equation

$$d\mathbf{X}_t = \mathbf{F}_t\mathbf{X}_t\,dt + \mathbf{G}_t\,d\mathbf{W}_t \qquad t \in T, \quad \mathbf{X}_0 \tag{9.3.1}$$

where T is some interval on the positive real line.

The linear observation process is again another m-vector stochastic differential equation

$$d\mathbf{Y}_t = \mathbf{H}_t\mathbf{X}_t\,dt + d\mathbf{V}_t \qquad t \in T, \quad \mathbf{Y}_0 = 0 \tag{9.3.2}$$

The following assumptions, which are similar to those in the discrete case, are made regarding eqs. 9.3.1 and 9.3.2:

1. The n-vector signal process $\{\mathbf{X}_t, t \in T\}$ and the m-vector observation process $\{\mathbf{Y}_t, t \in T\}$ are both defined on a complete probability space $(\Omega, \mathcal{F}, P)$.
2. The $n \times n$ nonsingular matrix $\mathbf{F}_t$, the $n \times r$ rectangular matrix $\mathbf{G}_t$, and the $m \times n$ rectangular matrix $\mathbf{H}_t$ are all nonrandom function of time such that

$$\begin{aligned}
&\int_{t\in T} |F_{ijt}|\,dt < \infty && i, j = 1, 2, \ldots, n \\
&\int_{t\in T} |G_{ijt}|^2\,dt < \infty && i = 1, 2, \ldots, n, \quad j = 1, 2, \ldots, r \\
&\int_{t\in T} |H_{ijt}|\,dt < \infty && i = 1, 2, \ldots, m, \quad j = 1, 2, \ldots, n
\end{aligned} \tag{9.3.3}$$

3. $\mathbf{W}_t$ is an r-vector of Brownian motion processes with covariance parameter matrix $\mathbf{Q}_t > 0$, given by

$$E\{d\mathbf{W}_t\,d\mathbf{W}_t^T\} = \mathbf{Q}_t\,dt$$

4. $\mathbf{V}_t$ is an m-vector of Brownian motion processes with covariance parameter matrix $\mathbf{R}_t > 0$, given by

$$E\{d\mathbf{V}_t\,d\mathbf{V}_t^T\} = \mathbf{R}_t\,dt$$

5. The Gaussian initial condition vector $\mathbf{X}_0$ and the Brownian motion processes $\{\mathbf{W}_t, t \in T\}$ and $\{\mathbf{V}_t, t \in T\}$ are mutually independent.
6. If $\mathbf{g}_t$ is some random process, then $E\{\mathbf{g}_t | \mathbf{Y}_s, s \le t\}$ will be represented by $E^t\mathbf{g}_t = \hat{\mathbf{g}}_t$.
7. The innovations process $\{\boldsymbol{\nu}_t, t \in T\}$ is also an m-vector Brownian motion process given by

$$d\boldsymbol{\nu}_t = d\mathbf{Y}_t - \mathbf{H}_t\hat{\mathbf{X}}_t\,dt \tag{9.3.4}$$

8. The error covariance matrix $\mathbf{P}_t = E(\hat{\mathbf{X}}_t - \mathbf{X}_t)(\hat{\mathbf{X}}_t - \mathbf{X}_t)^T$ is positive definite.

We now postulate the Kalman filter theorem for continuous systems.

Theorem 9.3.1 Continuous Kalman Filter

Let $\{\mathbf{X}_t, t \in T\}$ be a Gaussian signal process represented by eq. 9.3.1, and let $\{\mathbf{Y}_t, t \in T\}$ be a Gaussian observation process represented by eq. 9.3.2. Let assumptions 1 through 8 be satisfied. Further let

$$\int_{t \in T} |H_{ijt}|^2 \, dt < \infty$$

Then the conditional expectation $\hat{\mathbf{X}}_t$ satisfies the stochastic differential equation

$$d\hat{\mathbf{X}}_t = \mathbf{F}_t \hat{\mathbf{X}}_t \, dt + \mathbf{P}_t \mathbf{H}_t^T \mathbf{R}_t^{-1} \big(d\mathbf{Y}_t - \mathbf{H}_t \hat{\mathbf{X}}_t \, dt \big) \qquad t \in T \qquad (9.3.5)$$

and the covariance matrix $\mathbf{P}_t$ satisfies the matrix Riccati equation

$$\frac{d\mathbf{P}_t}{dt} = \mathbf{F}_t \mathbf{P}_t + \mathbf{P}_t \mathbf{F}_t^T + \mathbf{G}_t \mathbf{Q}_t \mathbf{G}_t^T - \mathbf{P}_t \mathbf{H}_t^T \mathbf{R}_t^{-1} \mathbf{H}_t \mathbf{P}_t \qquad t \in T \quad (9.3.6)$$

and the Kalman gain matrix $\mathbf{K}_t$ satisfies the equation

$$\mathbf{K}_t = \mathbf{P}_t \mathbf{H}_t \mathbf{R}_t^{-1} \qquad t \in T \qquad (9.3.7)$$

Proof. There are very many different proofs to this theorem, some rigorous and some heuristic. We give here only a heuristic proof showing that eqs. 9.3.5–9.3.7 are limiting cases of the discrete Kalman filter equations 9.2.31, 9.2.32, and 9.2.34. For a rigorous proof see Kallianpur (29, pp. 256–272), Kallianpur and Striebel (30), and Lipster and Shiryaev (34, p. 352).

We show that the stochastic differential equations 9.3.5 and 9.3.6 are a limiting case of eqs. 9.2.31 and 9.2.32. Since $\mathbf{F}_t$, $\mathbf{G}_t$, and $\mathbf{H}_t$ are matrix *nonrandom* functions, eq. 9.3.1 can be formally written as

$$d\mathbf{X}_t = \mathbf{F}_t \mathbf{X}_t \, dt + \mathbf{G}_t \mathbf{w}_t \, dt \qquad t \in T \qquad (9.3.8)$$

where the white noise process $\{\mathbf{w}_t\}$ is defined by $\mathbf{w}_t \, dt = d\mathbf{W}_t$. By defining $\mathbf{Z}_t \, dt = d\mathbf{Y}_t$, eq. 9.3.2 can be rewritten as

$$\mathbf{Z}_t = \mathbf{H}_t \mathbf{X}_t + \mathbf{v}_t \qquad t \in T \qquad (9.3.9)$$

where again the white noise process $\mathbf{v}_t$ is defined by $\mathbf{v}_t \, dt = d\mathbf{V}_t$.

For the sake of clarity we assume a *uniform* discretization interval $\Delta t = t_{k+1} - t_k$, $k = 0, 1, \ldots, n-1$. Discretization of eqs. 9.3.8 and 9.3.9 results in

$$\mathbf{X}_{k+1} = (\mathbf{I} + \mathbf{F}_k \Delta t)\mathbf{X}_k + \Delta t \, \mathbf{G}_k \mathbf{w}_k \qquad (9.3.10)$$

$$\mathbf{Z}_k = \mathbf{H}_k \mathbf{X}_k + \mathbf{v}_k \qquad (9.3.11)$$

where the subscript k stands for the value of the process at time $t = t_k$. Comparing eq. 9.3.10 to eq. 9.2.1, we find that

$$\mathbf{I} + \mathbf{F}_k \Delta t = \mathbf{\Phi}_{k+1,k} \qquad \Delta t \, \mathbf{G}_k = \mathbf{\Gamma}_k \tag{9.3.12}$$

We have now to find the equivalence for the variance parameters $\mathbf{Q}_t$ and $\mathbf{R}_t$ in the discrete domain.

From assumptions 3 and 4 we have $E\mathbf{w}_t\mathbf{w}_t^T \, dt^2 = \mathbf{Q}_t \, dt$ and $E\mathbf{v}_t\mathbf{v}_t^T \, dt^2 = \mathbf{R}_t \, dt$. Or

$$E\mathbf{w}_t\mathbf{w}_t^T = \frac{\mathbf{Q}_t}{dt}$$

$$E\mathbf{v}_t\mathbf{v}_t^T = \frac{\mathbf{R}_t}{dt}$$

Comparing this result with $E\mathbf{W}_k\mathbf{W}_k^T = \mathbf{Q}_k$ and $E\mathbf{V}_k\mathbf{V}_k^T = \mathbf{R}_k$ with Δt being the discretization interval, $\mathbf{Q}_t$ and $\mathbf{R}_t$ at time t_k can be given in terms of $\mathbf{Q}_k$ and $\mathbf{R}_k$ by

$$\begin{aligned} \frac{\mathbf{Q}_t^k}{\Delta t} &= \mathbf{Q}_k \\ \frac{\mathbf{R}_t^k}{\Delta t} &= \mathbf{R}_k \end{aligned} \tag{9.3.13}$$

First we find the limiting form of eq. 9.2.31 by substituting in it eqs. 9.3.12 and 9.3.13. Since we are taking the limiting form as $\Delta t \to 0$, the distinction between $\hat{X}_k(+)$ and $\hat{X}_k(-)$ in eq. 9.2.31 has been eliminated.

$$\begin{aligned} \hat{\mathbf{X}}_{k+1} &= (\mathbf{I} + \mathbf{F}_k \Delta t)\hat{\mathbf{X}}_k + (\mathbf{I} + \mathbf{F}_k \Delta t)\mathbf{P}_k\mathbf{H}_k^T\left(\mathbf{H}_k\mathbf{P}_k\mathbf{H}_k^T + \frac{\mathbf{R}_t^k}{\Delta t}\right)^{-1}(\mathbf{Z}_k - \mathbf{H}_k\hat{\mathbf{X}}_k) \\ &= \hat{\mathbf{X}}_k + \Delta t\,\mathbf{F}_k\hat{\mathbf{X}}_k + \Delta t\,(\mathbf{I} + \mathbf{F}_k \Delta t) \\ &\quad \times \mathbf{P}_k\mathbf{H}_k^T\left(\mathbf{H}_k\mathbf{P}_k\mathbf{H}_k^T \Delta t + \mathbf{R}_t^k\right)^{-1}(\mathbf{Z}_k - \mathbf{H}_k\hat{\mathbf{X}}_k) \\ &= \hat{\mathbf{X}}_k + \Delta t\,\mathbf{F}_k\hat{\mathbf{X}}_k + \Delta t\,\mathbf{P}_k\mathbf{H}_k^T\left(\mathbf{H}_k\mathbf{P}_k\mathbf{H}_k^T \Delta t + \mathbf{R}_t^k\right)^{-1}(\mathbf{Z}_k - \mathbf{H}_k\hat{\mathbf{X}}_k) \\ &\quad + \Delta t^2\,\mathbf{F}_k\mathbf{P}_k\mathbf{H}_k^T\left(\mathbf{H}_k\mathbf{P}_k\mathbf{H}_k^T \Delta t + \mathbf{R}_t^k\right)^{-1}(\mathbf{Z}_k - \mathbf{H}_k\hat{\mathbf{X}}_k) \end{aligned} \tag{9.3.14}$$

Subtracting $\hat{\mathbf{X}}_k$ from both sides of eq. 9.3.14, we have

$$\begin{aligned} \hat{\mathbf{X}}_{k+1} - \hat{\mathbf{X}}_k &= \mathbf{F}_k\hat{\mathbf{X}}_k \Delta t + \mathbf{P}_k\mathbf{H}_k^T\left(\mathbf{H}_k\mathbf{P}_k\mathbf{H}_k^T \Delta t + \mathbf{R}_t^k\right)^{-1} \\ &\quad \times (\mathbf{Z}_k - \mathbf{H}_k\hat{\mathbf{X}}_k)\,\Delta t + o(\Delta t) \end{aligned} \tag{9.3.15}$$

where $o(\Delta t) \to 0$ as $\Delta t \to 0$.

Dividing by Δt and taking the limit of eq. 9.3.15 as $\Delta t \to 0$, we obtain

$$d\hat{\mathbf{X}}_t = \mathbf{F}_t\hat{\mathbf{X}}_t\,dt + \mathbf{P}_t\mathbf{H}_t^T\mathbf{R}_t^{-1}\left(\mathbf{Z}_t\,dt - \mathbf{H}_t\hat{\mathbf{X}}_t\,dt\right) \qquad t \in T \qquad (9.3.16)$$

By substituting $d\mathbf{Y}_t$ for $\mathbf{Z}_t\,dt$ we obtain eq. 9.3.5.

Note. The term $\mathbf{H}_k\mathbf{P}_k\mathbf{H}_k^T$ appearing in the discrete formulation disappears in the continuous formulation.

The next step is to find the limiting form of eq. 9.2.32. Substituting eqs. 9.3.12 and 9.3.13 in eq. 9.2.32, we have

$$\begin{aligned}\mathbf{P}_{k+1} &= (\mathbf{I} + \mathbf{F}_k\,\Delta t)\mathbf{P}_k(\mathbf{I} + \mathbf{F}_k\,\Delta t)^T - (\mathbf{I} + \mathbf{F}_k\,\Delta t)\mathbf{P}_k\mathbf{H}_k^T \\ &\quad\times\left(\mathbf{H}_k\mathbf{P}_k\mathbf{H}_k^T + \frac{\mathbf{R}_t^k}{\Delta t}\right)^{-1}\mathbf{H}_k\mathbf{P}_k(\mathbf{I} + \mathbf{F}_k\,\Delta t)^T + \Delta t\,\mathbf{G}_k\frac{\mathbf{Q}_t^k}{\Delta t}\mathbf{G}_k^T\,\Delta t \\ &= (\mathbf{I} + \mathbf{F}_k\,\Delta t)\mathbf{P}_k(\mathbf{I} + \mathbf{F}_k\,\Delta t)^T - (\mathbf{I} + \mathbf{F}_k\,\Delta t)\mathbf{P}_k\mathbf{H}_k^T \\ &\quad\times\left(\mathbf{H}_k\mathbf{P}_k\mathbf{H}_k^T\,\Delta t + \mathbf{R}_t^k\right)^{-1}\mathbf{H}_k\mathbf{P}_k(\mathbf{I} + \mathbf{F}_k\,\Delta t)^T\Delta t + \mathbf{G}_k\mathbf{Q}_t^k\mathbf{G}_k^T\,\Delta t\end{aligned} \qquad (9.3.17)$$

Simplifying eq. 9.3.17, we obtain

$$\begin{aligned}\frac{\mathbf{P}_{k+1} - \mathbf{P}_k}{\Delta t} &= \mathbf{F}_k\mathbf{P}_k + \mathbf{P}_k\mathbf{F}_k^T - \mathbf{P}_k\mathbf{H}_k^T\left(\mathbf{H}_k\mathbf{P}_k\mathbf{H}_k^T\,\Delta t + \mathbf{R}_t^k\right)^{-1}\mathbf{H}_k\mathbf{P}_k \\ &\quad+\mathbf{G}_k\mathbf{Q}_t^k\mathbf{G}_k^T + o(\Delta t)\end{aligned} \qquad (9.3.18)$$

Taking the limit of eq. 9.3.18 as $\Delta t \to 0$,

$$\frac{d\mathbf{P}_t}{dt} = \mathbf{F}_t\mathbf{P}_t + \mathbf{P}_t\mathbf{F}_t^T + \mathbf{G}_t\mathbf{Q}_t\mathbf{G}_t^T - \mathbf{P}_t\mathbf{H}_t^T\mathbf{R}_t^{-1}\mathbf{H}_t\mathbf{P}_t \qquad t \in T$$

which is exactly eq. 9.3.6. Note that the term $\mathbf{H}_k\mathbf{P}_k\mathbf{H}_k^T$ drops out here also.

Substituting eqs. 9.3.12 and 9.3.13 in the Kalman gain matrix of eq. 9.2.5, we have

$$\mathbf{K}_k = \mathbf{P}_k\mathbf{H}_k^T\left(\mathbf{H}_k\mathbf{P}_k\mathbf{H}_k^T\,\Delta t + \mathbf{R}_t^k\right)^{-1}\Delta t \qquad (9.3.19)$$

We divide eq. 9.3.19 by Δt and take the limit as $\Delta t \to 0$. Thus

$$\lim_{\Delta t \to 0}\frac{\mathbf{K}_k}{\Delta t} = \mathbf{K}_t = \mathbf{P}_t\mathbf{H}_t\mathbf{R}_t^{-1} \qquad t \in T$$

which is eq. 9.3.7. □

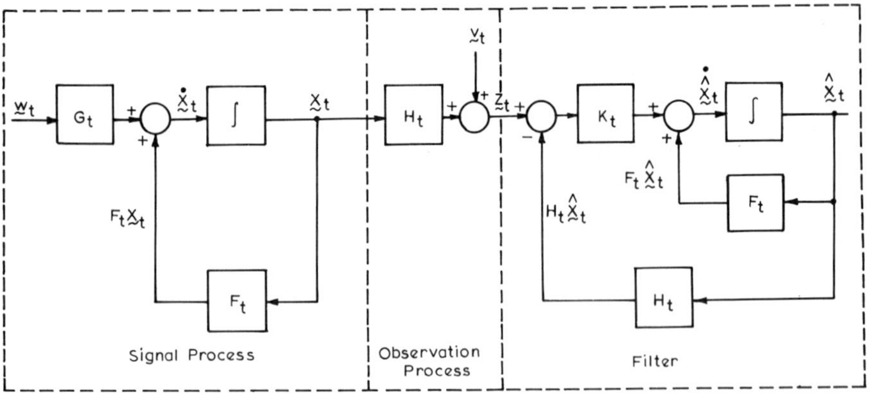

FIGURE 9.3.1

Since the signal and observation processes evolve continuously, there is no timing diagram corresponding to the discrete case. However, we give the block diagram implementation of eqs. 9.3.8, 9.3.9, 9.3.5 and 9.3.7 for the continuous Kalman filter in Figure 9.3.1.

Example 9.3.1

We now solve the continuous analog of the discrete example, Example 9.2.2. The signal process is given by

$$\dot{X}_t = 0 \qquad \mathbf{F} = 0, \quad \mathbf{Q} = 0, \quad \mathbf{H} = 1$$

and the observation process by

$$Y_t = X_t + v_t$$

with v_t, a white noise process distributed as $N(0, \sigma_v^2 \delta(t))$.

The Kalman gain k_t is obtained from eq. 9.3.7,

$$k_t = \frac{p_t}{\sigma_v^2}$$

The signal estimate is obtained from eq. 9.3.5,

$$\frac{d\hat{X}_t}{dt} = k_t(Y_t - \hat{X}_t)$$

The variance is obtained from eq. 9.3.6,

$$\frac{dp_t}{dt} = -\frac{p_t^2}{\sigma_v^2}$$

or,

$$\int_{p_0}^{p_t} \frac{dp_t}{p_t^2} = -\frac{1}{\sigma_v^2}\int_0^t dt$$

or

$$p_t = \frac{p_0}{1 + p_0 t/\sigma_v^2}$$

Hence the Kalman gain k_t is given by

$$k_t = \frac{p_0}{\sigma_v^2 + p_0 t}$$

and the signal estimate $\hat{X}_t$ is given by

$$\frac{d\hat{X}_t}{dt} = \frac{p_0}{\sigma_v^2 + p_0 t}\left(Y_t - \hat{X}_t\right)$$

Clearly as $t \to \infty$, $d\hat{X}_t/dt = 0 \Rightarrow \hat{X}_t = X_\infty$ a constant, and p_t is equal to zero as it should be.

9.4 KALMAN FILTER AS A SPECIAL CASE OF THE NONLINEAR FILTER

We now derive the Kalman filter as a special case of the general nonlinear filtering equation 8.5.7. Let $(\Omega, \mathfrak{F}, P)$ be a probability space, and let $\{\mathfrak{B}_t, t \in T\}$ be a filtration σ-field defined on it. The Gaussian signal process $\{\mathbf{X}_t, \mathfrak{B}_t, t \in T\}$ is the n-vector semimartingale with sample continuous trajectories given by

$$d\mathbf{X}_t = \mathbf{F}_t\mathbf{X}_t\,dt + \mathbf{G}_t\,d\mathbf{W}_t \qquad t \in T, \quad \mathbf{X}_0 \tag{9.4.1}$$

and the Gaussian observation process $\{\mathbf{Y}_t, \mathfrak{B}_t, t \in T\}$ is the m-vector semimartingale with sample continuous trajectories given by

$$d\mathbf{Y}_t = \mathbf{H}_t\mathbf{X}_t\,dt + d\mathbf{V}_t \qquad t \in T, \quad \mathbf{Y}_0 = 0 \tag{9.4.2}$$

$\mathbf{F}_t$, $\mathbf{G}_t$, and $\mathbf{H}_t$ are nonrandom matrix functions satisfying eq. 9.3.3. Let $\mathfrak{F}_t$ be the σ-field generated by the observations, that is, $\mathfrak{F}_t = \sigma\{\mathbf{Y}_s, s \le t, t \in T\}$. Let all the other assumptions of Theorem 9.3.1 hold.

We now substitute in the nonlinear filter equation 8.5.7 the following quantities:

$$\hat{\mathbf{f}}_t = \mathbf{F}_t\hat{\mathbf{X}}_t \qquad \hat{\mathbf{h}}_t = \mathbf{H}_t\hat{\mathbf{X}}_t$$

and write

$$d\hat{\mathbf{X}}_t = \mathbf{F}_t\hat{\mathbf{X}}_t\,dt + \left[E^{\mathfrak{F}_t}\left(\tilde{\mathbf{X}}_t\tilde{\mathbf{X}}_t^T\mathbf{H}_t^T + \frac{d}{dt}\langle\mathbf{M},\mathbf{V}^T\rangle_t\right)\right]\mathbf{R}_t^{-1}\,d\boldsymbol{\nu}_t \tag{9.4.3}$$

where $\tilde{\mathbf{X}}_t = \hat{\mathbf{X}}_t - \mathbf{X}_t$, $\mathbf{M}_t$ is given by $d\mathbf{M}_t = \mathbf{G}_t\, d\mathbf{W}_t$, and the innovations process $d\boldsymbol{\nu}_t = d\mathbf{Y}_t - \mathbf{H}_t\hat{\mathbf{X}}_t\, dt$.

By assumption $\mathbf{W}_t$ and $\mathbf{V}_t$ are independent, and hence $\langle \mathbf{M}, \mathbf{V}^T\rangle_t = 0$. Hence eq. 9.4.3 reduces to

$$d\hat{\mathbf{X}}_t = \mathbf{F}_t\hat{\mathbf{X}}_t\, dt + \left(E^{\mathscr{F}_t}\tilde{\mathbf{X}}_t\tilde{\mathbf{X}}_t^T\mathbf{H}_t^T\right)\mathbf{R}_t^{-1}\, d\boldsymbol{\nu}_t \qquad t \in T \tag{9.4.4}$$

Equation 9.4.4 clearly demonstrates that the first conditional moment involves the second conditional moment $E^{\mathscr{F}_t}\tilde{\mathbf{X}}_t\tilde{\mathbf{X}}_t^T$. We now define the conditional variance matrix

$$\hat{\mathbf{P}}_t = E^{\mathscr{F}_t}\tilde{\mathbf{X}}_t\tilde{\mathbf{X}}_t^T \tag{9.4.5}$$

and simplify eq. 9.4.4 to

$$d\hat{\mathbf{X}}_t = \mathbf{F}_t\hat{\mathbf{X}}_t\, dt + \hat{\mathbf{P}}_t\mathbf{H}_t^T\mathbf{R}_t^{-1}\, d\boldsymbol{\nu}_t \tag{9.4.6}$$

We have to find an expression for the conditional variance $\hat{\mathbf{P}}_t$. The error equation $d\tilde{\mathbf{X}}_t$ can be obtained by subtracting eq. 9.4.1 from eq. 9.4.6,

$$d\tilde{\mathbf{X}}_t = \mathbf{F}_t\tilde{\mathbf{X}}_t\, dt - \mathbf{G}_t\, d\mathbf{W}_t + \hat{\mathbf{P}}_t\mathbf{H}_t^T\mathbf{R}_t^{-1}\, d\boldsymbol{\nu}_t \tag{9.4.7}$$

We now apply the Ito–Doleans-Dade–Meyer rule, eq. 6.7.30, to $d(\tilde{\mathbf{X}}_t\tilde{\mathbf{X}}_t^T)$,

$$d\left(\tilde{\mathbf{X}}_t\tilde{\mathbf{X}}_t^T\right) = \tilde{\mathbf{X}}_t\, d\tilde{\mathbf{X}}_t^T + d\tilde{\mathbf{X}}_t\tilde{\mathbf{X}}_t^T + d\langle \mathbf{M}_{\tilde{\mathbf{X}}}^c, \mathbf{M}_{\tilde{\mathbf{X}}}^{c^T}\rangle_t + \Delta\tilde{\mathbf{X}}_t\left(\Delta\tilde{\mathbf{X}}_t^T\right) \tag{9.4.8}$$

The continuous martingale part $d\mathbf{M}_{\tilde{\mathbf{X}}}^c$ of $d\tilde{\mathbf{X}}_t$ from eq. 9.4.7 is $-\mathbf{G}_t\, d\mathbf{W}_t + \hat{\mathbf{P}}_t\mathbf{H}_t^T\mathbf{R}_t^{-1}\, d\boldsymbol{\nu}_t$. Since $\mathbf{X}_t$ is a continuous semimartingale, $\Delta\tilde{\mathbf{X}}_t = 0$. We now calculate the quadratic covariance process $d\langle \mathbf{M}_{\tilde{\mathbf{X}}}^c, \mathbf{M}_{\tilde{\mathbf{X}}}^{c^T}\rangle_t$,

$$\begin{aligned} d\langle \mathbf{M}_{\tilde{\mathbf{X}}}^c, \mathbf{M}_{\tilde{\mathbf{X}}}^{c^T}\rangle_t &= \langle -\mathbf{G}\, d\mathbf{W} + \hat{\mathbf{P}}\mathbf{H}^T\mathbf{R}^{-1}\, d\boldsymbol{\nu}, -d\mathbf{W}^T\mathbf{G}^T + d\boldsymbol{\nu}^T\mathbf{R}^{-1}\mathbf{H}\hat{\mathbf{P}}\rangle_t \\ &= \langle \mathbf{G}\, d\mathbf{W}, d\mathbf{W}^T\mathbf{G}^T\rangle_t + \langle \hat{\mathbf{P}}\mathbf{H}^T\mathbf{R}^{-1}\, d\boldsymbol{\nu}, d\boldsymbol{\nu}^T\mathbf{R}^{-1}\mathbf{H}\hat{\mathbf{P}}\rangle_t \end{aligned} \tag{9.4.9}$$

The second equation follows because $\mathbf{W}_t$ and $\boldsymbol{\nu}_t$ are independent. Since both $\mathbf{W}_t$ and $\boldsymbol{\nu}_t$ are Brownian motion processes, the quadratic covariance processes are given by $\langle d\mathbf{W}, d\mathbf{W}^T\rangle_t = \mathbf{Q}_t\, dt$ and $\langle d\boldsymbol{\nu}, d\boldsymbol{\nu}^T\rangle_t = \mathbf{R}_t\, dt$. Hence eq. 9.4.9 can be written as

$$\begin{aligned} d\langle \mathbf{M}_{\tilde{\mathbf{X}}}^c, \mathbf{M}_{\tilde{\mathbf{X}}}^{c^T}\rangle_t &= \mathbf{G}_t\mathbf{Q}_t\mathbf{G}_t^T\, dt + \hat{\mathbf{P}}_t\mathbf{H}_t^T\mathbf{R}_t^{-1}\mathbf{R}_t\mathbf{R}_t^{-1}\mathbf{H}_t\hat{\mathbf{P}}_t\, dt \\ &= \mathbf{G}_t\mathbf{Q}_t\mathbf{G}_t^T\, dt + \hat{\mathbf{P}}_t\mathbf{H}_t^T\mathbf{R}_t^{-1}\mathbf{H}_t\hat{\mathbf{P}}_t\, dt \end{aligned} \tag{9.4.10}$$

Substituting eq. 9.4.10 in eq. 9.4.8, we have

$$d\left(\tilde{\mathbf{X}}_t\tilde{\mathbf{X}}_t^T\right) = \tilde{\mathbf{X}}_t\, d\tilde{\mathbf{X}}_t^T + d\tilde{\mathbf{X}}_t\tilde{\mathbf{X}}_t^T + \mathbf{G}_t\mathbf{Q}_t\mathbf{G}_t^T\, dt + \hat{\mathbf{P}}_t\mathbf{H}_t^T\mathbf{R}_t^{-1}\mathbf{H}_t\hat{\mathbf{P}}_t\, dt \tag{9.4.11}$$

Since $d\boldsymbol{\nu}_t = d\mathbf{Y}_t - \mathbf{H}_t\hat{\mathbf{X}}_t\,dt$, we can substitute for $d\mathbf{Y}_t$ from eq. 9.4.2 and obtain

$$\begin{aligned} d\boldsymbol{\nu}_t &= \mathbf{H}_t(\mathbf{X}_t - \hat{\mathbf{X}}_t)\,dt + d\mathbf{V}_t \\ &= -\mathbf{H}_t\tilde{\mathbf{X}}_t\,dt + d\mathbf{V}_t \end{aligned} \tag{9.4.12}$$

Substituting for $d\boldsymbol{\nu}_t$ from eq. 9.4.12 into eq. 9.4.7, we can write the error equation as

$$d\tilde{\mathbf{X}}_t = \mathbf{F}_t\tilde{\mathbf{X}}_t\,dt - \mathbf{G}_t\,d\mathbf{W}_t - \hat{\mathbf{P}}_t\mathbf{H}_t^T\mathbf{R}_t^{-1}\mathbf{H}_t\tilde{\mathbf{X}}_t\,dt - \hat{\mathbf{P}}_t\mathbf{H}_t^T\mathbf{R}_t^{-1}\,d\mathbf{V}_t \tag{9.4.13}$$

We now substitute for $d\tilde{\mathbf{X}}_t$ in eq. 9.4.11 from eq. 9.4.13, resulting in

$$\begin{aligned} d(\tilde{\mathbf{X}}_t\tilde{\mathbf{X}}_t^T) &= (\tilde{\mathbf{X}}_t\tilde{\mathbf{X}}_t^T\mathbf{F}_t^T - \tilde{\mathbf{X}}_t\tilde{\mathbf{X}}_t^T\mathbf{H}_t^T\mathbf{R}_t^{-1}\mathbf{H}_t\hat{\mathbf{P}}_t + \mathbf{F}_t\tilde{\mathbf{X}}_t\tilde{\mathbf{X}}_t^T \\ &\quad - \hat{\mathbf{P}}_t\mathbf{H}_t^T\mathbf{R}_t^{-1}\mathbf{H}_t\tilde{\mathbf{X}}_t\tilde{\mathbf{X}}_t^T + \mathbf{G}_t\mathbf{Q}_t\mathbf{G}_t^T + \hat{\mathbf{P}}_t\mathbf{H}_t^T\mathbf{R}_t^{-1}\mathbf{H}_t\hat{\mathbf{P}}_t)\,dt \\ &\quad - (\tilde{\mathbf{X}}_t\,d\mathbf{W}_t^T\mathbf{G}_t^T + \mathbf{G}_t\,d\mathbf{W}_t\tilde{\mathbf{X}}_t^T + \tilde{\mathbf{X}}_t\,d\mathbf{V}_t^T\mathbf{R}_t^{-1}\mathbf{H}_t\hat{\mathbf{P}}_t \\ &\quad + \hat{\mathbf{P}}_t\mathbf{H}_t^T\mathbf{R}_t^{-1}\,d\mathbf{V}_t\tilde{\mathbf{X}}_t^T) \qquad t \in T \end{aligned} \tag{9.4.14}$$

We can now think of eq. 9.4.14 as the new signal process, and using the same observation process, eq. 9.4.2,

$$d\mathbf{Y}_t = \mathbf{H}_t\mathbf{X}_t\,dt + d\mathbf{V}_t \qquad t \in T \tag{9.4.15}$$

we can apply the nonlinear filter equation 8.5.7 and write

$$\begin{aligned} d\hat{\mathbf{P}}_t &= (\hat{\mathbf{P}}_t\mathbf{F}_t^T + \mathbf{F}_t\hat{\mathbf{P}}_t - \hat{\mathbf{P}}_t\mathbf{H}_t^T\mathbf{R}_t^{-1}\mathbf{H}_t\hat{\mathbf{P}}_t + \mathbf{G}_t\mathbf{Q}_t\mathbf{G}_t^T)\,dt \\ &\quad + E^{\mathcal{F}_t}\left[(\hat{\mathbf{P}}_t - \tilde{\mathbf{X}}_t\tilde{\mathbf{X}}_t^T)(\mathbf{H}_t\hat{\mathbf{X}}_t - \mathbf{H}_t\mathbf{X}_t)^T\right]\mathbf{R}_t^{-1}\,d\boldsymbol{\nu}_t \end{aligned} \tag{9.4.16}$$

In eq. 9.4.16 the quadratic covariance terms do not appear, since by assumption $\tilde{\mathbf{X}}_t$, $\mathbf{W}_t$, and $\mathbf{V}_t$ are all independent with zero mean ($\Rightarrow$ orthogonality). Let us now simplify the second term in the right-hand side of eq. 9.4.16,

$$\begin{aligned} &E^{\mathcal{F}_t}(\hat{\mathbf{P}}_t - \tilde{\mathbf{X}}_t\tilde{\mathbf{X}}_t^T)(\mathbf{H}_t\hat{\mathbf{X}}_t - \mathbf{H}_t\mathbf{X}_t)^T\mathbf{R}_t^{-1}\,d\boldsymbol{\nu}_t \\ &\quad = E^{\mathcal{F}_t}(\hat{\mathbf{P}}_t - \tilde{\mathbf{X}}_t\tilde{\mathbf{X}}_t^T)\tilde{\mathbf{X}}_t^T\mathbf{H}_t^T\mathbf{R}_t^{-1}\,d\boldsymbol{\nu}_t \qquad \text{since } \boldsymbol{\nu}_t \in \mathcal{F}_t \\ &\quad = -E^{\mathcal{F}_t}(\tilde{\mathbf{X}}_t\tilde{\mathbf{X}}_t^T)\tilde{\mathbf{X}}_t^T\mathbf{H}_t^T\mathbf{R}_t^{-1}\,d\boldsymbol{\nu}_t \qquad \text{since } E\tilde{\mathbf{X}}_t^T = 0 \text{ and } \hat{\mathbf{P}}_t \in \mathcal{F}_t \end{aligned} \tag{9.4.17}$$

Note that the term $\tilde{\mathbf{X}}_t^T\mathbf{H}_t^T\mathbf{R}_t^{-1}\,d\boldsymbol{\nu}_t$ is a scalar. By substituting eq. 9.4.17 into eq. 9.4.16, the conditional variance equation can be written as

$$\begin{aligned} d\hat{\mathbf{P}}_t &= (\hat{\mathbf{P}}_t\mathbf{F}_t^T + \mathbf{F}_t\hat{\mathbf{P}}_t - \hat{\mathbf{P}}_t\mathbf{H}_t^T\mathbf{R}_t^{-1}\mathbf{H}_t\hat{\mathbf{P}}_t + \mathbf{G}_t\mathbf{Q}_t\mathbf{G}_t^T)\,dt \\ &\quad - E^{\mathcal{F}_t}(\tilde{\mathbf{X}}_t\tilde{\mathbf{X}}_t^T)\tilde{\mathbf{X}}_t^T\mathbf{H}_t^T\mathbf{R}_t^{-1}\,d\boldsymbol{\nu}_t \end{aligned} \tag{9.4.18}$$

Since we have assumed that the process $\mathbf{X}_t$ itself is Gaussian, the distribution of $\hat{\mathbf{X}}_t$ can be proved to be Gaussian (Kallianpur and Striebel, 30), and hence $\tilde{\mathbf{X}}_t$ is also Gaussian. Since the third-order moments in a linear Gaussian case are zero, the term $E^{\mathcal{F}_t}(\tilde{\mathbf{X}}_t\tilde{\mathbf{X}}_t^T)\tilde{\mathbf{X}}_t^T\mathbf{H}_t^T\mathbf{R}_t^{-1}\,d\boldsymbol{\nu}_t = 0$. Hence we have

$$d\hat{\mathbf{P}}_t = \left(\hat{\mathbf{P}}_t\mathbf{F}_t^T + \mathbf{F}_t\hat{\mathbf{P}}_t - \hat{\mathbf{P}}_t\mathbf{H}_t^T\mathbf{R}_t^{-1}\mathbf{H}_t\hat{\mathbf{P}}_t + \mathbf{G}_t\mathbf{Q}_t\mathbf{G}_t^T\right) dt \qquad (9.4.19)$$

Since eq. 9.4.19 does not specifically depend on the observations, it is no longer the conditional variance but the unconditional variance which can be written as

$$d\mathbf{P}_t = \mathbf{F}_t\mathbf{P}_t + \mathbf{P}_t\mathbf{F}_t^T - \mathbf{P}_t\mathbf{H}_t\mathbf{R}_t^{-1}\mathbf{H}_t\mathbf{P}_t + \mathbf{G}_t\mathbf{Q}_t\mathbf{G}_t^T \qquad t \in T \quad (9.4.20)$$

For rigorous proof see Lipster and Shiryaev (34, p. 365).

Remarks. Equation 9.4.18 clearly brings out the fact that the nonlinear filter equation does not represent a closed form solution in the general case. As remarked earlier, the first conditional moment, eq. 9.4.4, involves the second conditional moment. The equation for the second conditional moment, eq. 9.4.18, involves the third conditional moment. Only in the linear Gaussian case the third conditional moment is zero, and thus the linear filter equations form a closed set which can be explicitly solved. Other finite dimensional filters for a class of nonlinear filtering problems have been developed by Benes (66). Again as remarked earlier, the signal estimate and the variance equations are uncoupled in the linear Gaussian case. Hence the variance equation can be solved independently and substituted into the signal estimate equation.

Problems

1. Show that the estimator

$$\hat{X}_k = \frac{1}{k}\sum_{i=1}^{k} Y_i$$

as given by eq. 9.1.2 is a minimum variance estimator.

2. A discrete signal process and a discrete observation process are given by

$$\begin{bmatrix} X_{i1} \\ X_{i2} \end{bmatrix} = \begin{bmatrix} X_1 \\ X_2 \end{bmatrix} \qquad i = 1, 2, \ldots, k$$

$$\begin{bmatrix} Y_{i1} \\ Y_{i2} \end{bmatrix} = \begin{bmatrix} X_1 \\ X_2 \end{bmatrix} + \begin{bmatrix} V_{i1} \\ V_{i2} \end{bmatrix} \qquad i = 1, 2, \ldots, k$$

where X_1 and X_2 are constants. V_{i1} and V_{i2} are zero mean white Gaussian noise sequences with covariance matrix

$$\begin{bmatrix} \sigma_{v_1}^2 & \sigma_{v_1 v_2} \\ \sigma_{v_1 v_2} & \sigma_{v_2}^2 \end{bmatrix}$$

Construct a recursive estimator $\hat{X}_{k_1}$ and $\hat{X}_{k_2}$.

3. A random variable X has a sample of k values $\{X_i, i = 1, 2, \ldots, k\}$. The unbiased estimators for the mean value μ and the variance σ^2 are given by

$$\hat{\mu}_k = \frac{1}{k} \sum_{i=1}^{k} X_i$$

$$\hat{\sigma}_k^2 = \frac{1}{k-1} \sum_{i=1}^{k} (X_i - \hat{\mu}_k)^2$$

Express these estimators in recursive form.

4. An integrator is driven by a white noise w_t which is normally distributed with zero mean and variance parameter σ_w^2. The output of the integrator is sampled at a constant interval $\Delta t = t_{k+1} - t_k$ for all k in the presence of a measurement noise sequence $\{v_k\}$ which has zero mean and variance σ_v^2. Find $p_k(+)$ and $p_{k+1}(-)$ for $\sigma_w^2 \Delta t \geq \sigma_v^2$ and $\sigma_v^2 > \sigma_w^2 \Delta t$.

5. Show that the error covariance update equation

$$\mathbf{P}_k(+) = (\mathbf{I} - \mathbf{K}_k \mathbf{H}_k)\mathbf{P}_k(-)$$

can be expressed in an alternate form as

$$\mathbf{P}_k^{-1}(+) = \mathbf{P}_k^{-1}(-) + \mathbf{H}_k^T \mathbf{R}_k^{-1} \mathbf{H}_k$$

6. A scalar signal process is modeled as

$$X_{k+1} = X_k + W_k \qquad k = 1, 2, \ldots, n$$

with $\{W_k\}$ a discrete white Gaussian noise sequence with zero mean and variance $\frac{1}{4}$. The initial state X_1 is modeled as a Gaussian random variable with mean value 1 and variance 2. The measurement process is a scalar process with

$$Y_k = X_k + V_k \qquad k = 1, 2$$

with $\{V_k\}$ a discrete white Gaussian noise sequence with zero mean and variance $\frac{1}{8}$. Obtain explicit expressions for $X_k(+)$, $X_k(-)$, $P_k(+)$, $P_k(-)$, and K_k for $k = 1, 2$.

7. The discrete Kalman filter was derived by minimizing the loss function $J_k = E\tilde{\mathbf{X}}_k^T(+)\tilde{\mathbf{X}}_k(+)$. Rederive the discrete Kalman filter if $J_k = \tilde{\mathbf{X}}_k^T(-)\mathbf{P}_k^{-1}(-)\tilde{\mathbf{X}}_k(-) + (\mathbf{Y}_k - \mathbf{H}_k\hat{\mathbf{X}}_k(-))^T\mathbf{R}^{-1}(\mathbf{Y}_k - \mathbf{H}_k\hat{\mathbf{X}}_k(-))$.

8. The discrete covariance matrix update equation 9.2.24 can also be given as

$$\mathbf{P}_k(+) = \mathbf{P}_k(-) - \mathbf{P}_k(-)\mathbf{H}_k^T\left(\mathbf{H}_k\mathbf{P}_k(-)\mathbf{H}_k^T + \mathbf{R}_k\right)^{-1}\mathbf{H}_k\mathbf{P}_k(-)$$

Show that this equation can also be expressed as

$$\mathbf{H}_k\mathbf{P}_k(+) = \mathbf{R}_k\left(\mathbf{H}_k\mathbf{P}_k(-)\mathbf{H}_k^T + \mathbf{R}_k\right)^{-1}\mathbf{H}_k\mathbf{P}_k(-)$$

and if $\mathbf{H}_k$ is nonsingular, then show that

$$|\mathbf{P}_k(+)| = \frac{|\mathbf{P}_k(-)|\,|\mathbf{R}_k|}{|\mathbf{H}_k\mathbf{P}_k(-)\mathbf{H}_k^T + \mathbf{R}_k|}$$

where $|\cdot|$ denotes the determinant.

9. A moving average time series model is given by

$$X_k = W_k + W_{k-1} \qquad X_0$$

where $\{W_k\}$ is a zero mean discrete white Gaussian noise sequence with unit variance. Assuming $P_0 = 1$ show that the optimal one-step predictor is given by

$$X_{k+1}(-) = \frac{k+1}{k+2}\left(X_k - \hat{X}_k(-)\right)$$

10. In the signal equations 9.3.1 $\mathbf{F}_t$ and $\mathbf{G}_t$ are constants,

$$\mathbf{F}_t = \begin{bmatrix} 0 & 1 \\ -1 & 0 \end{bmatrix} \qquad \mathbf{G}_t = \begin{bmatrix} a & 0 \\ 0 & b \end{bmatrix} \qquad \mathbf{X}_{t_0} = \begin{bmatrix} 1 \\ 3 \end{bmatrix}$$

The Brownian motion has the covariance parameter matrix

$$\mathbf{Q}_t = \begin{bmatrix} 1 & 0 \\ 0 & 2 \end{bmatrix}$$

Under the above conditions the solution to the stochastic differential equation can be given in the form

$$\mathbf{X}_t = \mathbf{\Phi}_{t,t_0}\mathbf{X}_{t_0} + \int_{t_0}^{t}\mathbf{\Phi}_{t,\tau}\mathbf{G}_\tau\,d\mathbf{W}_\tau \qquad t \in T$$

The covariance matrix of $\mathbf{X}_t$ defined by $\mathbf{P}_{Xt} = E(\mathbf{X}_t - \boldsymbol{\mu}_{Xt})(\mathbf{X}_t - \boldsymbol{\mu}_{Xt})^T$ can be expressed by

$$\mathbf{P}_{Xt} = \boldsymbol{\Phi}_{t,t_0}\mathbf{P}_{X_{t_0}}\boldsymbol{\Phi}_{t,t_0}^T + \int_{t_0}^{t}\boldsymbol{\Phi}_{t,\tau}\mathbf{G}_\tau\mathbf{Q}_\tau\mathbf{G}_\tau^T\boldsymbol{\Phi}_{t,\tau}^T\,d\tau$$

Find $\boldsymbol{\mu}_{Xt}$ and $\mathbf{P}_{Xt}$ and comment on their nature as $t \to \infty$.

11. Discuss the nature of $\boldsymbol{\mu}_{Xt}$ and $\mathbf{P}_{Xt}$ in Problem 10 as $t \to \infty$ and $\mathbf{F}_t$ is changed to

$$\mathbf{F}_t = \begin{bmatrix} 0 & 1 \\ -1 & -2\zeta \end{bmatrix}$$

12. In Example 11, W_{1t} is changed to $Ct + W_{1t}$, where C is a constant > 0. Discuss the nature of $\boldsymbol{\mu}_{Xt}$ and $\mathbf{P}_{Xt}$ as $t \to \infty$.

13. The signal process of a dynamic system is given by

$$dX_t = aX_t\,dt + dW_t \qquad t \in T$$

and the observation process is given by

$$Y_t\,dt = bX_t\,dt + dV_t \qquad t \in T$$

where W_t and V_t are Brownian motion processes with variance parameters σ_w^2 and σ_v^2, respectively. Find the filter equations for $d\hat{X}_t$ and P_{Xt}. Find an expression for the steady-state value of P_{Xt} as $t \to \infty$.

14. The signal process of a dynamic system is given by

$$\begin{bmatrix} dX_{1t} \\ dX_{2t} \end{bmatrix} = \begin{bmatrix} 0 & 1 \\ 0 & 0 \end{bmatrix}\begin{bmatrix} X_{1t}\,dt \\ X_{2t}\,dt \end{bmatrix} \qquad t \in T, \quad \begin{bmatrix} X_{10} \\ X_{20} \end{bmatrix}, \quad \begin{bmatrix} p_{X_{10}} \\ p_{X_{20}} \end{bmatrix}$$

and the observation process is given by

$$Y_t\,dt = [1 \quad 0]\begin{bmatrix} X_{1t}\,dt \\ X_{2t}\,dt \end{bmatrix} + dV_t$$

Derive the filter equations.

15. The signal and observation processes are given by the stochastic differential equations

$$d\mathbf{X}_t = (\mathbf{F}_{0t} + \mathbf{F}_{1t}\mathbf{X}_t + \mathbf{F}_{2t}\mathbf{Y}_t)\,dt + \mathbf{G}_t\,d\mathbf{W}_t \qquad t \in T$$

$$d\mathbf{Y}_t = (\mathbf{H}_{0t} + \mathbf{H}_{1t}\mathbf{X}_t + \mathbf{H}_{2t}\mathbf{Y}_t)\,dt + \mathbf{J}_t\,d\mathbf{W}_t \qquad t \in T$$

where $\mathbf{X}_t$ and $\mathbf{Y}_t$ are n- and m-dimensional processes, and $\{W_t\}$ is an $(m + n)$-dimensional Brownian motion process. $\mathbf{F}_{it}$ and $\mathbf{H}_{it}$ $(i = 0, 1, 2)$, $\mathbf{G}_t$, and $\mathbf{J}_t$ are suitably dimensioned matrices with individual functions of $\mathbf{F}_{it}$ and $\mathbf{H}_{it}$ being integrable for $t \in T$ and with functions of $\mathbf{G}_t$ and $\mathbf{J}_t$ being square integrable for $t \in T$.

a. Find the nonlinear representation for the conditional mean and the variance from Theorem 8.4.1.

b. Derive the Kalman filter equations and show that they are a special case of part a.

10 APPLICATION OF NONLINEAR FILTERING TO FAULT DETECTION PROBLEMS

10.1 INTRODUCTION

We have seen in the last two chapters how the application of the nonlinear filtering theorem to nonlinear systems *generally* leads to a system of optimal filters which are not closed (infinite dimensional). The filter equations satisfy an infinite set of stochastic differential equations involving conditional moments of increasingly higher order, and in the linear Gaussian case we have a closed form solution. Since closed form solutions may not be possible in general, we make assumptions regarding higher order moments so as to reduce the filter equations to a finite dimensional form. This may lead to suboptimal schemes.

We have already seen in the last chapter that in a linear system perturbed by Gaussian noise, the signal process can be estimated from the observations using the Kalman filter. However, if a fault develops in the system at any random time, the Kalman filter will not be able to track the fault immediately, and large initial errors will develop in the signal estimate. To limit these large errors, the Kalman filter has to be reparametrized, for which we need the estimates of both time and the amount of fault. Thus the information from the observations has to be used both in tracking the states and for fault detection. A survey of fault detection problems in dynamic systems has been discussed by Willsky (60). For a certain class of fault detection problems the nonlinear filtering theorem derived in Chapter 8 can be used to obtain suboptimal schemes (Davis, 10; Hibey, 71). In these schemes it has been proposed that the Brownian motion nature of the innovations process be utilized for an adaptive scheme to improve on the Kalman filter performance.

10.2 FAULT DETECTION WITH CHANGE IN PLANT PARAMETER f_t

The analysis in this section follows that of Davis (10). The problem will be formulated as a scalar, and the generalization to a vector case is straightforward.

Let $(\Omega, \mathcal{F}, P)$ be a complete probability space. The signal process $\{X_t, t \in T\}$ is given by the stochastic differential equation

$$dX_t = f_t X_t \, dt + g_t \, dW_t \qquad t \in T, \quad X_0 \tag{10.2.1}$$

where f_t and g_t are functions of time (not random processes) satisfying the conditions

$$\int_{t \in T} |f_t| \, dt < \infty \qquad \int_{t \in T} |g_t|^2 \, dt < \infty$$

and $\{W_t\}$ is a Brownian motion process with parameter σ_w^2. X_0 is a Gaussian random variable independent of $\{W_t\}$ representing the initial condition, and T is the time interval $[0, \infty)$.

The observation process $\{Y_t, t \in T\}$ is given by another stochastic differential equation,

$$dY_t = h_t X_t \, dt + dV_t \qquad t \in T, \quad Y_0 = 0 \tag{10.2.2}$$

where h_t is a function of time (not a random process) satisfying the condition

$$\int_{t \in T} |h_t|^2 \, dt < \infty$$

and $\{V_t\}$ is another Brownian motion process with parameter σ_v^2 and independent of the Brownian motion process $\{W_t\}$ and initial condition X_0.

$\{X_t, t \in T\}$ and $\{Y_t, t \in T\}$ are sample continuous and are measurable with respect to the σ-field $\mathcal{B}_t$ defined by $\mathcal{B}_t \supset \sigma\{X_0, X_s, Y_s, s \le t, t \in T\}$. Further let $\mathcal{F}_t$ be the σ-field generated by the observations $\{Y_s, s \le t, t \in T\}$.

Let us now assume that at some random time τ, a fault occurs which causes the plant parameter f_t to change from f_{0t} to f_{1t}, as shown in Figure 10.2.1. We assume that $\{\tau \le t\}$ is $\mathcal{B}_t$-measurable.

Let Z_t be a $\mathcal{B}_t$-measurable random process defined as the indicator function

$$Z_t = I_{\{t \ge \tau\}} = \begin{cases} 1 & t \ge \tau \\ 0 & t < \tau \end{cases} \tag{10.2.3}$$

Corresponding to this sudden change, f_t in eq. 10.2.1 can be represented in terms of the random process Z_t by

$$\begin{aligned} f_t &= f_{0t}(1 - Z_t) + f_{1t} Z_t \\ &= f_{0t} + (f_{1t} - f_{0t}) Z_t \\ &= f_{0t} + \Delta f_t \, Z_t \end{aligned} \tag{10.2.4}$$

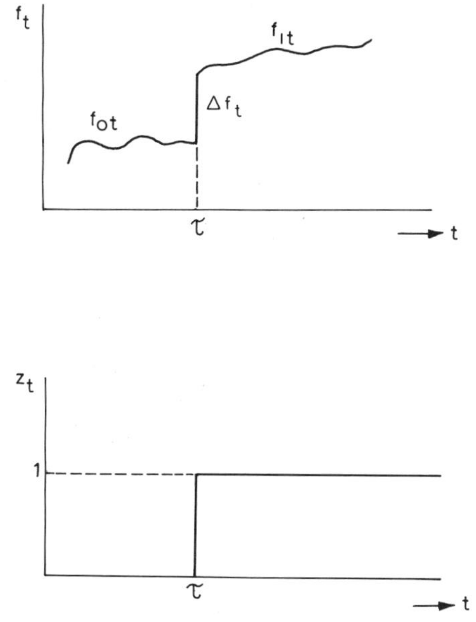

FIGURE 10.2.1

where Δf_t (Figure 10.2.1) represents the change in the plant parameter f_t at random time τ. The signal process of eq. 10.2.1 changes to the stochastic differential equation

$$dX_t = (f_{0t} + \Delta f_t Z_t) X_t \, dt + g_t \, dW_t \qquad t \in T, \quad X_0 \tag{10.2.5}$$

The signal process which was originally linear has been transformed into a nonlinear one because of the multiplicative term $Z_t X_t$. We have to find a stochastic differential equation corresponding to the process Z_t.

We now assume that the process of fault occurrence is a Poisson process N_t with parameter λ independent of W_t and V_t. As a consequence the random variable τ representing the interarrival times of the fault is exponentially distributed as

$$P\{\tau \leq x\} = 1 - e^{-\lambda x} \tag{10.2.6}$$

and we assume that it is independent of X_0, V_t, and W_t.

As shown in Chapter 3, the process $N_t - \lambda t$ is a Poisson martingale. τ is an $\mathcal{F}_t$ stopping time, and Z_t is the Poisson process stopped at time τ. By Doob's optional stopping theorem, Theorem 3.3.1, a stopped martingale is also a martingale. Hence the process $Z_t - \lambda(t \wedge \tau)$ is a $\mathcal{B}_t$-martingale, where $(t \wedge \tau)$ represents $\min(t, \tau)$. Or

$$Z_t - \lambda(t \wedge \tau) = M_t \qquad t \in T \tag{10.2.7}$$

However, the quantity $t \wedge \tau$ can be represented by

$$t \wedge \tau = \int_0^t (1 - Z_s)\, ds \qquad t \in T \tag{10.2.8}$$

as shown below.

CASE 1. $t < \tau$. Since s is also less than τ, we have $Z_s = 0$ and

$$t \wedge \tau = \int_0^t ds = t$$

CASE 2. $t \geq \tau$. Here eq. 10.2.8 can be split as

$$\int_0^t (1 - Z_s)\, ds = \int_0^\tau (1 - Z_s)\, ds + \int_\tau^t (1 - Z_s)\, ds$$

In the first integral on the right-hand side $s < \tau$ and $Z_s = 0$, and in the second integral $s > \tau$ and $Z_s = 1$. Hence

$$t \wedge \tau = \int_0^\tau ds + 0 = \tau$$

Substituting eq. 10.2.8 into eq. 10.2.7,

$$Z_t - \lambda \int_0^t (1 - Z_s)\, ds = M_t \tag{10.2.9}$$

Due to the fault occurring at random time τ we have the following signal model:

$$dX_t = (f_{0t} + \Delta f_t Z_t) X_t\, dt + g_t\, dW_t \qquad t \in T, \quad X_0 \tag{10.2.10a}$$

$$dZ_t = \lambda(1 - Z_t)\, dt + dM_t \qquad t \in T, \quad Z_0 = 0 \tag{10.2.10b}$$

with the observation process remaining

$$dY_t = h_t X_t\, dt + dV_t \qquad t \in T \quad Y_0 = 0 \tag{10.2.11}$$

As seen earlier, the product $X_t Z_t$ makes eq. 10.2.10a nonlinear. We can apply the Ito–Doleans-Dade–Meyer rule, eq. 6.7.28, to $X_t Z_t$ to obtain a stochastic differential equation,

$$d(X_t Z_t) = X_{t-}\, dZ_t + Z_{t-}\, dX_t + d\langle M_X^c, M_Z^c \rangle_t + \Delta X_t \Delta Z_t \tag{10.2.12}$$

By definition the process $\{Z_t\}$ is purely discontinuous and the process $\{X_t\}$ is continuous. Hence $M_Z^c = 0 = \Delta X_t$, and eq. 10.2.12 can be simplified to yield

$$d(X_t Z_t) = X_t\, dZ_t + Z_t\, dX_t \qquad t \in T \tag{10.2.13}$$

We now define another stochastic process, $Q_t = X_t Z_t$ to linearize eq. 10.2.10a. Substituting the values of dX_t and dZ_t from eq. 10.2.10 into eq. 10.2.13, we have

$$dQ_t = X_t\lambda(1 - Z_t)\,dt + X_t\,dM_t + Z_t f_{0t} X_t\,dt + Z_t^2\,\Delta f_t X_t\,dt + Z_t g_t\,dW_t \tag{10.2.14}$$

Since Z_t is the indicator function, $Z_t^2 = Z_t$, and hence eq. 10.2.14 can be rewritten as

$$dQ_t = \left[Q_t(f_{1t} - \lambda) + X_t\lambda\right] dt + X_t\,dM_t + Z_t g_t\,dW_t \qquad t \in T \tag{10.2.15}$$

Thus we have augmented the original signal process X_t with two other processes, Z_t and Q_t. The augmented signal model is now described by

$$d\begin{bmatrix} X_t \\ Q_t \end{bmatrix} = \begin{bmatrix} f_{0t} & \Delta f_t \\ \lambda & f_{1t} - \lambda \end{bmatrix}\begin{bmatrix} X_t \\ Q_t \end{bmatrix} dt + \begin{bmatrix} g_t & 0 \\ Z_t g_t & X_t \end{bmatrix}\begin{bmatrix} dW_t \\ dM_t \end{bmatrix} \qquad t \in T, \quad \begin{bmatrix} X_0 \\ 0 \end{bmatrix} \tag{10.2.16}$$

$$dZ_t = \lambda(1 - Z_t)\,dt + dM_t \qquad t \in T, \quad Z_0 = 0 \tag{10.2.17}$$

with the same observation process

$$dY_t = h_t X_t\,dt + dV_t \qquad t \in T \tag{10.2.11}$$

Note that the augmented signal model is now linear in X_t, Z_t, and Q_t. We can now apply the nonlinear filtering formula given by

$$d\hat{\mathbf{X}}_t = \mathbf{F}\hat{\mathbf{X}}_t\,dt + E^{\mathcal{F}_t}\left[\tilde{\mathbf{X}}_t\tilde{\mathbf{X}}_t^T\mathbf{H}^T + \frac{d}{dt}\langle \mathbf{W}, \mathbf{V}^T\rangle_t\right]\mathbf{R}^{-1}\,d\boldsymbol{v}_t \tag{10.2.18}$$

to the system of equations 10.2.16, 10.2.17, and 10.2.11.

The innovations process $d\boldsymbol{v}_t$ is given by

$$d\boldsymbol{v}_t = d\mathbf{Y}_t - \mathbf{H}\hat{\mathbf{X}}_t\,dt \tag{10.2.19a}$$

In eq. 10.2.18

$$\mathbf{F} = \begin{bmatrix} f_{0t} & \Delta f_t \\ \lambda & f_{1t} - \lambda \end{bmatrix} \qquad \mathbf{H} = [h_t \quad 0] \qquad \mathbf{R} = \frac{1}{\sigma_v^2} \tag{10.2.20}$$

Substituting for **H** in eq. 10.2.19a, the innovations process is given by

$$d\nu_t = dY_t - h_t \hat{X}_t\, dt \qquad (10.2.19b)$$

Substituting eq. 10.2.20 into eq. 10.2.18, we can write the filter equations as

$$\begin{bmatrix} d\hat{X}_t \\ d\hat{Q}_t \end{bmatrix} = \begin{bmatrix} f_{0t} & \Delta f_t \\ \lambda & f_{1t} - \lambda \end{bmatrix} \begin{bmatrix} \hat{X}_t \\ \hat{Q}_t \end{bmatrix} dt + E^{\mathcal{F}_t} \begin{bmatrix} \tilde{X}_t^2 & \tilde{X}_t \tilde{Q}_t \\ \tilde{X}_t \tilde{Q}_t & \tilde{Q}_t^2 \end{bmatrix} \begin{bmatrix} h_t \\ 0 \end{bmatrix} \frac{1}{\sigma_v^2} d\nu_t$$

$$(10.2.21)$$

The quadratic covariance terms are zero since both W_t and M_t are assumed independent of V_t.

In a similar manner the filter equations for dZ_t can be written as

$$d\hat{Z}_t = \lambda(1 - \hat{Z}_t)\, dt + \frac{1}{\sigma_v^2} E^{\mathcal{F}_t}(\tilde{X}_t \tilde{Z}_t) h_t\, d\nu_t \qquad (10.2.22)$$

since $\langle M, V \rangle_t = 0$.

In eq. 10.2.21 $E^{\mathcal{F}_t} \tilde{X}_t^2$ is, by definition, the conditional variance $\hat{P}_t$. Thus the signal estimate equations (filter equations) can be given by

$$d\hat{X}_t = (f_{0t} \hat{X}_t + \Delta f_t \hat{Q}_t)\, dt + \frac{1}{\sigma_v^2} \hat{P}_t h_t\, d\nu_t \qquad t \in T, \quad \hat{X}_0 \qquad (10.2.23a)$$

$$d\hat{Q}_t = \lambda \hat{X}_t + (f_{1t} - \lambda) \hat{Q}_t\, dt + \frac{1}{\sigma_v^2} E^{\mathcal{F}_t}(\tilde{X}_t \tilde{Q}_t) h_t\, d\nu_t \qquad t \in T, \quad \hat{Q}_0 = 0$$

$$(10.2.23b)$$

$$d\hat{Z}_t = \lambda(1 - \hat{Z}_t)\, dt + \frac{1}{\sigma_v^2} E^{\mathcal{F}_t}(\tilde{X}_t \tilde{Z}_t) h_t\, d\nu_t \qquad t \in T, \quad \hat{Z}_0 = 0 \quad (10.2.23c)$$

Since $\tilde{X}_t \tilde{Q}_t = (\hat{X}_t - X_t)(\hat{Q}_t - Q_t) = \hat{X}_t \hat{Q}_t - X_t \hat{Q}_t - \hat{X}_t Q_t + X_t Q_t$, we have

$$E^{\mathcal{F}_t}(\tilde{X}_t \tilde{Q}_t) = E^{\mathcal{F}_t}(X_t Q_t) - \hat{X}_t \hat{Q}_t \qquad (10.2.24)$$

Similarly,

$$E^{\mathcal{F}_t}(\tilde{X}_t \tilde{Z}_t) = E^{\mathcal{F}_t}(\hat{X}_t - X_t)(\hat{Z}_t - Z_t) = \hat{Q}_t - \hat{X}_t \hat{Z}_t \qquad (10.2.25)$$

Using eqs. 10.2.24 and 10.2.25, the signal estimate equations 10.2.23 can be rewritten as

$$d\hat{X}_t = \left(f_{0t}\hat{X}_t + \Delta f_t \hat{Q}_t\right) dt + \frac{\hat{P}_t h_t}{\sigma_v^2} d\nu_t \qquad t \in T, \quad \hat{X}_0 \tag{10.2.26a}$$

$$d\hat{Q}_t = \left[\lambda \hat{X}_t + (f_{1t} - \lambda)\hat{Q}_t\right] dt + \frac{h_t}{\sigma_v^2}\left[E^{\mathscr{F}_t}(X_t Q_t) - \hat{X}_t\hat{Q}_t\right] d\nu_t$$

$$t \in T, \quad \hat{Q}_0 = 0 \tag{10.2.26b}$$

$$d\hat{Z}_t = \lambda\left(1 - \hat{Z}_t\right) dt + \frac{h_t}{\sigma_v^2}\left(\hat{Q}_t - \hat{X}_t\hat{Z}_t\right) d\nu_t \qquad t \in T, \quad \hat{Z}_0 = 0$$

$$\tag{10.2.26c}$$

Equations 10.2.26 will form a recursive filtering scheme, but for the unknown quantities $\hat{P}_t = E^{\mathscr{F}_t}\tilde{X}_t^2$ and $E^{\mathscr{F}_t}(X_t Q_t)$.

We now find a stochastic differential equation for $\hat{P}_t$ as discussed in Chapter 9, and the steps are indicated below. The stochastic differential equation for the error propagation $\tilde{X}_t$ is obtained by subtracting eq. 10.2.5 from eq. 10.2.26a, resulting in

$$d\tilde{X}_t = \left(f_{0t}\tilde{X}_t + \Delta f_t \tilde{Q}_t\right) dt + \frac{\hat{P}_t h_t}{\sigma_v^2} d\nu_t - g_t\, dW_t \qquad t \in T \tag{10.2.27}$$

The Ito–Doleans-Dade–Meyer rule for $d\tilde{X}_t^2$ yields

$$d\tilde{X}_t^2 = 2\tilde{X}_t\, d\tilde{X}_t + d\langle M_{\tilde{X}}, M_{\tilde{X}}\rangle_t \tag{10.2.28}$$

where $M_{\tilde{X}}$ the martingale associated with the semimartingale $\tilde{X}_t$ is given by

$$dM_{\tilde{X}_t} = \frac{\hat{P}_t h_t}{\sigma_v^2} d\nu_t - g_t\, dW_t$$

Hence the quadratic variance process $d\langle M_{\tilde{X}}, M_{\tilde{X}}\rangle_t$ is given by

$$\begin{aligned} d\langle M_{\tilde{X}}, M_{\tilde{X}}\rangle_t &= \langle \frac{\hat{P}h}{\sigma_v^2} d\nu - g\, dW, \frac{\hat{P}h}{\sigma_v^2} d\nu - g\, dW\rangle_t \\ &= \frac{\hat{P}_t^2 h_t^2}{\sigma_v^4}\sigma_v^2\, dt + g_t^2\sigma_w^2\, dt \end{aligned} \tag{10.2.29}$$

Substituting eqs. 10.2.27 and 10.2.29 into eq. 10.2.28, we have a new signal process for $\tilde{X}_t^2$,

$$d\tilde{X}_t^2 = \left(2\tilde{X}_t^2 f_{0t} + 2\Delta f_t \tilde{X}_t \tilde{Q}_t + \frac{\hat{P}_t^2 h_t^2}{\sigma_v^2} + g_t^2 \sigma_w^2\right) dt + 2\tilde{X}_t \frac{\hat{P}_t h_t}{\sigma_v^2} d\nu_t - 2\tilde{X}_t g_t \, dW_t \tag{10.2.30}$$

From eqs. 10.2.19b and 10.2.11 the innovations process $d\nu_t$ can be given by

$$d\nu_t = h_t(X_t - \hat{X}_t)\, dt + dV_t = -h_t \tilde{X}_t \, dt + dV_t \tag{10.2.31}$$

Substituting eq. 10.2.31 into eq. 10.2.30, we have

$$d\tilde{X}_t^2 = \left(2\tilde{X}_t^2 f_{0t} + 2\Delta f_t \tilde{X}_t \tilde{Q}_t + g_t^2 \sigma_w^2 + \frac{\hat{P}_t^2 h_t^2}{\sigma_v^2} - 2\tilde{X}_t^2 \frac{P_t h_t^2}{\sigma_v^2}\right) dt$$

$$+ 2\tilde{X}_t \frac{\hat{P}_t h_t}{\sigma_v^2} dV_t - 2\tilde{X}_t g_t \, dW_t \tag{10.2.32}$$

The nonlinear filtering formula can now be applied to eq. 10.2.32, resulting in

$$d\hat{P}_t = \left[2\hat{P}_t f_{0t} + 2\Delta f_t E^{\mathcal{F}_t}(\tilde{X}_t \tilde{Q}_t) + g_t^2 \sigma_w^2 - \frac{\hat{P}_t^2 h_t^2}{\sigma_v^2}\right] dt$$

$$+ E^{\mathcal{F}_t} \frac{1}{\sigma_v^2}\left[(\hat{P}_t - \tilde{X}_t^2) h_t \tilde{X}_t + \frac{d}{dt}\left\langle \frac{2\tilde{X}\hat{P}h}{\sigma_v^2} V - 2\tilde{X}gW, V\right\rangle_t\right] d\nu_t$$

$$= \left[2\hat{P}_t f_{0t} + 2\Delta f_t E^{\mathcal{F}_t}(\tilde{X}_t \tilde{Q}_t) + g_t^2 \sigma_w^2 - \frac{\hat{P}_t^2 h_t^2}{\sigma_v^2}\right] dt$$

$$+ E^{\mathcal{F}_t} \frac{1}{\sigma_v^2}\left[\hat{P}_t h_t \tilde{X}_t - \tilde{X}_t^3 h_t + \frac{d}{dt} \frac{2\tilde{X}_t \hat{P}_t h_t \sigma_v^2 t}{\sigma_v^2}\right] d\nu_t \tag{10.2.33}$$

Since $E^{\mathcal{F}_t} \tilde{X}_t = 0$, eq. 10.2.33 reduces to

$$d\hat{P}_t = \left[2\hat{P}_t f_{0t} + 2\Delta f_t E^{\mathcal{F}_t}(\tilde{X}_t \tilde{Q}_t) + g_t^2 \sigma_w^2 - \frac{\hat{P}_t^2 h_t^2}{\sigma_v^2}\right] dt - \frac{h_t}{\sigma_v^2} E^{\mathcal{F}_t} \tilde{X}_t^3 \, d\nu_t$$

$$\hat{P}_0 = P_{00} \tag{10.2.34}$$

where the initial variance is $P_{00} = E(\hat{X}_0 - X_0)^2$.

If $\Delta f_t = 0$, then $P\{X_t|\mathcal{F}_t\}$ is normally distributed (Kallianpur and Striebel, 30) so that $E^{\mathcal{F}_t}\tilde{X}_t^3 = 0$, yielding

$$d\hat{P}_t = \left(2\hat{P}_t f_{0t} + g_t^2\sigma_w^2 - \frac{\hat{P}_t^2 h_t^2}{\sigma_v^2}\right) dt \tag{10.2.35}$$

the familiar Riccati equation, and $\hat{P}_t$ becomes the unconditional variance P_t. This was derived for the matrix case in Chapter 9.

The filter equation 10.2.34 for $\hat{P}_t$ involves the higher moment $E^{\mathcal{F}_t}\tilde{X}_t^3$, and hence the system does not have a closed form solution. In a similar manner we can also write a filter equation for $E^{\mathcal{F}_t}(X_tQ_t)$, which will again involve higher order joint moments. We have to invoke approximation techniques to obtain a closed form solution, and as a consequence we have to settle for suboptimal schemes. We approximate $E^{\mathcal{F}_t}(X_tQ_t)$ as

$$E^{\mathcal{F}_t}(X_tQ_t) = E^{\mathcal{F}_t}(X_t^2Z_t) = E^{\mathcal{F}_t}X_t^2E^{\mathcal{F}_t}Z_t = \hat{P}_t\hat{Z}_t$$

under the assumption that X_t^2 and Z_t are independent.

By definition we have

$$\begin{aligned}\hat{Z}_t &= E^{\mathcal{F}_t}Z_t = 0 \cdot P(t < \tau|\mathcal{F}_t) + 1 \cdot 0(t \geq \tau|\mathcal{F}_t)\\ &= P(t \geq \tau|\mathcal{F}_t)\end{aligned} \tag{10.2.36}$$

Basically the random variable $\hat{Z}_t$ is a probability function conditioned on the observations. We can now set a threshold value $\gamma \in [0, 1]$, which will be determined by some criterion of performance linked to the probabilities of false and missed alarms. Having set the threshold value γ, the estimated time of failure τ is obtained from

$$\hat{\tau} = \inf_t\{\hat{Z}_t \geq \gamma\} \tag{10.2.37}$$

We adopt the following recursive suboptimal scheme for the realization of the filter. Using the approximation for $E^{\mathcal{F}_t}(X_tQ_t)$, we substitute in the filter equation 10.2.26a $\Delta f_t = 0$, $\hat{P}_t = P_{0t}$ for $t < \hat{\tau}$, and $f_{0t} = f_{1t}$, $\hat{P}_t = P_{1t}$ for $t \geq \hat{\tau}$. Thus the suboptimal scheme has the following filter equations:

$$d\hat{X}_t = f_{0t}\hat{X}_t\,dt + \frac{h_t}{\sigma_v^2}P_{0t}\,d\nu_t \qquad t < \hat{\tau},\quad \hat{X}_0 \tag{10.2.38a}$$

$$d\hat{Q}_t = [\lambda\hat{X}_t + (f_{1t} - \lambda)\hat{Q}_t]\,dt + \frac{h_t}{\sigma_v^2}(P_{0t}\hat{Z}_t - \hat{X}_t\hat{Q}_t)\,d\nu_t \qquad t < \hat{\tau},\quad \hat{Q}_0 = 0 \tag{10.2.38b}$$

$$d\hat{Z}_t = \lambda(1 - \hat{Z}_t)\,dt + \frac{h_t}{\sigma_v^2}(\hat{Q}_t - \hat{X}_t\hat{Z}_t)\,d\nu_t \qquad t < \hat{\tau},\quad \hat{Z}_0 = 0 \tag{10.2.38c}$$

where $d\nu_t = dY_t - h_t\hat{X}_t\,dt$, $t < \hat{\tau}$. Since $\Delta f_t = 0$ for $t < \hat{\tau}$, the variance equation is obtained from eq. 10.2.35 by substituting P_{0t} for $\hat{P}_t$,

$$dP_{0t} = \left(2P_{0t}f_{0t} + g_t^2\sigma_w^2 - \frac{P_{0t}^2 h_t^2}{\sigma_v^2}\right)dt \qquad t < \hat{\tau} \tag{10.2.39}$$

with the initial variance given by $P_{00} = E(\hat{X}_0 - X_0)^2$.

Equations 10.2.38 solved recursively yield the suboptimal estimate $\hat{Z}_t$ of the random variable Z_t. We now test at every instant of time whether $\hat{Z}_t$ has exceeded the threshold value γ. If it has not, we go back to the filter equations 10.2.38. At the time $\hat{Z}_t$ crosses the threshold value γ we obtain the estimate $\hat{\tau}$ of the failure time, and the signal estimate equation changes to

$$d\hat{X}_t = f_{1t}\hat{X}_t\,dt + \frac{h_t}{\sigma_v^2}P_{1t}\,d\nu_t \qquad t \geq \hat{\tau}, \quad \hat{X}_{\hat{\tau}} \tag{10.2.40}$$

with the corresponding variance equation

$$dP_{1t} = \left(2P_{1t}f_{1t} + g_t^2\sigma_w^2 - \frac{P_{1t}^2 h_t^2}{\sigma_v^2}\right)dt \qquad t \geq \hat{\tau} \tag{10.2.41}$$

whose initial variance $P_{1\hat{\tau}} = P_{0\hat{\tau}}$.

For $t \geq \hat{\tau}$ we do not need the equations for $\hat{Q}_t$ and $\hat{Z}_t$ since these variables need to be computed only up to time $\hat{\tau}$.

Remarks

1. The suboptimal filters, eqs. 10.2.38–10.2.41, are two different Kalman filters, one for $t < \hat{\tau}$ and another one for $t \geq \hat{\tau}$.

2. The Kalman filter adjusts very slowly to changes in the parameters. Even though in the long run the Kalman filter may adjust to the new parameter f_{1t}, in the short run the errors due to a change in parameter from f_{0t} to f_{1t} may be intolerable. We may have to implement some type of adaptive scheme to limit the errors to within tolerance levels.

3. Instead of a step change from f_{0t} to f_{1t} in the plant parameter, we might also have a ramp change from f_{0t} to f_{1t}, which can also be analyzed by an analogous procedure (Section 10.5).

4. All stochastic differential equations, and in particular the filter equations 10.2.38–10.2.41, are to be interpreted in the Ito sense. To find solutions to these equations using a computer we have to introduce correction terms and convert them into the Stratonovich form, as discussed in Chapter 7.

10.3 FAULT DETECTION WITH CHANGE IN SIGNAL NOISE PARAMETER g_t

In many of the inertial navigation systems the type of model we encounter is one in which the signal noise parameter changes suddenly. The analysis in this section follows Krishnan (32). See also Hibey (71).

The signal process $\{X_t, t \in T\}$ is defined by the Ito stochastic differential equation

$$dX_t = fX_t\,dt + g\,dW_t \qquad t \in T, \quad X_0 \tag{10.3.1}$$

where f and g are constants and $\{W_t, t \in T\}$ is a Brownian motion process with parameter σ_w^2. X_0 is a Gaussian random variable independent of $\{W_t, t \in T\}$ and $\{V_t, t \in T\}$ representing the initial condition of eq. 10.3.1.

The observation process $\{Y_t, t \in T\}$ is also an Ito stochastic differential equation,

$$dY_t = hX_t\,dt + dV_t \qquad t \in T, \quad Y_0 = 0 \tag{10.3.2}$$

where h is a constant and $\{V_t, t \in T\}$ is another Brownian motion process with parameter σ_v^2, independent of $\{W_t, t \in T\}$. As described in Section 10.2, $\mathcal{B}_t \supset \sigma\{X_0, X_s, Y_s, W_s, V_s, s \leq t, t \in T\}$ and $\mathcal{F}_t = \sigma\{Y_s, s \leq t, t \in T\}$.

At some random time τ a fault occurs so that the signal noise parameter g in eq. 10.3.1 changes from g to $g + b$, where b is an unknown random variable. We again assume that $\{\tau \leq t\}$ is $\mathcal{B}_t$-measurable and is independent of X_0, W_t, and V_t. As a consequence of the fault the signal process changes to

$$dX_t = fX_t\,dt + (g + b)\,dW_t \qquad t \geq \tau, \quad t \in T \tag{10.3.3}$$

Under normal operating conditions the signal estimate is given by the Kalman filter equations. The sudden change in the signal noise parameter will induce large errors since the Kalman filter cannot immediately track sudden changes. In order to reparametrize the filter equations we should estimate the time of fault τ and the magnitude of the fault b.

Just as in Section 10.2, we introduce the $\mathcal{B}_t$-measurable indicator function Z_t given by eq. 10.2.3, and eqs. 10.3.1 and 10.3.3 can be combined to yield

$$dX_t = fX_t\,dt + (g + bZ_t)\,dW_t \qquad t \in T, \quad X_0 \tag{10.3.4a}$$

with the corresponding stochastic differential equation for Z_t given by

$$dZ_t = \lambda(1 - Z_t)\,dt + dM_t \qquad t \in T, \quad Z_0 = 0 \tag{10.3.4b}$$

where M_t is the discontinuous $\mathcal{B}_t$-martingale associated with the stopped Poisson process Z_t. The observation process corresponding to the signal processes, eqs. 10.3.4, is $\{Y_t, t \in T\}$, given by eq. 10.3.2,

$$dY_t = hX_t\,dt + dV_t \qquad t \in T, \quad Y_0 = 0 \tag{10.3.2}$$

Using the nonlinear filtering formula, eq. 10.2.12, we can write the filter equations for the estimates $\hat{X}_t$ and $\hat{Z}_t$,

$$d\hat{X}_t = f\hat{X}_t\,dt + \frac{h}{\sigma_v^2}\hat{P}_{Xt}\,d\nu_t \qquad t < \hat{\tau}, \quad \hat{X}_0 \tag{10.3.5a}$$

$$d\hat{Z}_t = \lambda(1 - \hat{Z}_t)\,dt + \frac{h}{\sigma_v^2}\hat{P}_{XZt}\,d\nu_t \qquad t < \hat{\tau}, \quad \hat{Z}_0 = 0 \tag{10.3.5b}$$

where we have defined

$$\begin{aligned} \hat{P}_{Xt} &= E^{\mathcal{G}_t}\tilde{X}_t^2 \\ \hat{P}_{XZt} &= E^{\mathcal{G}_t}(\tilde{X}_t\tilde{Z}_t) \end{aligned} \tag{10.3.6}$$

and $d\nu_t = dY_t - h\hat{X}_t\,dt$.

In deriving eqs. 10.3.5 we have also used the fact that W_t and V_t are independent and M_t is a discontinuous $\mathcal{B}_t$-martingale, and hence the quadratic covariance processes $\langle W, V\rangle_t$ and $\langle M, V\rangle_t$ are zero.

It is interesting to note that the filter equation 10.3.5a is the same for the signal processes of eq. 10.3.4a and eq. 10.3.1. Thus large errors in the estimate manifest themselves immediately after the occurrence of the fault.

The unknown quantities in eqs. 10.3.5 are the second conditional moments $\hat{P}_{Xt}$ and $\hat{P}_{XZt}$. To determine them we need the stochastic differential equation for the propagation of the error $\tilde{X}_t$. Subtracting eq. 10.3.4a from eq. 10.3.5a, we obtain

$$d\tilde{X}_t = f\tilde{X}_t\,dt + \frac{h}{\sigma_v^2}\hat{P}_{Xt}\,d\nu_t - (g + bZ_t)\,dW_t \tag{10.3.7}$$

The innovations process ν_t, eq. 10.3.6, can also be written as

$$d\nu_t = h(X_t - \hat{X}_t)\,dt + dV_t = -h\tilde{X}_t\,dt + dV_t \tag{10.3.8}$$

which when substituted into eq. 10.3.7 yields

$$d\tilde{X}_t = f\tilde{X}_t\,dt - \frac{h^2}{\sigma_v^2}\tilde{X}_t\hat{P}_{Xt}\,dt + \frac{h}{\sigma_v^2}\hat{P}_{Xt}\,dV_t - (g + bZ_t)\,dW_t \tag{10.3.9}$$

Using the Ito–Doleans-Dade–Meyer rule, eq. 10.2.22, for $d\tilde{X}_t^2$ yields

$$\begin{aligned} d\tilde{X}_t^2 = {} & \left[2f\tilde{X}_t^2 - \frac{2h^2}{\sigma_v^2}\tilde{X}_t^2\hat{P}_{Xt} + \frac{h^2}{\sigma_v^2}\hat{P}_{Xt}^2 + (g + bZ_t)^2\sigma_w^2\right]dt \\ & + \frac{2h}{\sigma_v^2}\tilde{X}_t\hat{P}_{Xt}\,dV_t - 2\tilde{X}_t(g + bZ_t)\,dW_t \end{aligned} \tag{10.3.10}$$

Applying the nonlinear filtering equation 10.2.12 and using the relation $Z_t^2 = Z_t$, we obtain

$$d\hat{P}_{Xt} = \left\{2f\hat{P}_{Xt} - \frac{h^2}{\sigma_v^2}\hat{P}_{Xt}^2 + \sigma_w^2\left[g^2 + (2gb + b^2)\hat{Z}_t\right]\right\} dt + \frac{h}{\sigma_v^2} s_{X^3t}\, d\nu_t$$

$$t < \hat{\tau}, \quad \hat{P}_{X0} \qquad (10.3.11a)$$

where we have defined $s_{X^3t} = E^{\mathcal{F}_t}\tilde{X}_t^3$.

In an exactly analogous manner we can write the filter equation for $d\hat{P}_{XZt}$,

$$d\hat{P}_{XZt} = \left[(f - \lambda)\hat{P}_{XZt} - \frac{h^2}{\sigma_v^2}\hat{P}_{Xt}\hat{P}_{XZt}\right] dt + \frac{h}{\sigma_v^2} s_{X^2Zt}\, d\nu_t \qquad t < \hat{\tau}, \quad P_{XZ0}$$

$$(10.3.11b)$$

where we have defined $s_{X^2Zt} = E^{\mathcal{F}_t}\tilde{X}_t^2 Z_t$.

We can again find a set of filter equations for s_{X^3t} and s_{X^2Zt}, thus yielding an expanding set of equations as mentioned earlier. To form a closed set of equations corresponding to a suboptimal filter we shall use eqs. 10.3.5 and 10.3.11 as the filter equations and use an adaptive algorithm, as described in the next section, to drive the terms s_{X^3t} and s_{X^2Zt} to zero. We can substitute an a priori estimate for b in eq. 10.3.11a.

From eqs. 10.3.5b and 10.3.11b we are in a position to estimate the time of fault. By definition,

$$\hat{Z}_t = E^{\mathcal{F}_t}Z_t = P(t \geq \tau | \mathcal{F}_t) \qquad (10.3.12)$$

Hence Z_t is a probability function conditioned on the observations.

We again define a threshold function $\gamma \in [0, 1]$, the value of which can be set by some criterion of performance linked to the probabilities of false and missed alarms. Having set the threshold value γ, the estimated time of failure τ is obtained from

$$\hat{\tau} = \inf_t \{\hat{Z}_t \geq \gamma\} \qquad (10.3.13)$$

After the occurrence of the fault the state equations can be written as

$$dX_t = fX_t\, dt + (g + b)\, dW_t \qquad t \geq \tau, \quad X_\tau \qquad (10.3.14a)$$

$$db_t = 0 \qquad t \geq \tau, \quad b \qquad (10.3.14b)$$

where we have introduced a new state b and omitted the state Z_t, which is not of any concern after the fault has occurred. Using the nonlinear filtering result, eq. 10.2.12, and the Ito–Doleans-Dade–Meyer rule, 10.2.22, we can write the filter equations

$$d\hat{X}_t = f\hat{X}_t\,dt + \frac{h}{\sigma_v^2}\hat{P}_{Xt}\,d\nu_t \qquad t \geq \hat{\tau}, \quad \hat{X}_{\hat{\tau}} \tag{10.3.15a}$$

$$d\hat{b}_t = \frac{h}{\sigma_v^2}\hat{P}_{Xbt}\,d\nu_t \qquad t \geq \hat{\tau}, \quad \hat{b} \tag{10.3.15b}$$

where the conditional error covariances $\hat{P}_{Xt} = E^{\mathcal{G}_t}\tilde{X}_t^2$ and $\hat{P}_{Xbt} = E^{\mathcal{G}_t}\tilde{X}_t\tilde{b}_t$ are given by

$$d\hat{P}_{Xt} = \left[2f\hat{P}_{Xt} - \frac{h^2}{\sigma_v^2}\hat{P}_{Xt}^2 + \sigma_w^2(g+\hat{b})^2 + \hat{P}_{bt}\right]dt + \frac{h}{\sigma_v^2}s_{X^3 t}\,d\nu_t$$

$$t \geq \hat{\tau}, \quad \hat{P}_{X\hat{\tau}} \tag{10.3.16a}$$

$$d\hat{P}_{Xbt} = \left(f\hat{P}_{Xbt} - \frac{h^2}{\sigma_v^2}\hat{P}_{Xt}\hat{P}_{Xbt}\right)dt + \frac{h}{\sigma_v^2}s_{X^2bt}\,d\nu_t \qquad t \geq \hat{\tau}, \quad \hat{P}_{Xb\hat{\tau}}$$

$$\tag{10.3.16b}$$

The conditional covariance matrix $\hat{P}_{bt} = E^{\mathcal{G}_t}\tilde{b}_t^2$ in eq. 10.3.16a is given by

$$d\hat{P}_{bt} = \left(\frac{-h^2}{\sigma_v^2}\hat{P}_{Xbt}^2\right)dt + \frac{h}{\sigma_v^2}s_{Xb^2 t}\,d\nu_t \qquad t \geq \hat{\tau}, \quad \hat{P}_{b\hat{\tau}} \tag{10.3.16c}$$

where we have defined $s_{X^3 t} = E^{\mathcal{G}_t}\tilde{X}_t^3$, $s_{X^2bt} = E^{\mathcal{G}_t}\tilde{X}_t^2\tilde{b}$, and $s_{Xb^2 t} = E^{\mathcal{G}_t}\tilde{X}_t\tilde{b}^2$. We can now apply the adaptive algorithm to be described in the next section to yield a closed form suboptimal filter.

Note. There is no stochastic differential equation corresponding to $\hat{P}_{Zt}$ in the set of eqs. 10.3.11 because $Z_t^2 = Z_t$, whereas we do have a stochastic differential equation for $\hat{P}_{bt}$ since $b_t^2 \neq b_t$.

Summary of Suboptimal Filter Scheme. The system equations before fault are

$$\begin{aligned} dX_t &= fX_t\,dt + (g + bZ_t)\,dW_t \qquad t < \tau, \quad X_0 \\ dZ_t &= \lambda(1 - Z_t)\,dt + dM_t \qquad t < \tau, \quad Z_0 = 0 \\ dY_t &= hX_t\,dt + dV_t \qquad t \in T, \quad Y_0 = 0 \end{aligned} \tag{10.3.17}$$

The corresponding filter equations are

$$
\begin{aligned}
d\hat{X}_t &= f\hat{X}_t\,dt + \frac{h}{\sigma_v^2}\hat{P}_{Xt}\,d\nu_t \qquad t < \hat{\tau}, \quad \hat{X}_0 \\
d\hat{Z}_t &= \lambda(1 - \hat{Z}_t)\,dt + \frac{h}{\sigma_v^2}\hat{P}_{XZt}\,d\nu_t \qquad t < \hat{\tau}, \quad \hat{Z}_0 = 0 \\
d\hat{P}_{Xt} &= \left\{2f\hat{P}_{Xt} - \frac{h^2}{\sigma_v^2}\hat{P}_{Xt}^2 + \sigma_w^2\left[g^2 + (2g\hat{b} + \hat{b}^2)\hat{Z}_t\right]\right\}dt + \frac{h}{\sigma_v^2}s_{X^3t}\,d\nu_t \\
&\qquad t < \hat{\tau}, \quad \hat{P}_{X0} \\
d\hat{P}_{XZt} &= \left[(f - \lambda)\hat{P}_{XZt} - \frac{h^2}{\sigma_v^2}\hat{P}_{Xt}\hat{P}_{XZt}\right]dt + \frac{h}{\sigma_v^2}s_{X^2Zt}\,d\nu_t \\
&\qquad t < \hat{\tau}, \quad \hat{P}_{XZ0}
\end{aligned}
\tag{10.3.18}
$$

The system equations after the occurrence of the fault are

$$
\begin{aligned}
dX_t &= fX_t\,dt + (g + b)\,dW_t \qquad t \geq \tau, \quad X_\tau \\
db_t &= 0 \qquad t \geq \tau, \quad b
\end{aligned}
\tag{10.3.19}
$$

The corresponding filter equations are

$$
\begin{aligned}
d\hat{X}_t &= f\hat{X}_t\,dt + \frac{h}{\sigma_v^2}\hat{P}_{Xt}\,d\nu_t \qquad t \geq \hat{\tau}, \quad \hat{X}_\tau \\
d\hat{b}_t &= \frac{h}{\sigma_v^2}\hat{P}_{Xbt}\,d\nu_t \qquad t \geq \hat{\tau}, \quad \hat{b} \\
d\hat{P}_{Xt} &= \left\{2f\hat{P}_{Xbt} - \frac{h^2}{\sigma_v^2}\hat{P}_{Xt}^2 + \sigma_w^2\left[(g + b)^2 + \hat{P}_{bt}\right]\right\}dt \\
&\quad + \frac{h}{\sigma_v^2}s_{X^3t}\,d\nu_t \qquad t > \hat{\tau}, \quad \hat{P}_{X\hat{\tau}} \\
d\hat{P}_{Xbt} &= \left(f\hat{P}_{Xbt} - \frac{h^2}{\sigma_v^2}\hat{P}_{Xt}\hat{P}_{Xbt}\right)dt + \frac{h}{\sigma_v^2}s_{X^2bt}\,d\nu_t \qquad t \geq \hat{\tau}, \quad \hat{P}_{Xb\hat{\tau}} \\
d\hat{P}_{bt} &= -\frac{h^2}{\sigma_v^2}\hat{P}_{Xbt}^2\,dt + \frac{h}{\sigma_v^2}s_{Xb^2t}\,d\nu_t \qquad t \geq \hat{\tau}, \quad \hat{P}_{b\hat{\tau}}
\end{aligned}
\tag{10.3.20}
$$

Note. All stochastic differential equations, eqs. 10.3.17–10.3.20, are to be interpreted in the Ito sense. To obtain computational results, these equations have to be transformed into the Stratonovich form by applying correction terms.

In the next section we describe an adaptive scheme to obtain better estimates of the Kalman filter, eqs. 10.3.18 and 10.3.20.

10.4 ADAPTIVE ALGORITHM

Different types of adaptive algorithms for Kalman filters have been described by Mehra (36, 37). We investigate a different type of an adaptive algorithm for the problem under discussion. We consider the signal process $\{X_t, t \in T\}$ of the form

$$dX_t = fX_t\,dt + g(X_t)\,dW_t \qquad t \in T, \quad X_0 \tag{10.4.1}$$

and the observation process $\{Y_t, t \in T\}$ of the form

$$dY_t = hX_t\,dt + dV_t \qquad t \in T \tag{10.4.2}$$

where f and h are constants and the σ-fields $\{\mathcal{B}_t, t \in T\}$ and $\{\mathcal{F}_t, t \in T\}$ are as defined in the previous sections.

The optimal filter equations are

$$d\hat{X}_t = f\hat{X}_t\,dt + \frac{K_t}{\sigma_v^2}\,d\nu_t \qquad t \in T, \quad \hat{X}_0 \tag{10.4.3}$$

$$d\hat{P}_t = \left[2f\hat{P}_t - \frac{h^2}{\sigma_v^2}\hat{P}_t^2 + \sigma_w^2 E^{\mathcal{F}_t} g^2(X_t)\right] dt + \frac{h}{\sigma_v^2} s_t\,d\nu_t \qquad t \in T, \quad \hat{P}_0 \tag{10.4.4}$$

where $K_t = \hat{P}_t h$, $s_t = E^{\mathcal{F}_t}\tilde{X}_t^3$, σ_v^2 and σ_w^2 are the variance parameters associated with the Brownian motion processes $\{V_t\}$ and $\{W_t\}$, respectively, and ν_t is the innovations process given by

$$d\nu_t = dY_t - h\hat{X}_t\,dt \tag{10.4.5}$$

We can again write an optimal filter equation for s_t by the now familiar method of writing the stochastic differential equation for $d\tilde{X}_t^3$ using the Ito–Doleans-Dade–Meyer rule and then using the nonlinear filtering equation. Thus

$$ds_t = \left\{3fs_t - \frac{3h^2}{\sigma_v^2}\hat{P}_t s_t + 3\sigma_w^2 E^{\mathcal{F}_t}[\tilde{X}_t g^2(X_t)]\right\} dt + \frac{h}{\sigma_v^2}\left(E^{\mathcal{F}_t}\tilde{X}_t^4 - 3\hat{P}_t^2\right) d\nu_t \qquad t \in T \tag{10.4.6}$$

Several approximation schemes are in existence for eq. 10.4.4 or, eq. 10.4.6. We can set $E^{\mathscr{F}_t} g^2(X_t) = g^2(\hat{X}_t)$ (extended Kalman), in which case $s_t = 0$. A second approximation (Jazwinski, 23) is to set

$$E^{\mathscr{F}_t} g^2(X_t) = g^2(\hat{X}_t) + \left[g_x^2(\hat{X}_t) + g(\hat{X}_t) g_{xx}(\hat{X}_t) \right] \hat{P}_t$$

and $s_t = 0$.

A third approximation (Gran and Kozin, 17) is to set $E^{\mathscr{F}_t} \tilde{X}_t^4 = 3\hat{P}_t^2$ and expand $g^2(X_t)$ to any suitable order. The essential feature of the above schemes is that once the approximations are made, the gain K_t in eq. 10.4.3 is fixed. The resulting filters perform adequately in certain ranges of signal space and system parameters. In certain other cases they may diverge.

In the adaptive filtering algorithm described below, the gain K_t is varied by feeding back the present information about the filter. This information is obtained from the innovations process, ν_t which is a Brownian motion process under optimal conditions, having the same statistics as the observation noise process $\{V_t\}$. With a suboptimal filter $\hat{X}_t$ is no longer an optimal estimate, and hence the innovations process is no longer a Brownian motion. The non-Brownian motion nature of the innovations process is utilized to vary the gain K_t. It is reasonable to assume that the suboptimal filter may not be too far away from the optimal filter, and as a consequence the suboptimal innovations process ν_t can be modeled by a simple first-order autoregressive process (Stoica and Soderstrom, 52),

$$d\nu_t' = \alpha_t \nu_t' \, dt + dV_t \qquad t \in [t_0, t_1] \tag{10.4.7}$$

where ν_t' is the parametrized model for the observed innovations process ν_t. Clearly when α_t is driven to zero then the solution of eq. 10.4.7 will have the same characteristics as that of the optimal innovations process.

If we now consider s_t in eq. 10.4.4 as the control, then it is intuitively clear that for each setting of s_t there will be a corresponding innovations process ν_t that can be modeled by an α_t. Therefore, a relationship whose exact form is unknown exists between s_t and α_t. Let τ be the time interval of a moving window and let $[t_0, t_1] \in T$ be the time interval over which α_t is estimated. We shall also assume that α_t is slowly varying with respect to time. The solution to the differential equation 10.4.7 is given by

$$\nu_t' = e^{\alpha_t (t - t_0)} \nu_{t_0}' + \int_{t_0}^{t} e^{\alpha_t (t - \xi)} \, dV_\xi \qquad t \in [t_0, t_1] \tag{10.4.8}$$

α_t can now be estimated by matching ν_t' given by eq. 10.4.8 to the observed innovations process ν_t in the mean square sense over the time interval $[t, t + \tau]$. If $\hat{\alpha}_t$ is the estimator of α_t, then

$$\hat{\alpha}_t = \arg \left\{ \min_{\alpha} \frac{1}{\tau} E \int_t^{t+\tau} \left(\nu_\xi' - \nu_\xi \right)^2 d\xi \right\} \qquad t \in [t_0, t_1] \tag{10.4.9}$$

Equation 10.4.9 shows that the innovations process has to be observed during the time interval $[t_0, t_1 + \tau]$.

Since the true relationship between s_t and α_t is unknown we can model α_t by

$$\dot{\alpha}'_t = A\alpha_t + Ak(s - s_0) \qquad t \in [t_0, t_1],\ \alpha'_{t_0} \tag{10.4.10}$$

where A, k, and s_0 are constants to be determined. The differential equation 10.4.10 is chosen to be linear for simplicity.

The solution to eq. 10.4.10 is given by

$$\alpha'_t = \alpha'_{t_0} e^{A(t-t_0)} + k(s - s_0)[e^{A(t-t_0)} - 1] \qquad t \in [t_0, t_1] \tag{10.4.11}$$

The constants A, k, and s_0 can be estimated in the time interval $[t_0, t_1]$ using the minimum mean square error criterion. Thus the estimates $\hat{A}$, $\hat{k}$, and $\hat{s}_0$ are obtained from

$$\hat{A}, \hat{k}, \hat{s}_0 = \arg\left\{ \min_{A, k, s_0} \frac{1}{t_1 - t_0} \int_{t_0}^{t_1} \left(\alpha'_\xi - \hat{\alpha}_\xi\right)^2 d\xi \right\} \qquad [t_0, t_1] \in T \tag{10.4.12}$$

where α'_ξ and $\hat{\alpha}_\xi$ are obtained from eqs. 10.4.11 and 10.4.9 respectively.

Having obtained $\hat{A}$, $\hat{k}$, and $\hat{s}_0$ the new control $\hat{s}$ is obtained from the criterion that α'_t must be driven to zero in the time interval T_0, that is, $\alpha'_{t_0+T_0} = 0$. Substituting this condition in eq. 10.4.11 yields

$$\hat{s} = \frac{e^{\hat{A}T_0}\alpha'_{t_0}}{\hat{k}(1 - e^{\hat{A}T_0})} + \hat{s}_0 \tag{10.4.13}$$

The interval T_0 should be so chosen that it is of the same order as the moving window τ, so that the control s will not drive α'_t past zero before $\hat{\alpha}_t$ can be reevaluated.

The sequence of operations for the algorithm can be given as follows, and is shown in Figure 10.4.1:

1. Choose the moving window τ and the update interval T_0 in eq. 10.4.13. (T_0 is of the same order as τ.)
2. Initialize the procedure by choosing a "suitable" value for s in eq. 10.4.4 for the initial time t_0.
3. Observe and record the resulting innovations process ν_t from the initial time t_0 to the time $t_1 + \tau$. Estimate the coefficient $\hat{\alpha}_t$ from eq. 10.4.9 for the observation interval $[t, t + \tau]$, $t \in [t_0, t_1]$.
4. Estimate the coefficients A, k, and s_0 in eq. 10.4.10 during the interval $[t_0, t_1]$ using the least-squares minimization procedure of eq. 10.4.12.
5. Compute the new value of $\hat{s}$ which will drive α'_t to zero in the interval T_0.
6. Consider t_1 to be the initial time and repeat the procedure from step 3.

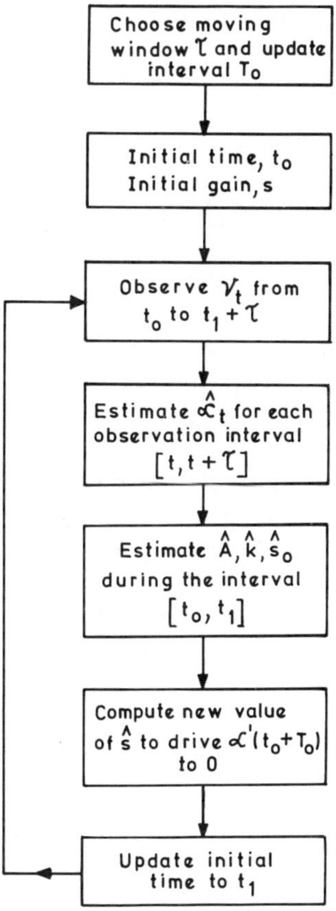

FIGURE 10.4.1

The above algorithm is suggested as a possible method of improving the Kalman filter estimates for the fault detection problem. It has neither been implemented nor has its stability been analyzed.

10.5 MODELING OTHER SYSTEM CHANGES

In the previous sections we have indicated two types of faults occurring in systems. In addition the following types of changes can be modeled along similar lines. Additive bias in the state equation is modeled as

$$dX_t = fX_t\,dt + bZ_t\,dt + g\,dW_t \qquad t \in T, \quad X_0 \tag{10.5.1}$$

An increase in observation noise can be modeled as

$$dY_t = hX_t\,dt + (1 + bZ_t)\,dV_t \qquad t \in T \tag{10.5.2}$$

and an additive bias in the observation equation is modeled as

$$dY_t = hX_t\,dt + bZ_t\,dt + dV_t \qquad t \in T \tag{10.5.3}$$

Finally a change in the measurement gain can be modeled as

$$dY_t = (h + bZ_t)X_t\,dt + dV_t \qquad t \in T \tag{10.5.4}$$

In the above equations Z_t is the indicator function defined by eq. 10.2.3, and all changes are step changes.

Ramp changes also can be taken into account in a similar manner. For example, the dynamic equations of Section 10.3 in the case of a ramp change in the signal noise parameter g_t can be modeled as

$$\begin{aligned}
dX_t &= fX_t\,dt + (g + b\xi_t)\,dW_t \qquad t \in T, \quad X_0 \\
d\xi_t &= Z_t\,dt \qquad t \in T, \quad \xi_0 = 0 \\
dZ_t &= \lambda(1 - Z_t)\,dt + dM_t \qquad t \in T, \quad Z_0 = 0 \\
dY_t &= hX_t\,dt + dV_t \qquad t \in T, \quad Y_0 = 0
\end{aligned} \tag{10.5.5}$$

where we have introduced an extra signal $\xi_t = \int_0^t Z_s\,ds$.

Problems

1. Equations 10.2.38–10.2.41 represent the suboptimal filter equations for the fault detection problem, and they are Ito stochastic differential equations. Convert these stochastic differential equations into the Stratonovich form by finding the correction terms.

2. Equations 10.3.18 and 10.3.20 represent suboptimal filter equations, and again they are Ito stochastic differential equations. Convert them into the Stratonovich form by finding the correction terms.

3. The signal process is given by

$$dX_t = fX_t\,dt + bZ_t\,dt + g\,dW_t \qquad t \in T, \quad X_0$$

and the observation process by

$$dY_t = hX_t\,dt + dV_t \qquad t \in T, \quad Y_0 = 0$$

where b is an additive bias in the state equation with all other processes, parameters, and σ-fields as defined in the text. Formulate the filter equations and the corresponding Stratonovich form.

4. If now the signal process is given by

$$dX_t = fX_t\,dt + g\,dW_t \qquad t \in T, \quad X_0$$

formulate the filter equations and the corresponding Stratonovich form for the following observation processes:

a. $dY_t = hX_t\,dt + bZ_t\,dt + dV_t \qquad t \in T, \quad Y_0 = 0$
where b is an additive bias.

b. $dY_t = hX_t\,dt + (1 + bZ_t)\,dV_t \qquad t \in T, \quad Y_0 = 0$
where b is an increase in the observation noise.

c. $dY_t = (h + bZ_t)X_t\,dt + dV_t \qquad t \in T, \quad Y_0 = 0$
where b is a change in measurement gain.

5. Derive eqs. 10.5.5 for a ramp change in the signal noise parameter g_t and formulate the filter equations and the corresponding Stratonovich form.

11 OPTIMAL SMOOTHING

In this section we consider interpolation or smoothing problems and derive stochastic differential equations satisfied by smoothed estimates using the techniques developed in the nonlinear filtering theory of Chapter 8. The material in this chapter follows along the lines of Venimadhavan (56), Viswanathan (57), and Venimadhavan and Viswanathan (55).

11.1 SMOOTHING PROBLEMS

Let $(\Omega, \mathcal{F}, P)$ be a complete probability space. Let $\{X_t(\omega), t \in T\}$ be a signal process with continuous trajectories defined on the complete probability space characterized by an Ito stochastic differential equation,

$$dX_t(\omega) = f_t(X_t(\omega))\, dt + dW_t(\omega) \qquad t \in T, \quad X_0 \tag{11.1.1}$$

Let $\{Y_t(\omega), t \in T\}$ be an observation process with continuous trajectories defined on the same probability space and represented by another Ito stochastic differential equation,

$$dY_t(\omega) = h_t(X_t(\omega))\, dt + dV_t(\omega) \qquad t \in T, \quad Y_0 = 0 \tag{11.1.2}$$

The processes $\{W_t, t \in T\}$ and $\{V_t, t \in T\}$, not necessarily independent, are Brownian motion processes with parameters σ_w^2 and σ_v^2, respectively. The initial condition X_0 is a Gaussian random variable independent of both $\{W_t\}$ and

$\{V_t\}$. The functions f_t and h_t are nonanticipative functionals of X_t such that

$$\begin{aligned}
&\int_{t\in T} E|f_t(X_t)|\,dt < \infty \\
&\int_{t\in T} E|h_t(X_t)|\,dt < \infty \\
&\int_{t\in T} E|f_t|^2(X_t)\,dt < \infty \\
&\int_{t\in T} E|h_t|^2(X_t)\,dt < \infty
\end{aligned} \qquad (11.1.3)$$

Let us define the σ-fields $\mathcal{B}_t \supset \sigma\{X_s, Y_s, W_s, V_s, s \le t,\ t \in T\}$ and $\mathcal{F}_t = \sigma\{Y_s, s \le t, t \in T\}$.

Since $\{W_t\}$ and $\{V_t\}$ are Brownian motion processes, $\mathcal{B}_s$ is independent of both $\sigma\{W_{t_2} - W_{t_1}, s < t_1 < t_2\}$ and $\sigma\{V_{t_2} - V_{t_1}, s < t_1 < t_2\}$. The last two conditions in eqs. 11.1.3 ensure the existence of a measurable modification of the conditional expectations $E^{\mathcal{F}_t} f_t(X_t)$ and $E^{\mathcal{F}_t} h_t(X_t)$.

We saw in Section 8.3 that if another random process $\psi_\tau(X_\tau)$, $\tau \in T$ is measurable with respect to the σ-field $\mathcal{B}_\tau$, then $E^{\mathcal{F}_t}\psi_\tau(X_\tau)$ is called the filtered estimate if $\tau = t$, the smoothed estimate if $\tau < t$, and the predicted estimate if $\tau > t$. In the previous chapters we have been considering only the *filtered* estimates for which we have derived stochastic differential equations. We derive in this chapter the stochastic differential equations satisfied by the *smoothed* estimates.

Smoothing problems themselves can be classified as follows:

1. Fixed point smoothing, where $\tau < t$ is a *fixed instant of time* for all $t \in T$, and the stochastic differential equation for the estimate $E^{\mathcal{F}_t}\psi_\tau(X_\tau)$ is to be determined.

2. Fixed interval smoothing, where the *interval* $T = [0, B]$, $B < \infty$, *is fixed*, τ is any point in $T = [0, B]$, and the stochastic differential equation for the estimate $E^{\mathcal{F}_B}\psi_\tau(X_\tau)$, $\tau \in T$, is to be determined.

3. Fixed lag smoothing, where $a \in T$ is a *fixed delay*, and the stochastic differential equation for the estimate $E^{\mathcal{F}_t}\psi_{t-a}(X_{t-a})$, $t \in T$, $t \ge a$, is to be determined.

We have shown in Theorem 8.1.1 that the innovations process $\nu_t(\omega)$ defined by

$$d\nu_t(\omega) = dY_t(\omega) - E^{\mathcal{F}_t} h_t(X_t(\omega))\,dt \qquad t \in T,\quad \nu_0 = 0 \quad (11.1.4)$$

is also a Brownian motion process and an $\mathcal{F}_t$-martingale so that $\mathcal{F}_s$ and $\sigma\{\nu_{t_1} - \nu_{t_2}, s < t_1 < t_2, s, t_1, t_2 \in T\}$ are independent.

We now state the following nonlinear filtering theorem similar to eq. 8.4.38 for continuous trajectories.

Theorem 11.1.1

Let the signal process $\{X_t, t \in T\}$ and the observation process $\{Y_t, t \in T\}$ be the unique solutions to the stochastic differential equations 11.1.1 and 11.1.2, respectively, with f_t and h_t satisfying conditions 11.1.3. Let the associated σ-fields $\mathcal{B}_t$ and $\mathcal{F}_t$ be as defined earlier. Under these conditions the filtered estimate $\hat{X}_t = E^{\mathcal{F}_t} X_t$ satisfies the Ito stochastic differential equation

$$d\hat{X}_t = \hat{f}_t\, dt + \frac{1}{\sigma_v^2} E^{\mathcal{F}_t}\left(X_t h_t - \hat{X}_t \hat{h}_t + \frac{d}{dt}\langle W, V\rangle_t \right) d\nu_t \qquad t \in T, \quad \hat{X}_0 \tag{11.1.5}$$

which can be written in a alternate form as

$$d\hat{X}_t = \hat{f}_t\, dt + \frac{1}{\sigma_v^2}\left[\operatorname{cov}^{\mathcal{F}_t}(X_t h_t) + E^{\mathcal{F}_t}\frac{d}{dt}\langle W, V\rangle_t \right] d\nu_t \qquad t \in T, \quad \hat{X}_0 \tag{11.1.6}$$

where the conditional covariance is given by

$$\operatorname{cov}^{\mathcal{F}_t}(X_t h_t) = E^{\mathcal{F}_t}(X_t h_t) - E^{\mathcal{F}_t} X_t E^{\mathcal{F}_t} h_t \tag{11.1.7}$$

The proof is exactly similar to that given in Theorem 8.4.1, except that the process $\{X_t, t \in T\}$ has sample continuous trajectories. In the following sections we discuss only the scalar case. Extension to the vector case is straightforward.

11.2 MARTINGALE REPRESENTATION FOR SMOOTHED ESTIMATES

We can now state the following theorem on the representation of smoothed estimates.

Theorem 11.2.1 Fixed Point Smoothing

Let the signal process $\{X_t, \mathcal{B}_t, t \in T\}$ be given by

$$dX_t(\omega) = f_t(X_t(\omega))\, dt + dW_t(\omega) \qquad t \in T, \quad X_0 \tag{11.2.1}$$

Let the observation process $\{Y_t, \mathcal{B}_t, t \in T\}$ be given by

$$dY_t(\omega) = h_t(X_t(\omega))\,dt + dV_t(\omega) \qquad t \in T, \quad Y_0 = 0 \qquad (11.2.2)$$

The processes $\{W_t, t \in T\}$ and $\{V_t, t \in T\}$ are now independent Brownian motion processes with parameters σ_w^2 and σ_v^2, respectively, with X_0 being a zero mean Gaussian random variable independent of $\{W_t\}$ and $\{V_t\}$, and the functionals f_t and h_t satisfy conditions 11.1.3. Let $\tau < t$ be a fixed instant of time. Under these conditions the smoothed estimate $E^{\mathcal{F}_t}X_\tau$, $\tau < t$, $t \in T$, satisfies the equation

$$E^{\mathcal{F}_t}X_\tau = E^{\mathcal{F}_\tau}X_\tau + \frac{1}{\sigma_v^2}\int_\tau^t \left[E^{\mathcal{F}_s}(X_\tau h_s) - E^{\mathcal{F}_s}X_\tau E^{\mathcal{F}_s}h_s\right] d\nu_s \qquad \tau < t, \quad t \in T$$

(11.2.3)

Proof. Let us define $\xi_t = E^{\mathcal{F}_t}X_\tau$, $t > \tau$, which from Example 3.4.1 is a square integrable martingale. But from eq. 8.4.6 of Theorem 8.4.1, ξ_t admits of a representation

$$\xi_t = \xi_\tau + \int_\tau^t \psi_s(\omega)\,d\nu_s \qquad \tau < t, \quad t \in T \qquad (11.2.4)$$

where $\{\nu_t, t \in T\}$ is the innovations process given by eq. 11.1.4, and $\psi_s(\omega)$ is a nonanticipative, $\mathcal{F}_s$-measurable random process satisfying the condition

$$\int_\tau^t E|\psi_s|^2(\omega)\,ds < \infty$$

Let $\{g_t(\omega), \mathcal{F}_t, t \in T\}$ be any random process satisfying the conditions of Lemma 6.5.1, and let Z_t be the square integrable $\mathcal{F}_t$-martingale represented by

$$Z_t = \int_\tau^t g_s(\omega)\,d\nu_s \qquad (11.2.5)$$

We proceed in a manner analogous to the proof of Theorem 6.6.3.

From eq. 4.3.5 of Theorem 4.3.2 we have for the square integrable $\mathcal{F}_t$-martingales ξ_t and Z_t

$$E\xi_t Z_t = E\langle \xi, Z\rangle_t + E\nu_t = E\langle \xi, Z\rangle_t$$

But from eq. 6.5.21 we have

$$E\langle \xi, Z\rangle_t = E\int_\tau^t \psi_s(\omega) g_s(\omega)\,d\langle \nu, \nu\rangle_s$$

Since the innovations process ν_t is a Brownian motion process, $d\langle \nu, \nu\rangle_t = \sigma_v^2\, dt$, and therefore

$$E\xi_t Z_t = \sigma_v^2 E\int_\tau^t \psi_s(\omega) g_s(\omega)\, ds \tag{11.2.6}$$

We can also find $E\xi_t Z_t$ by a different route as follows:

$$\begin{aligned} E\xi_t Z_t = E\left(E^{\mathcal{F}_t} X_\tau\right) Z_t &= E E^{\mathcal{F}_t}(X_\tau Z_t) \qquad \text{since } Z_t \in \mathcal{F}_t \\ &= E X_\tau Z_t \end{aligned} \tag{11.2.7}$$

Substituting for dY_t from eq. 11.2.2 into eq. 11.1.4, we find that

$$d\nu_t = dV_t + h_t(X_t)\, dt - E^{\mathcal{F}_t} h_t(X_t)\, dt \tag{11.2.8}$$

so that substituting for $d\nu_t$ in eq. 11.2.5 we obtain

$$Z_t = \int_\tau^t g_s(\omega)\, dV_s + \int_\tau^t \left[h_s(X_s) - E^{\mathcal{F}_s} h_s(X_s)\right] g_s(\omega)\, ds \tag{11.2.9}$$

Substituting for Z_t from eq. 11.2.9 into eq. 11.2.7,

$$\begin{aligned} E\xi_t Z_t = E X_\tau Z_t &= E X_\tau \int_\tau^t g_s(\omega)\, dV_s + E X_\tau \int_\tau^t \left[h_s(X_s) - E^{\mathcal{F}_s} h_s(X_s)\right] g_s\, ds \\ &= E\left[X_\tau E^{\mathcal{B}_\tau}\int_\tau^t g_s(\omega)\, dV_s\right] + E\int_\tau^t \left[X_\tau h_s(X_s) - X_\tau E^{\mathcal{F}_s} h_s(X_s)\right] g_s\, ds \\ &= 0 + E\int_\tau^t \left[X_\tau h_s(X_s) - X_\tau E^{\mathcal{F}_s} h_s(X_s)\right] g_s\, ds \\ &= E\int_\tau^t \left\{E^{\mathcal{F}_s}\left[X_\tau h_s(X_s)\right] - E^{\mathcal{F}_s} X_\tau E^{\mathcal{F}_s} h_s(X_s)\right\} g_s\, ds \end{aligned} \tag{11.2.10}$$

Combining eqs. 11.2.10 and 11.2.6 we have

$$E\int_\tau^t \left\{\sigma_v^2 \psi_s - \left[E^{\mathcal{F}_s}(X_\tau h_s) - E^{\mathcal{F}_s} X_\tau E^{\mathcal{F}_s} h_s\right]\right\} g_s\, ds = 0 \tag{11.2.11}$$

Since g_s is an arbitrary random process, we infer from eq. 11.2.11

$$\psi_s = \frac{1}{\sigma_v^2}\left[E^{\mathcal{F}_s}(X_\tau h_s) - E^{\mathcal{F}_s} X_\tau E^{\mathcal{F}_s} h_s\right] \tag{11.2.12}$$

Substituting for ψ_s in eq. 11.2.4 we obtain the desired result, eq. 11.2.3. □

From Theorem 11.2.1 we have the following corollaries for fixed interval and fixed lag smoothing.

Corollary 11.2.1 Fixed Interval Smoothing

Let T be a fixed interval $[0, B]$. Then

$$E^{\mathcal{F}_B} X_\tau = E^{\mathcal{F}_\tau} X_\tau + \frac{1}{\sigma_v^2} \int_\tau^B \left[E^{\mathcal{F}_s}(X_\tau h_s) - E^{\mathcal{F}_s} X_\tau E^{\mathcal{F}_s} h_s \right] dv_s \qquad \tau \in T \tag{11.2.13}$$

Corollary 11.2.2 Fixed Lag Smoothing

Let $a \in T$ be a fixed lag. Then for $(\tau + a) \in T$ we have

$$E^{\mathcal{F}_{\tau+a}} X_\tau = E^{\mathcal{F}_\tau} X_\tau + \frac{1}{\sigma_v^2} \int_\tau^{\tau+a} \left[E^{\mathcal{F}_s}(X_\tau h_s) - E^{\mathcal{F}_s} X_\tau E^{\mathcal{F}_s} h_s \right] dv_s \qquad (\tau + a) \in T \tag{11.2.14}$$

The differential equations 11.2.3, 11.2.13, and 11.2.14 satisfied by the smoothed estimates can be expressed in a more compact form by defining the conditional covariance function similar to eq. 11.1.7,

$$\operatorname{cov}^{\mathcal{F}_s}(X_\tau h_s) = E^{\mathcal{F}_s}(X_\tau h_s) - E^{\mathcal{F}_s} X_\tau E^{\mathcal{F}_s} h_s \tag{11.2.15}$$

Using eq. 11.2.15 we can write for fixed point smoothing, eq. 11.2.3,

$$E^{\mathcal{F}_t} X_\tau = E^{\mathcal{F}_\tau} X_\tau + \frac{1}{\sigma_v^2} \int_\tau^t \operatorname{cov}^{\mathcal{F}_s}(X_\tau h_s)\, dv_s \qquad \tau < t, \quad t \in T \tag{11.2.16}$$

for fixed interval smoothing, eq. 11.2.13,

$$E^{\mathcal{F}_B} X_\tau = E^{\mathcal{F}_\tau} X_\tau + \frac{1}{\sigma_v^2} \int_\tau^B \operatorname{cov}^{\mathcal{F}_s}(X_\tau h_s)\, dv_s \qquad \tau \in T, \quad T = [0, B] \tag{11.2.17}$$

and for fixed lag smoothing, eq. 11.2.14,

$$E^{\mathcal{F}_{\tau+a}} X_\tau = E^{\mathcal{F}_\tau} X_\tau + \frac{1}{\sigma_v^2} \int_\tau^{\tau+a} \operatorname{cov}^{\mathcal{F}_s}(X_\tau h_s)\, dv_s \qquad (\tau + a) \in T \tag{11.2.18}$$

11.3 LINEAR SMOOTHING PROBLEM

In Chapter 9 we derived the Kalman filter as a special case of the general nonlinear filtering representation. Next we derive the Kalman smoother from the representations given by eqs. 11.2.16–11.2.18. Again, only the scalar case is considered. Extension to the vector case is straightforward.

Let $(\Omega, \mathfrak{F}, P)$ be a complete probability space. The signal process $\{X_t, t \in T\}$ and the observation process $\{Y_t, t \in T\}$, both having continuous trajectories, are defined on the complete probability space and characterized by the following stochastic differential equations:

$$\begin{aligned} dX_t &= f_t X_t \, dt + g_t \, dW_t \qquad t \in T, \quad X_0 \\ dY_t &= h_t X_t \, dt + dV_t \qquad t \in T, \quad Y_0 = 0 \end{aligned} \tag{11.3.1}$$

where W_t and V_t are again independent Brownian motion processes with variance parameters σ_w^2 and σ_v^2, respectively, X_0 is a zero mean Gaussian random variable independent of W_t and V_t, and f_t and h_t are nonrandom functions satisfying the usual regularity conditions.

We have already shown in Theorem 9.3.1 that the conditional expectation $\hat{X}_t = E^{\mathfrak{F}_t} X_t$ with $\mathfrak{F}_t = \sigma\{Y_s, s \le t, t \in T\}$ satisfies the stochastic differential equation

$$d\hat{X}_t = f_t \hat{X}_t \, dt + \frac{1}{\sigma_v^2} \hat{p}_t h_t \, d\nu_t \qquad t \in T, \quad X_0 \tag{11.3.2}$$

and the "conditional"† variance $\hat{p}_t = E^{\mathfrak{F}_t}(\hat{X}_t - X_t)^2$ satisfies

$$\frac{d\hat{p}_t}{dt} = 2 f_t \hat{p}_t + g_t^2 \sigma_w^2 - \frac{\hat{p}_t^2 h_t^2}{\sigma_v^2} \qquad t \in T, \quad \hat{p}_0 \tag{11.3.3}$$

where

$$d\nu_t = dY_t - h_t \hat{X}_t \, dt$$

The filtered estimate $\hat{X}_t$ is a Gaussian process, and the "conditional" variance $\hat{p}_t$ satisfies the deterministic Riccati equation 11.3.3.

Theorem 11.3.1 Fixed Point Kalman Smoother

Let the signal and observation processes be governed by eq. 11.3.1. Let $\tau \in T$ be a fixed point. The fixed point smoothed estimate $E^{\mathfrak{F}_t} X_\tau$, $\tau < t$, satisfies the

†As shown by eq. 9.4.20, the "conditional" variance $\hat{p}_t$ is the unconditional variance p_t for the linear Gaussian case.

Ito stochastic differential equation

$$E^{\mathcal{F}_t} X_\tau = E^{\mathcal{F}_\tau} X_\tau + \frac{1}{\sigma_v^2} \int_\tau^t h_s \operatorname{cov}^{\mathcal{F}_s}(X_\tau X_s)\, d\nu_s \qquad \tau < t, \quad t \in T \qquad (11.3.4)$$

The conditional covariance $\operatorname{cov}^{\mathcal{F}_t}(X_\tau X_t)$ satisfies the Ito stochastic differential equation

$$\operatorname{cov}^{\mathcal{F}_t}(X_\tau X_t) = \hat{p}_\tau + \int_\tau^t \left(f_s - \frac{h_s^2}{\sigma_v^2} \hat{p}_s \right) \operatorname{cov}^{\mathcal{F}_s}(X_\tau X_s)\, ds \qquad \tau < t, \quad t \in T$$

(11.3.5)

The conditional variance $\operatorname{var}^{\mathcal{F}_t} X_\tau$ satisfies the Ito stochastic differential equation

$$\operatorname{var}^{\mathcal{F}_t} X_\tau = \hat{p}_\tau - \frac{1}{\sigma_v^2} \int_\tau^t h_s^2 \left[\operatorname{cov}^{\mathcal{F}_s}(X_\tau X_s)\right]^2 ds \qquad \tau < t, \quad t \in T \quad (11.3.6)$$

Proof. It has been shown by Kallianpur and Striebel (30) that the conditional distribution of $X_{\tau_1}, X_{\tau_2}, \ldots, X_{\tau_k}, \tau_j \in [0, t], j = 1, \ldots, k$, given $\mathcal{F}_t$, is Gaussian. (We have used this to derive eq. 9.4.19 also.)

By substituting $h_s X_s$ for $h_s(X_s)$ in eq. 11.2.16, we obtain

$$E^{\mathcal{F}_t} X_\tau = E^{\mathcal{F}_\tau} X_\tau + \frac{1}{\sigma_v^2} \int_\tau^t \operatorname{cov}^{\mathcal{F}_s}(X_\tau X_s) h_s\, d\nu_s \qquad \tau < t, \quad t \in T$$

which is eq. 11.3.4.

To prove the second part of the theorem we find expressions for $E^{\mathcal{F}_t}(X_\tau X_t)$ and $E^{\mathcal{F}_t} X_\tau E^{\mathcal{F}_t} X_t$ since

$$\operatorname{cov}^{\mathcal{F}_t}(X_\tau X_t) = E^{\mathcal{F}_t}(X_\tau X_t) - E^{\mathcal{F}_t} X_\tau E^{\mathcal{F}_t} X_t \qquad (11.3.7)$$

We find first an expression or $E^{\mathcal{F}_t}(X_\tau X_t)$. Since

$$dX_t = f_t X_t\, dt + g_t\, dW_t \qquad t > \tau, \quad t \in T, \quad X_\tau \qquad (11.3.8)$$

and $\tau \in T$ is a fixed point, the stochastic differential equation satisfied by $d(X_\tau X_t)$ is

$$d(X_\tau X_t) = X_\tau\, dX_t = X_\tau X_t f_t\, dt + X_\tau g_t\, dW_t \qquad t > \tau, \quad t \in T, \quad X_\tau^2$$

(11.3.9)

As explained in the previous chapters, eq. 11.3.9 will be treated as the new signal process with the same observation process Y_t given by

$$dY_t = h_t X_t\, dt + dV_t \qquad t \in T \qquad (11.3.10)$$

We now apply eq. 11.1.6 of the nonlinear filtering theorem, Theorem 11.1.1, to eqs. 11.3.9 and 11.3.10, and using the fact that W_t and V_t are independent, we obtain the following filtered representation:

$$dE^{\mathcal{F}_t}(X_\tau X_t) = f_t E^{\mathcal{F}_t}(X_\tau X_t) + \frac{h_t}{\sigma_v^2}\operatorname{cov}(X_\tau X_t, X_t)\,d\nu_t$$

$$t > \tau, \quad t \in T, \quad E^{\mathcal{F}_\tau}X_\tau^2 \tag{11.3.11}$$

We can also write eq. 11.3.11 in integral form as

$$E^{\mathcal{F}_t}(X_\tau X_t) = E^{\mathcal{F}_\tau}X_\tau^2 + \int_\tau^t f_s E^{\mathcal{F}_s}(X_\tau X_s)\,ds$$
$$+ \frac{1}{\sigma_v^2}\int_\tau^t h_s \operatorname{cov}^{\mathcal{F}_s}(X_\tau X_s, X_s)\,d\nu_s \qquad t > \tau, \quad t \in T \tag{11.3.12}$$

To find an expression for $E^{\mathcal{F}_t}X_\tau E^{\mathcal{F}_t}X_t$ we note that

$$dE^{\mathcal{F}_t}X_\tau = \frac{h_t}{\sigma_v^2}\operatorname{cov}^{\mathcal{F}_t}(X_\tau X_t)\,d\nu_t \qquad \tau < t, \quad t \in T$$
$$dE^{\mathcal{F}_t}X_t = f_t E^{\mathcal{F}_t}X_t\,dt + \frac{h_t}{\sigma_v^2}\hat{p}_t\,d\nu_t \qquad \tau < t, \quad t \in T \tag{11.3.13}$$

We now apply the Ito rule of eq. 6.4.7 to the product

$$Y_t = E^{\mathcal{F}_t}X_\tau E^{\mathcal{F}_t}X_t$$

with

$$a_{1t} = 0 \qquad b_{1t} = \frac{h_t}{\sigma_v^2}\operatorname{cov}^{\mathcal{F}_t}(X_\tau X_t)$$

$$a_{2t} = f_t E^{\mathcal{F}_t}X_t \qquad b_{2t} = \frac{h_t}{\sigma_v^2}\hat{p}_t$$

and obtain the stochastic differential equation

$$d\left(E^{\mathcal{F}_t}X_\tau E^{\mathcal{F}_t}X_t\right) = E^{\mathcal{F}_t}X_\tau\left(f_t E^{\mathcal{F}_t}X_t\,dt + \frac{h_t}{\sigma_v^2}\hat{p}_t\,d\nu_t\right) + E^{\mathcal{F}_t}X_t\frac{h_t}{\sigma_v^2}\operatorname{cov}^{\mathcal{F}_t}(X_\tau X_t)\,d\nu_t$$
$$+ \frac{h_t^2}{\sigma_v^2}\hat{p}_t\operatorname{cov}^{\mathcal{F}_t}(X_\tau X_t)\,dt \qquad \tau < t, \quad t \in T, \quad \left(E^{\mathcal{F}_\tau}X_\tau\right)^2 \tag{11.3.14}$$

or in integral form,

$$E^{\mathcal{F}_t}X_\tau E^{\mathcal{F}_t}X_t = \left(E^{\mathcal{F}_\tau}X_\tau\right)^2 + \int_\tau^t f_s E^{\mathcal{F}_s}X_\tau E^{\mathcal{F}_s}X_s\, ds + \frac{1}{\sigma_v^2}\int_\tau^t h_s^2 \hat{p}_s \operatorname{cov}^{\mathcal{F}_s}(X_\tau X_s)\, ds$$

$$+ \frac{1}{\sigma_v^2}\int_\tau^t h_s\left[E^{\mathcal{F}_s}X_\tau \hat{p}_s + E^{\mathcal{F}_s}X_s \operatorname{cov}^{\mathcal{F}_s}(X_\tau X_s)\right] d\nu_s$$

$$\tau < t, \quad t \in T \qquad (11.3.15)$$

Subtracting eq. 11.3.15 from eq. 11.3.12, we obtain

$$\operatorname{cov}^{\mathcal{F}_t}(X_\tau X_t) = E^{\mathcal{F}_\tau}X_\tau^2 - \left(E^{\mathcal{F}_\tau}X_\tau\right)^2 + \int_\tau^t f_s\left[E^{\mathcal{F}_s}(X_\tau X_s) - E^{\mathcal{F}_s}X_\tau E^{\mathcal{F}_s}X_s\right] ds$$

$$- \frac{1}{\sigma_v^2}\int_\tau^t h_s^2 \hat{p}_s \operatorname{cov}^{\mathcal{F}_s}(X_\tau X_s)\, ds \qquad \tau < t, \quad t \in T \qquad (11.3.16)$$

with the stochastic integrals with respect to the innovations process vanishing due to the conditional Gaussian property. Equation 11.3.16 is eq. 11.3.5. □

By an exactly analogous procedure eq. 11.3.6 can be obtained. An alternate approach to linear fixed point smoothing problems is given by Bagchi (1).

Theorem 11.3.2 Fixed Interval Kalman Smoother

Let the signal and observation processes be governed by eq. 11.3.1. Let T be a fixed interval $[0, B]$, and let τ be *any* point in this interval. The fixed interval smoothed estimator $E^{\mathcal{F}_B}X_\tau$, $\tau \in T$, satisfies

$$dE^{\mathcal{F}_B}X_\tau = \left[f_\tau E^{\mathcal{F}_B}X_\tau + \frac{\sigma_w^2 g_\tau^2}{\hat{p}_\tau}\left(E^{\mathcal{F}_B}X_\tau - E^{\mathcal{F}_\tau}X_\tau\right)\right] dt \qquad \tau \in T$$

$$(11.3.17)$$

with the boundary condition $E^{\mathcal{F}_B}X_B = X_B$.

The conditional variance $\operatorname{var}^{\mathcal{F}_B}X_\tau$ satisfies

$$d\operatorname{var}^{\mathcal{F}_B}X_\tau = \left[2\left(f_\tau + \frac{\sigma_w^2 g_\tau^2}{\hat{p}_\tau}\right)\operatorname{var}^{\mathcal{F}_B}X_\tau - \sigma_w^2 g_\tau^2\right] d\tau \qquad \tau \in T \qquad (11.3.18)$$

with the boundary condition $\operatorname{var}^{\mathcal{F}_B}X_B = \hat{p}_B$.

Here also the conditional distribution of X_τ, given $\mathcal{F}_\tau$, is Gaussian (Kallianpur and Striebel, 30).

Proof. From Corollary 11.2.1 we have for the fixed interval smoother,

$$E^{\mathcal{F}_B} X_\tau = E^{\mathcal{F}_\tau} X_\tau + \frac{1}{\sigma_v^2} \int_\tau^B \operatorname{cov}^{\mathcal{F}_s}(X_\tau X_s) h_s \, d\nu_s \qquad \tau < B \tag{11.3.19}$$

Solving for $\operatorname{cov}^{\mathcal{F}_s}(X_\tau X_s)$ from eq. 11.3.5, we have

$$\operatorname{cov}^{\mathcal{F}_s}(X_\tau X_s) = \hat{p}_\tau \exp\left[\int_\tau^s \left(f_u - \frac{h_u^2 \hat{p}_u}{\sigma_v^2}\right) du\right] \tag{11.3.20}$$

Substituting eq. 11.3.20 into eq. 11.3.19, we obtain

$$E^{\mathcal{F}_B} X_\tau + \frac{\hat{p}_\tau}{\sigma_v^2} \int_\tau^B h_s \exp\left[\int_\tau^s \left(f_u - \frac{h_u^2 \hat{p}_u}{\sigma_v^2}\right) du\right] d\nu_s \tag{11.3.21}$$

which can be written as

$$E^{\mathcal{F}_B} X_\tau = E^{\mathcal{F}_\tau} X_\tau + \frac{\hat{p}_\tau}{\sigma_v^2} Z_\tau \tag{11.3.22}$$

where

$$Z_\tau = \int_\tau^B h_s \exp\left[\int_\tau^s \left(f_u - \frac{h_u^2 \hat{p}_u}{\sigma_v^2}\right) du\right] d\nu_s \tag{11.3.23}$$

From eq. 11.3.23 we can write the stochastic differential equation satisfied by Z_τ as

$$dZ_\tau = -\left(f_\tau - \frac{h_\tau^2 \hat{p}_\tau}{\sigma_v^2}\right) Z_\tau \, d\tau - h_\tau \, d\nu_\tau \qquad Z_B = 0 \tag{11.3.24}$$

The negative sign is due to the solution being backward in time.

From eq. 11.3.22 we have

$$dE^{\mathcal{F}_B} X_\tau = d\hat{X}_\tau + \frac{1}{\sigma_v^2} d(\hat{p}_\tau Z_\tau) \tag{11.3.25}$$

From eq. 11.3.13,

$$d\hat{X}_\tau = f_\tau \hat{X}_\tau \, d\tau + \frac{h_\tau}{\sigma_v^2} \hat{p}_\tau \, d\nu_\tau \qquad \tau \in T \tag{11.3.26}$$

Applying the Ito rule of eq. 6.4.7 to $d(\hat{p}_\tau Z_\tau)$ with

$$d\hat{p}_\tau = 2f_\tau \hat{p}_\tau + \sigma_w^2 g_\tau^2 - \frac{h_\tau^2 \hat{p}_\tau^2}{\sigma_v^2}$$

$$dZ_\tau = -\left(f_\tau - \frac{h_\tau^2 \hat{p}_\tau}{\sigma_v^2}\right) Z_\tau \, d\tau - h_\tau \, dv_\tau \tag{11.3.27}$$

we obtain

$$d(\hat{p}_\tau Z_\tau) = -\hat{p}_\tau \left[\left(f_\tau - \frac{h_\tau^2 \hat{p}_\tau}{\sigma_v^2}\right) Z_\tau \, d\tau + h_\tau \, dv_\tau\right]$$

$$+ Z_\tau \left(2f_\tau \hat{p}_\tau + \sigma_w^2 g_\tau^2 - \frac{h_\tau^2 \hat{p}_\tau^2}{\sigma_v^2}\right) dt \tag{11.3.28}$$

Substituting eqs. 11.3.26 and 11.3.28 in eq. 11.3.25, we have

$$dE^{\mathcal{F}_B} X_\tau = f_\tau \hat{X}_\tau \, d\tau + \frac{1}{\sigma_v^2} Z_\tau (f_\tau \hat{p}_\tau + \sigma_w^2 g_\tau^2) \, d\tau \tag{11.3.29}$$

However, from eq. 11.3.22,

$$Z_\tau = \frac{\sigma_v^2}{\hat{p}_\tau} (E^{\mathcal{F}_B} X_\tau - \hat{X}_\tau) \tag{11.3.30}$$

Substituting eq. 11.3.30 into eq. 11.3.29, there results

$$dE^{\mathcal{F}_B} X_\tau = f_\tau E^{\mathcal{F}_B} X_\tau + \frac{\sigma_w^2 g_\tau^2}{\hat{p}_\tau} (E^{\mathcal{F}_B} X_\tau - \hat{X}_\tau) \, d\tau$$

which is eq. 11.3.17. □

Finally combining the results of the fixed point and fixed interval smoothing problems according to the following scheme;

$$E^{\mathcal{F}_0} X_0 \xrightarrow[\text{smoothing}]{\text{fixed point}} E^{\mathcal{F}_\tau} X_0 \xrightarrow[\text{smoothing}]{\text{fixed interval}} E^{\mathcal{F}_t} X_{t-a}$$

yields the following result for the fixed lag smoother..

Theorem 11.3.3 Fixed Lag Kalman Smoother

Let the signal and observation processes be governed by eq. 11.3.1. Let $a \in T$ be a fixed delay. The conditional distribution of X_{t-a} given $\mathcal{F}_t$, $t > a$, $t \in T$, is Gaussian (Kallianpur and Striebel, 30). The fixed lag smoothed estimate satisfies the Ito stochastic differential equation

$$E^{\mathcal{F}_t} X_{t-a} = E^{\mathcal{F}_0} X_0 + \int_0^{t-a} \left(f_s + \frac{\sigma_w^2 g_s^2}{\hat{p}_s} \right) E^{\mathcal{F}_t} X_s \, ds$$

$$- \int_0^{t-a} \frac{\sigma_w^2 g_s^2}{\hat{p}_s} \hat{X}_s \, ds + \frac{1}{\sigma_v^2} \int_0^t h_s \operatorname{cov}^{\mathcal{F}_s}(X_0 X_s) \, d\nu_s$$

$$t > a, \quad t \in T \qquad (11.3.31)$$

The conditional covariance $\operatorname{cov}^{\mathcal{F}_t}(X_{t-a} X_t)$ satisfies the Ito stochastic differential equation

$$\frac{d \operatorname{cov}^{\mathcal{F}_t}(X_{t-a} X_t)}{dt} = \left(f_t + f_{t-a} + \frac{\sigma_w^2 g_{t-a}^2}{\hat{p}_{t-a}} - \frac{h_t^2 \hat{p}_t}{\sigma_v^2} \right) \operatorname{cov}^{\mathcal{F}_t}(X_{t-a} X_t)$$

$$t > a, \quad t \in T, \quad \operatorname{cov}^{\mathcal{F}_a}(X_0 X_a) \qquad (11.3.32)$$

The conditional variance $\operatorname{var}^{\mathcal{F}_t} X_{t-a}$ satisfies the Ito stochastic differential equation

$$\frac{d}{dt} \operatorname{var}^{\mathcal{F}_t} X_{t-a} = 2 \left(f_{t-a} + \frac{\sigma_w^2 g_{t-a}^2}{\hat{p}_{t-a}} \right) \operatorname{var}^{\mathcal{F}_t} X_{t-a}$$

$$- \frac{h_t^2}{\sigma_v^2} \left[\operatorname{cov}^{\mathcal{F}_t}(X_{t-a} X_t) \right]^2 - \sigma_w^2 g_{t-a}^2$$

$$t > a, \quad t \in T, \quad \operatorname{var}^{\mathcal{F}_a} X_0 \qquad (11.3.33)$$

Problems

1. Prove eq. 11.3.6 of Theorem 11.3.1, namely,

$$\operatorname{var}^{\mathcal{F}_t} X_\tau = \hat{p}_\tau - \frac{1}{\sigma_v^2} \int_\tau^t h_s^2 \left[\operatorname{cov}^{\mathcal{F}_s}(X_\tau X_s) \right]^2 ds \qquad \tau < t, \quad t \in T$$

2. Let the signal and observation processes be given by

$$dX_t = f_t(X_t) \, dt + dW_t \qquad t \in T, \quad X_0$$

$$dY_t = h_t(X_t) \, dt + J_t(X_t) \, dV_t \qquad t \in T$$

with the usual assumptions on W_t, V_t, and X_0. Find the fixed point smoothing equations corresponding to eqs. 11.3.4–11.3.6.

3. Similar to the smoothing theorem, Theorem 11.2.1, we can also enunciate a prediction theorem. Let the signal and observation processes be given by

$$dX_t = f_t(X_t)\,dt + dW_t \qquad t \in T, \quad X_0$$

$$dY_t = h_t(X_t)\,dt + dV_t \qquad t \in T, \quad Y_0 = 0$$

with the usual assumptions of Theorem 11.2.1. Let t be a *fixed* point, and let $\tau < t$, $t \in T$. Show that the predicted (extrapolated) estimate $E^{\mathcal{F}_\tau} X_t$, $\tau < t$, is given by

$$E^{\mathcal{F}_\tau} X_t = E^{\mathcal{F}_0} X_t + \int_0^\tau \Big[E^{\mathcal{F}_s} \frac{d}{ds} \langle E^{\mathcal{B}_s} X_t, V \rangle_s$$

$$+ E^{\mathcal{F}_s} \big\{ E^{\mathcal{B}_s} X_t \big(h_s - E^{\mathcal{F}_s} h_s\big)\big\} \Big]\, dv_s$$

4. Show that the solution for

$$\operatorname{cov}^{\mathcal{F}_t}(X_\tau X_t) = \hat{p}_\tau + \int_\tau^t \left(f_s - \frac{h_s^2}{\sigma_s^2} \hat{p}_s \right) \operatorname{cov}^{\mathcal{F}_s}(X_\tau X_s)\, ds$$

is given by

$$\operatorname{cov}^{\mathcal{F}_t}(X_\tau X_t) = \hat{p}_\tau \exp\left[\int_\tau^t \left(f_u - \frac{h_u^2 \hat{p}_u}{\sigma_v^2} \right) du \right]$$

5. Prove eq. 11.3.18 of Theorem 11.3.2, namely,

$$d\operatorname{var}^{\mathcal{F}_B} X_\tau = \left[2\left(f_\tau + \frac{\sigma_w^2 g_\tau^2}{\hat{p}_t} \right) \operatorname{var}^{\mathcal{F}_B} X_\tau - \sigma_w^2 g_\tau^2 \right] d\tau \qquad \tau \in T$$

with boundary condition $\operatorname{var}^{\mathcal{F}_B} X_B = \hat{p}_B$.

6. Show that

$$Z_t = \int_t^B h_s \exp\left[\int_t^s \left(f_u - \frac{h_u^2 \hat{p}_u}{\sigma_v^2} \right) du \right] dv_s$$

is the solution to the stochastic differential equation

$$dZ_t = -\left(f_t - \frac{h_t^2 \hat{p}_t}{\sigma_v^2} \right) Z_t\, dt - h_t\, dv_t \qquad Z_B = 0$$

7. Prove the fixed lag Kalman smoother theorem, Theorem 11.3.3.

REFERENCES

1. Bagchi, A. (1975) "A martingale approach to continuous time linear smoothing," *SIAM J. Appl. Math.*, **28**, 276–281.
2. Balakrishnan, A. V. (1974) "A note on the structure of optimal stochastic controls," *Appl. Math. Optimization*, **1**, 87–94.
3. Balakrishnan, A. V. (1972) "A martingale approach to linear recursive state estimation," *SIAM J. Control*, **10**, 754–766.
4. Bhat, B. R. (1981) *Modern probability theory*, Wiley Eastern, New Delhi.
5. Bremaud, P. (1981) *Point processes and queues*, Springer-Verlag, New York.
6. Burrill, C. W. (1972) *Measure, integration and probability*, McGraw-Hill, New York.
7. Chien, T.-T. (1972) *An adaptive technique for redundant sensor navigation system*, Ph.D. Thesis, Massachusetts Institute of Technology.
8. Clark, J. M. C. (1969) *Conditions for one to one correspondence between an observation process and its innovations*, Tech. Rep., Center for Computing and Automation, Imperial College, London.
9. Davis, M. H. A. (1977) *Linear estimation and stochastic control*, Chapman and Hall, London.
10. Davis, M. H. A. (1975) "The application of nonlinear filtering to fault detection in linear systems," *IEEE Trans. Automatic Control*, **20**, 257–259.
11. Dellacherie, C., and Meyer, P. A. (1978) *Probabilities and potentials*, North-Holland, Amsterdam.
12. De S. Lazaro, J. (1981) *Lecture notes on stochastic processes*, Tata Institute of Fundamental Research, Bangalore.
13. Doleans-Dade, C., and Meyer, P. A. (1970) "Intergrales stochastiques par rapport aux martingales locales," *Seminar of Probabilities IV*, *Lecture Notes in Mathematics*, no. **124**, Springer-Verlag, New York, 77–107.
14. Doob, J. L. (1953) *Stochastic processes*, Wiley, New York.
15. Fujisaki, M., Kallianpur, G., and Kunita, H. (1972) "Stochastic differential equations for nonlinear filtering problem," *Osaka J. Math.*, **9**, 19–40.

16. Gelb, A., Ed. (1974) *Applied optimal estimation*, M.I.T. Press, Cambridge.

17. Gran, R., and Kozin, F. (1973) "Nonlinear filtering applied to the modelling of earthquake data," *Proc. 4th Symp. on nonlinear estimation and its applications*, San Diego.

18. Halmos, P. R. (1974) *Measure theory*, Springer-Verlag, New York.

19. Hazewinkel, M. and Willems, J. C., Eds. (1981) *Stochastic systems, the mathematics of filtering and identification and applications*, Reidel, Dordrecht.

20. Hibey, J. L., Snyder, D. L., and Van Schuppen, J. H. (1978) "Error probability bounds for continuous time decision problems," *IEEE Trans. Inform. Theory*, **24**, 608–622.

21. Ito, K. (1961) *Lectures on stochastic processes*, Tata Institute of Fundamental Research, Bombay.

22. Jazwinski, A. H. (1970) *Stochastic processes and filtering theory*, Academic Press, New York.

23. Jazwinski, A. H. (1966) "Filtering for nonlinear dynamical systems," *IEEE Trans. Automatic Control*, **11**, 765–766.

24. Kailath, T. (1974) "A view of three decades of linear filtering theory," *IEEE Trans. Inform. Theory*, **20**, 146–181.

25. Kailath, T., and Geesey, R. A. (1971) "Innovations approach to least squares estimation, part IV: recursive estimation given lumped covariance functions," *IEEE Trans. Automatic Control*, **16**, 720–726.

26. Kailath, T., and Frost, P. (1971) "Innovations approach to least squares estimation, part III: nonlinear estimation in white Gaussian noise," *IEEE Trans. Automatic Control*, **16**, 217–226.

27. Kailath, T., and Frost, P. (1968) "Innovations approach to least squares estimation, part II: linear smoothing in additive white noise," *IEEE Trans. Automatic Control*, **13**, 655–660.

28. Kailath, T. (1968) "Innovations approach to least squares estimation, part I: linear filtering in additive white noise," *IEEE Trans. Automatic Control*, **13**, 646–654.

29. Kallianpur, G. (1980) *Stochastic filtering theory*, Springer-Verlag, New York.

30. Kallianpur, G., and Striebel, C. (1969) "Stochastic differential equations in statistical estimation problems," *Multivariate analysis*, vol. II, Krishnaiah, P. R., Ed., Academic Press, New York.

31. Kalman, R. E., and Bucy, R. S. (1961) "New results in linear filtering and prediction theory," *Trans. ASME, J. Basic Eng., ser. D*, **83**, 95–108.

32. Krishnan, V. (1982) "Fault detection by adaptive nonlinear filtering," *J. Indian Inst. Sci.* (Bangalore), **63**, 249–262.

33. Kunita, H., and Watanabe, S. (1967) "On square integrable martingales," *Nagoya Math. J.*, **31**, 209–245.

34. Lipster, R. S., and Shiryaev, A. N. (1977–1978) *Statistics of random processes*, vols. I and II, Springer-Verlag, New York.

35. Maybeck, P. S. (1979) *Stochastic models, estimation and control, vol. I*, Academic Press, New York.

36. Mehra, R. K. (1972) "Approaches to adaptive filtering," *IEEE Trans. Automatic Control*, **17**, 693–698.

37. Mehra, R. K. (1970) "On the identification of variances and adaptive Kalman filtering," *IEEE Trans. Automatic Control*, **15**, 175–184.

38. Meyer, P. A. (1970) "Martingales and stochastic integrals," *Lecture Notes in Mathematics*, **284**, Springer-Verlag, New York.

39. Meyer, P. A. (1970) "Non-square integrable martingales," *Lecture Notes in Mathematics*, **190**, Springer-Verlag, New York.

40. Meyer, P. A. (1970) "Square integrable martingales," *Lecture Notes in Mathematics*, **190**, Springer-Verlag, New York.

41. Meyer, P. A. (1966) *Probability and potentials*, Blaisdell, Waltham.

42. Meyer, P. A. (1963) "Decomposition of supermartingales: the uniqueness theorem," *Ill. J. Math.*, **7**, 1–17.

43. Meyer, P. A. (1962) "A decomposition theorem for supermartingales," *Ill. J. Math.*, **6**, 193–205.

44. Neveu, J. (1965) *Mathematical foundations of the calculus of probability*, Holden-Day, San Francisco.

45. Papoulis, A. (1965) *Probability, random variables and stochastic processes*, McGraw-Hill, New York.

46. Segall, A. (1976) "Recursive estimation for discrete time processes," *IEEE Trans. Inform. Theory*, **22**, 631–634.

47. Segall, A. (1976) "Stochastic processes in estimation theory," *IEEE Trans. Inform. Theory*, **22**, 275–286.

48. Segall, A., Davis, M. H. A., and Kailath, T. (1975) "Nonlinear filtering with counting observations," *IEEE Trans. Inform. Theory*, **21**, 143–149.

49. Segall, A., and Kailath, T. (1975) "The modelling of randomly modulated jump processes," *IEEE Trans. Inform. Theory*, **21**, 135–143.

50. Segall, A. (1973) *A martingale approach to modelling estimation and detection of jump processes*, Ph.D. Thesis, Stanford University, Stanford.

51. Shiryaev, A. N. (1978) *Optimal stopping rules*, Springer-Verlag, New York.

52. Stoica, P., and Soderstrom, T. (1977) "A method for the identification of linear systems using the generalized least squares principle," *IEEE Trans. Automatic Control*, **22**, 631–634.

53. Stratonovich, R. L. (1966) "A new form of representation of stochastic integrals and equations," *SIAM J. Control*, **4**, 362–371.

54. Varadhan, S. R. S. (1980) *Diffusion problems and partial differential equations*, Tata Institute of Fundamental Research, Bombay.

55. Venimadhavan, C. E., and Viswanathan, J. (1976) "Stochastic differential equations for linear smoothing problems," *IEEE Trans. Automatic Control*, **21**, 269–271.

56. Venimadhavan, C. E. (1975) *A martingale approach to smoothing problems*, Ph.D. Thesis, School of Automation, Indian Institute of Science, Bangalore.

57. Viswanathan, J. (1975) *Estimation problems in affine hereditory differential systems*, Ph.D. Thesis, School of Automation, Indian Institute of Science, Bangalore.

58. Whittakar, E. J., and Watson, G. N. (1963) *A course of modern analysis*, Cambridge University Press, Cambridge.

59. Williams, D. (1979) *Diffusions, Markov processes and martingales*, Wiley, New York.

60. Willsky, A. (1976) "A survey of design methods for failure detection in dynamic systems," *Automatica*, **12**, 601–611.

61. Wong, E. (1973) "Recent progress in stochastic processes; a survey," **19**, *IEEE Trans. Inform. Theory*, 262–275.

62. Wong, E. (1971) "Representation of martingales, quadratic variations and applications," *SIAM J. Control*, **9**, 621–633.

63. Wong, E. (1971) *Stochastic processes in information and dynamical systems*, McGraw-Hill, New York.

64. Wong, E., and Zakai, M. (1966) "On the relationship between ordinary and stochastic differential equations and applications to stochastic problems in control theory," *Proc. 3rd IFAC Congress*, paper 3-B.

65. Allinger, D., and Mitter, S. K. (1981) "New results in innovations problem for nonlinear filtering," *Stochastics*, **5**.

66. Benes, V. E. (1981) "Exact finite dimensional filters for certain diffusions with nonlinear drift," *Stochastics*, **5**, 65–92.

67. Bichteler, K. (1981) "Stochastic integration and L^p theory of semimartingales," *Annals Probabil.*, **9**, 49–89.

68. Davis, M. H. A. (1981) "New approach to filtering for nonlinear systems," *Proc. IEEE*, **128**, Part D, No. 5, 166–172.

69. Girsanov, I. V. (1960) "On transforming a certain class of stochastic processes by absolutely continuous substitution of measures," *Theory Prob. Applic.* **5**, 285–301.

70. Hammer, J. (1982) "On some properties of conditional moments in nonlinear filtering," *SIAM J. Control and Optimization*, **20**, 497–505.

71. Hibey, J. L. (1981) "Performance bounds for differential systems incurring abrupt random changes," *IEEE Trans. Automatic Control*, **26**, 553–554.

72. Ito, K., Ed. (1978) *Proceedings of international symposium on stochastic differential equations*, Wiley, New York.

73. Karlin, S. and Taylor, H. M. (1975) *First course in stochastic processes*, 2nd ed., Academic Press, New York.

74. Stroock, D. W. (1982) *Topics in stochastic differential equations*, Tata Institute of Fundamental Research, Bombay.

75. Yavin, Y. (1981) "An alternative approach to nonlinear filtering," *Int. J. System Science*, **12**, 795–812.

INDEX